your baby's **first** year

The National Childbirth Trust

your baby's **first** year

The Essential Guide for New Parents

MITCHELL BEAZLEY

contents

foreword

The National Childbirth Trust has been supporting new parents for 50 years, listening to their concerns, providing accessible information, and establishing networks of support. This book is the companion to our successful book, *Your Birth Year*, and in a similar way it too provides not just a handbook of practical information, but a guide and helpmate – this time for the exciting first year after birth.

When you give birth, you give life not only to a baby but a brand new person, an individual with his own unique way of relating to the world. At the same time, a new existence begins for you: you become a parent, beginning your own complex journey to a new identity and outlook. At this time of change it is important to remember that, just as there is no one right way to paint a picture, there is no single correct way to bring up your baby or to become a mother or father. Parenting is an art not a science; however, there is a body of evidence-based knowledge that can help you to find your way through the early months and years. At the National Childbirth Trust we believe that parents should be provided with useful, factual, research-based information so that they can become experts in their own right, and make the choices that are appropriate for their own particular baby, themselves, and their families.

Your Baby's First Year clearly and accessibly gives all the most up-to-date information that you need to make the transition to parenthood, and to care for your baby with confidence and assurance. Chronologically ordered, and with special chapters on feeding and sleeping, this book addresses the key concerns at various stages in the first year after birth – from the exciting, confusing, amazing early weeks to the busy, sociable, active, later months. You may choose to read the book from cover to cover, concentrate on those chapters that describe your current stage, or simply dip in and out when you feel the need for some information and reassurance. At the back of the book are listings of useful organizations that will be able to provide further support for various circumstances – both the common and more unusual.

Becoming a parent is an emotional journey that everyone experiences in his or her own unique way. There are choices to be made and skills that you can learn, but the really important bit, the essential and lasting element, is the relationship you create with your child. How you organize your days, the choices you make about feeding methods, sleeping arrangements, and all the other aspects of being a parent in the modern world, will influence how your relationship unfolds, but it is not the sum of what being a parent means. In this important first year you are building the foundation of a relationship that will stretch far beyond the early weeks and months; in the busy days ahead, remember to take time to enjoy your baby whenever you can. Parenting is demanding – love is the reward.

1 THE FIRST FEW HOURS

- The birth
- What to expect during the first minutes
- Your baby's appearance at birth
- Greeting your baby
- Your baby's wellbeing
- Preparing to leave your birthing room
- Medical intervention at birth
- If you have a caesarean
- Premature birth
- Giving birth to twins

The birth

The birth of your baby is a momentous occasion and one that you and your partner will remember for the rest of your lives. It marks the end of your baby's nine-month period of growth and development in the womb and the start of her journey into the world as an independent human being. It also heralds the moment that you will finally meet her face to face.

Anticipating the moment of birth

Like many other mothers-to-be, you may be experiencing a sense of excitement at the thought of seeing your baby for the first time. You may be wondering if your baby will be a boy or a girl. And who will the baby look like? You may also be looking forward to becoming a mother, whether it is for the first or a subsequent time. What will it feel like to hold your baby, to stroke her, to kiss her? How will this baby be different from your other children?

However, some women having their first baby worry that they may not be able to love her sufficiently or be a "good" mother to her. They may also worry that they will become isolated from their social circle of friends who have not yet had babies. Other mothers-to-be find the financial implications of raising a child to be a real concern, while others may be taking time out from a career and be keen to get back to work. Whatever your feelings are in anticipation of meeting your baby, it is important to acknowledge that they are usually a normal response to the life-changing event that you are about to experience.

"I was worried about whether I would love my baby at first sight, so was unprepared for the huge rush of love that overcame me in those first moments after birth."

While some new mothers quickly discover a sense of fulfilment and identity in their new role, others may take time to find a way of relating comfortably to their new baby, as well as maintaining a sense of self. However you feel, it is important that your feelings are acknowledged as being normal, and that you are fully supported in finding a way of parenting that is right for you and your family.

Birth partners

Although most fathers are now present during the birth of their babies, your own partner may feel concerned about accompanying you through the emotional and physical ups and downs of labour. It may even prove stressful for him, especially if he feels unsure of how best to support you. For many partners, participating in the birth process is a positive and rewarding experience, and is seen as a natural part of welcoming the arrival of their new son or daughter. However, some fathers can feel overwhelmed by the all-encompassing power

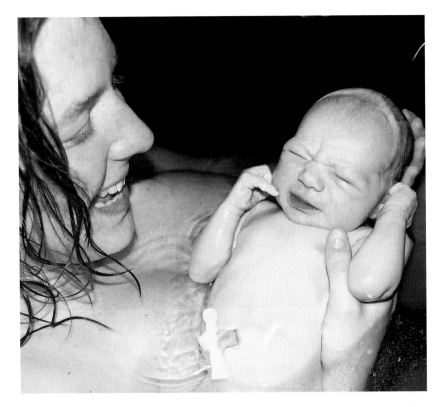

Holding your baby for the first time may be accompanied by an overwhelming surge of emotions. The "love-at-first-sight" feeling is facilitated by the hormone oxytocin.

BIRTH PARTNERS – DOULAS

Research shows that the constant one-to-one presence of a female care-giver during labour can reduce the chances of a woman needing a caesarean birth by 50 percent, reduces the likelihood of her needing an epidural or narcotic drugs for pain management, increases successful breastfeeding and positive parent-baby relationships, and decreases her chances of developing postnatal depression.⊙

A doula, or female birth attendant, can be anyone that you choose to support you during labour and birth. She may be a sister, mother, or a friend, or you may even have employed a woman who works as a doula. She may therefore be trained or untrained, but she will ideally be a mother, or even a grandmother, herself, and someone with whom you and your partner have built up a relationship of trust over time.

The role of your doula is to support your emotional and practical needs throughout labour and during the early postnatal period. She does not undertake any clinical tasks, as these are the responsibility of your midwife or other medical practitioners. In the initial hours following birth your doula can help to maintain privacy and a safe environment for you. She can offer support with breast-feeding and assist with comfort measures so that you and your partner can concentrate on "being" with your baby in the way that is right for you. She can also be a valuable resource for talking through the events of your labour during the days following birth. (For more information see www.doula.org.uk)

that labour has over the mother, and admit a sense of helplessness at not being able to control events on her behalf. This is one reason why some parents decide to have an additional birth partner, perhaps the mother's own mother or sister. Alternatively, they may choose to employ a doula (a female birth attendant – *see* box, right) for additional emotional support during labour.

It is possible that the father of your baby is no longer your partner and that it is not a part of your current relationship for him to be emotionally supportive or physically close. However, your ex-partner may still wish to be present at the birth and you may be agreeable to this. In such cases it can be a good idea for you to have an additional birth partner, who you trust will help you feel safe and nurtured throughout your labour.

Catching the first sight of your baby

The first glimpse of a new baby is a unique experience for every parent and you may well find yourselves filled with a sense of awe. If you haven't found out the sex of your baby already from your antenatal tests, it is likely that your first reaction will be to discover if you have a girl or a boy. This will be quickly followed by a request for reassurance from your midwife that your baby is "all right".

Many new mothers experience an immediate overwhelming love-at-first-sight feeling towards their babies and the strength of such emotion can sometimes

"I was not at all worried when I held my baby in my arms after a wonderful birth and felt... nothing. I didn't feel anything negative for her, just calm. This deep and passionate love for her only started to grow after a couple of months."

prove a surprise. Oxytocin, the hormone responsible for stimulating your womb to contract during labour, also produces a feeling of euphoria following a normal physiological birth. Oxytocin has been referred to as the "love hormone" for the feel-good effects it has on a new mother, and it certainly facilitates the falling-in-love process with your baby.

However, for some women it can take a few days, weeks, or even months, to begin to experience deep feelings for their newborn baby. If you find that this is the case for you, it does not mean that you do not, or cannot, love your baby, just that taking more time to adjust to the huge transition of meeting her face-to-face is normal for you.

Sometimes, particularly following a long and difficult labour, mothers may feel too exhausted to muster much enthusiasm towards their new baby, and may even feel resentful or angry towards her. It may also be the case that your newborn baby is quite different from who you were expecting. Perhaps your baby is a girl and you were thinking it would be a boy. Maybe the appearance of your baby has taken you by surprise, or perhaps she has an unexpected disability. It is important that you allow yourself time to rest and also time to come to terms with the birth of your baby.

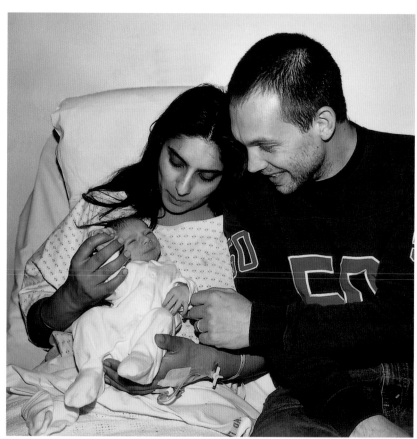

BECOMING A FAMILY

The first few hours can be an important bonding time with your baby for both you and your partner, when you may start to feel the special closeness of being a family.

For a new father, the fact that his baby has been born safely and his partner has survived the extraordinary powers of childbirth can feel emotionally overwhelming. The first 24 hours can also be a precious time for bonding with his new son or daughter. The initial moments that you spend together as a new family, whether it is your first or third baby, should involve enjoying a sense of pride and special closeness between you all.

Feelings about the birth

It is important to remember that giving birth to your baby is a huge physical and emotional achievement, regardless of the type of birth you eventually ended up having. However, sometimes women can feel embarrassed or ashamed about how they behaved during labour. Perhaps you shouted or swore, which may be unusual behaviour for you, or perhaps you opened your bowels – something that you would not normally do in the presence of other people. You should be aware that these things are common in labour and that your midwife will not be shocked or offended. Afterwards, you may find it helpful to talk through all your feelings with your partner. Indeed, as you both set out along the path of parenting, you may later regard your labour as the beginning of a more intimate level of communication between the two of you.

If your labour and birth were not exactly as you had planned, it is possible that, along with the immediate joy and delight you feel at having given birth, you are left with a sense of sadness or disappointment. Some new mothers feel upset for not having given birth without pain-relieving drugs, for example, if they had a vaginal birth. Although many women want to give birth naturally, without any intervention at all, when it is your first baby you cannot know beforehand what labour will be like or how you will deal with your contractions. It is important to remember that individualized, one-to-one physical and emotional support is highly important and many hospitals don't provide it. For many units interventional methods such as epidurals and narcotic drugs are the norm, and that is what women are offered. Perhaps, in the circumstances, by accepting diamorphine, pethidine, or an epidural you felt more in control of your birth experience, and were better able to participate emotionally with the process.

Whatever kind of birth you have had, you can feel proud of yourself as you did the best you could in an unknown situation. However, be aware that you may find it helpful to talk through your birth experience again with your midwife during the early postnatal days, especially if you feel that you did not receive the positive emotional or physical support that you needed, or that your own choices were disrespected in any way.

What to expect during the first minutes

The first few minutes following the birth of your baby are physiologically critical to the wellbeing of both you and your newborn. It is the time when the placenta begins to separate from the wall of your womb, and when your baby begins to take her first breaths.

"The moment my daughter was born and I looked down at her into her extremely alert eyes, it was as if we'd been waiting to meet each other for ever, and this was finally 'hello'."

It is a good idea to consider beforehand how you would like to meet your baby at birth: whether you would like your midwife to guide her into your arms or onto your tummy, or if you would like to reach out and lift her up when you are ready. Immediate contact with your body provides essential warmth for your baby as well as familiarity with the sounds and smells that she has been used to. Although warm towels may be used to cover her outer body, skin-to-skin contact is the best way to encourage your newborn to establish her breathing.

While you are enjoying the very first moments with your baby, your midwife will be mentally assessing her condition using a checklist known as the Apgar Score (*see* p.23). At the same time she will continue to attend to your physical needs, as the birth process is not clinically complete until your placenta is delivered.

Despite a sense of euphoria, you may feel weak and shaky for a short while after the birth as a result of the physical stress of labour. As long as you have not lost an excessive amount of blood this should soon pass. Some women believe that taking Arnica tablets (a homeopathic remedy) at regular intervals throughout labour, and for the first few postnatal days, helps to heal any physical trauma, such as bruising, and assists with the normal emotional shock of giving birth. If you have given birth in a hospital or a midwife-led unit, then while your midwife is waiting for your placenta to be delivered she will ask you and your partner to check the details written on two name bands. These will then be placed on your baby's ankle and wrist so that she can be identified during your stay.

Third stage of labour

This is the time from when your baby is born until your placenta is safely delivered, and it can be managed in one of the following two ways:

PHYSIOLOGICAL DELIVERY OF PLACENTA
If you have opted for a physiological third stage (following a labour and birth with no intervention), then no action should be taken by your midwife until your baby's cord has stopped pulsating and your placenta has separated from the wall of your womb and been expelled by your own effort (usually with one gentle push).

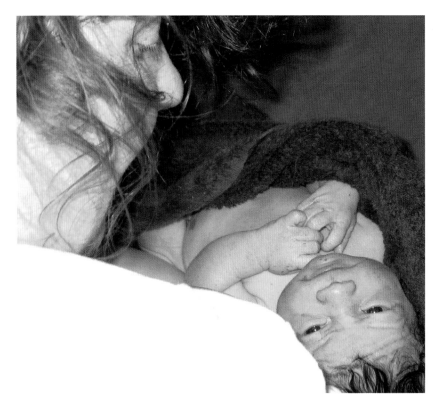

This generally occurs around 20–30 minutes after birth and the cord can then be cut. If there is any delay in your third stage of labour, encouraging your baby to suckle at your breast can stimulate the oxytocin in your body to make your womb contract enough to expel the placenta without any further intervention. A small quantity of blood loss is normal around the moment of birth and until the placenta is delivered, but your midwife will be watching to ensure that this does not become excessive.

Some fathers like to cut their new baby's umbilical cord. If your partner has struggled to be actively involved in the labour, this may be a way for him to feel included as he helps to bring the birth process to completion.

ACTIVELY MANAGED DELIVERY OF PLACENTA

This is the option usually offered to women giving birth in hospital. It involves being given an injection of syntometrine in your thigh just as your baby is born. Your baby's cord will be clamped and cut a few moments after her birth and, following a further five to seven minutes, your midwife will guide your placenta out by pulling gently on the end of the cord left at your vulva. You can find out more information in the *Third Stage of Labour* booklet, which is published by AIMS (Association of Improvement of Maternity Services) – go to www.aims.org.uk.

see also

your baby's wellbeing   22–3

If you have an actively managed third stage, the placenta will be retained if it is not delivered promptly within a few minutes, as the syntometrine makes the womb contract and hold onto the placenta if it is not expelled in time. If this happens, you may need to undergo a short operation during which a doctor will remove your placenta by hand. You will usually be offered an epidural (if you have not already had one), or a spinal anaesthetic for pain relief. If you opt for a physiological third stage the time is not so critical: the placenta will take longer to separate and be expelled. If your placenta is not delivered within approximately 30 minutes to an hour (or much sooner if you are losing blood), you can try breastfeeding, moving around, emptying your bladder, or an injection of syntometrine to stimulate the womb to contract. Until your placenta is safely delivered from the wall of your womb there is a greater risk of you haemorrhaging, and a large loss of blood at birth can mean it takes longer to recover postnatally. If the haemoglobin and ferritin levels in your blood are reduced after the birth, you may be offered a blood transfusion.

Perineal tears and stitches

Your midwife will check to see if there are any tears in your perineum at the time that your placenta is delivered and will inform you if she thinks that you need stitches (sutures). Although most midwives have suturing skills, especially those attending home births, if the midwife attending you in hospital is not able to suture, she will ask a doctor to do it.

"First degree" tears, ones that involve skin only, do not usually require sutures. "Second degree" tears, ones that involve some tissue as well as the skin, are sometimes left unsutured as long as the sides of the wound fit closely together and there is no bleeding. The reason for not suturing a second degree tear is because stitches may increase the amount of perineal pain that you experience during your early postnatal days, which can in turn affect your enjoyment of and interaction with your baby.⊙ However, there is mixed evidence about the time it takes for unsutured wounds to heal.⊙ A "third degree" tear involves the tissues of your bowel, and this requires a specialist to suture the area. Whatever the situation, some local anaesthetic will be injected into your vaginal wall so you should not feel any discomfort during the procedure. Evidence shows that the continuous method of suturing gives less pain than single stitches.⊙ Although an episiotomy (*see* p.236) should be a very rare occurrence during a normal physiological birth, this will almost always need sutures.

The "fourth stage"

Before your midwife leaves the room, or your home if you have had a home birth, you will be offered the opportunity to look at your placenta if you wish, as it remains your property until you say otherwise. Some parents have been known to

save the placenta to cook and eat at a later date, as they believe it contains important nutritional value for the postnatal mother; others believe that the ceremonial burying of the placenta returns it to the earth, giving it proper honour for the work it has done in nurturing and supporting the baby's life in the womb. You will then be left alone to enjoy some privacy together with your new baby, and traditionally you will be brought some well-deserved tea and toast. If you have had your baby at home, you will be able to enjoy this in the comfort of your own bed with your family surrounding you. This can be a very special moment, as you introduce your baby to her older siblings – if they have not been present during the birth.

FAMILY INTRODUCTIONS

Once you have had your baby you can Introduce her to her siblings, or other family members. This can be a special time for you all.

Your baby's appearance at birth

The normal appearance at birth of a well baby that has been born at term, after at least 37 weeks of gestation, may be different from what you were expecting, especially if this is your first baby.

A PROTECTIVE SUBSTANCE

Your baby may not look exactly as you were expecting. For example, her skin may be covered in vernix, which protected her in the womb.

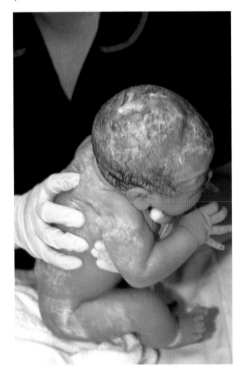

Your newborn baby will initially appear blueish in colour, although her body and face quickly begin to turn pink as the changes occurring within her respiratory system during the first minute after birth allow her to breathe air. However, her hands and feet may retain a blue tinge over the next 24 hours. If you are of Afro-Caribbean or Asian ethnicity, the initial blueness will be more noticeable around your baby's mouth, eyes, nose, and on the palms of her hands and soles of her feet. She will also still be curled up, and damp from the amniotic waters, perhaps even a little streaked with blood from birth. Her features will appear soft and rounded and she may have plenty of straight or curly hair on her head or none at all. She will have a fine film of down-like hair all over her body as well. Sometimes the skin of a newborn can be partially covered with a white creamy substance called "vernix", which has protected her while she was encased in the amniotic fluids. This will naturally dissolve into the skin within a few days.

If you have had a long labour, your baby's head may appear slightly pointed or asymmetrical at first. This is a normal occurrence due to the soft bones of her skull needing to overlap a little (known as moulding) in order to allow her head to negotiate the birth passage successfully. It will smooth out into a more rounded shape within a few days. Some babies are born with a slight swelling (caput) at the top of the head, which is caused by the skull pressing against the cervix during the birth process. Again, this will usually disappear within a few days.

Your baby's eyes will be a dark blue or grey colour – the colour is common to all newborns; her true eye colour may not show up for some weeks or even months. You will notice that she has creases in the palms of her hands and on the soles of her feet. If you are of Afro-Caribbean or Asian ethnicity it is likely that your baby's skin pigmentation will be paler in these areas yet darker around the nipples and genitalia. You may also find a shadowy bluish-black mark, or marks, over or around her lower back area. This is known as a Mongolian Blue Spot and is a normal variation in skin pigmentation. You may also notice that your baby's nipples appear slightly swollen; this is no cause for concern. It is a normal reaction to the withdrawal of the hormone oestrogen, which occurs as you and your baby are separated at birth – it will resolve itself within the first few weeks. The pale gristle-like end of her umbilical cord will be tightly closed off with a white plastic clamp that cannot be opened or fall off until the cord begins to dry out. The plastic will be cut by the midwife at your postnatal examination approximately three days later.

Your baby's behaviour straight after birth

Your baby has been used to a dark, warm environment in the womb, where all the sounds were muffled. She will therefore be highly sensitive to light, air temperature, and sound when she is born. A warm room with low light and soft sounds will provide her with an ideal place for a gentle entry into the world.

Your baby may not cry immediately and this is normal; it is not necessary to stimulate her in any particular way. The release of her chest from the compression of the birth canal as she is born, coupled with the sensation of relatively cooler air on her skin, will usually cause her to gasp and show continued efforts to breathe. If she does utter a cry within the first minute this may not be prolonged, although some babies scream enthusiastically for a few moments and then become quiet. If she seems slow to make an effort to breathe, your midwife may dry her gently with a towel or blow on her face a little to stimulate some reaction. This is usually sufficient to remind her that she has been born and now needs to breathe in air.

Your baby may open her eyes almost straightaway, especially if the lighting is low, and when you hold her in your arms the distance between your eyes and hers will be just right for her range of focus. The first prolonged eye contact you make with your baby may be the point at which you fall in love with her.

It is likely that the behaviour of your new baby will follow a particular pattern. After the immediate moments of activity following the birth she will then spend a quiet period looking around her, taking in her parents' faces as well as her new environment. An hour or two later, and especially if she has had a feed, you may find that she will fall asleep for some time. This is an important part of her recovery from the activity of being born.

Effects of pain relief on your baby's behaviour at birth

If you have chosen to have narcotic drugs (diamorphine or pethidine) during labour there is a possibility that your baby will be slow to establish her breathing, as one of the side effects of opiates is to depress the respiratory system. Although your midwife will have tried to ensure that you were given the injection at least four hours before your baby was expected to be born, as the drowsy effects of the drug tend to wear off after this period, babies come when they are ready and sometimes surprise even the experts. If your baby is not making good efforts to breathe within one minute, your midwife will call for assistance from another midwife who will take your baby to the resuscitaire to give her oxygen through a mask. Depending on your hospital facilities there will be a resuscitaire either in your birthing room or in a nearby room, where your baby's father can accompany the staff with your baby.

ASSISTANCE IN A HOME BIRTH
Although diamorphine or pethidine are available to you when you are having your baby at home, it is more likely that you will manage your labour using natural methods of pain relief as well as maybe some entonox (gas and air). Should your baby need some extra help to breathe at a home birth, the midwife has oxygen and other resuscitation equipment with her, as well as, usually, a second midwife for back-up assistance. It is possible for the midwife to help your baby to breathe with the oxygen (bag and mask) until you and your baby are transferred to hospital, should this become necessary.

Greeting your baby

Once you and your partner have been left alone with your new baby, you will naturally want to inspect her closely all over, despite reassurances from your midwife that she is physiologically well. This is a normal part of greeting your baby.

You will notice how soft and sensitive her skin is and marvel at how perfectly formed her tiny fingers and toes are. You will want to study her face for family likenesses, and when you stroke her palms you will feel how strongly she is already able to grip your fingers. As you trace your fingertips over the top of her head you will find that she has a small soft area in her skull; this is the spot where several of the skull bones meet but are not completely joined together yet, known as a fontanelle. She will have another smaller fontanelle at the back of her head near the base. These areas remain soft at birth. The rear fontanelle will close over within 6–8 weeks; the larger one can stay slightly open for up to 18 months old.

Holding your baby close, with her skin against yours, keeps her warm and helps her to establish a regular breathing pattern – as well as encouraging her to seek out your breast. You will notice how her normal breathing pattern is more rapid than yours and that she breathes through her nose. If you stroke her cheek you will see that she turns towards your finger using her natural reflex to root for food. She will enjoy you and your partner gently touching her and talking to her; your voices will be familiar from when she was in the womb and the sounds will be comforting. You may notice that she already responds to your words, she blinks, and is able to engage her eyes with yours. Your partner can enjoy plenty of cuddles, too. Many new parents express an anxiety about holding their newborn on account of the baby's fragility, but remember that she has already endured the process of birth, which means she is actually remarkably strong.

Spending undisturbed time together with your baby during the first hours after birth is an important part of establishing the beginnings of a healthy parent/child relationship. You will become increasingly used to what makes her happy and what makes her cross over the next few days, and your learning of this will continue for the rest of your life.

Your baby's first feed

Your midwife should be aware of your choice of method for feeding your baby and will be there to support you accordingly. However, if you have not yet decided which method of feeding you want to use, or even if you think that you will bottle

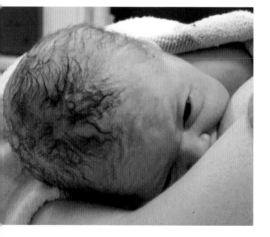

BREASTFEEDING YOUR BABY

Your baby has a natural rooting reflex to feed, but you can help her to get used to breastfeeding by offering her your breast frequently in the first 24 hours.

feed, it is still worth giving your baby one or two breastfeeds following birth. Through this process your baby can gain some benefit from the nutritive colostrum (*see* box, below right). You also benefit from the effects of the hormone oxytocin that are released again during breastfeeding as it helps to minimalize your blood loss following birth (known as lochia – *see* p.24.)

Babies will instinctively seek out the breast within the first hours after birth if they are not inhibited by the after-effects of any diamorphine or pethidine that may have been administered to the mother during labour (*see* p.19). Maintaining skin-to-skin contact also encourages your baby to look for nourishment. Research shows that if your baby suckles at the breast within the first hour after birth, you are more likely to continue breastfeeding.⊙ Do not worry if she only licks or nuzzles at your breast; she will still be swallowing a little of the colostrum that is so essentially rich in nutrition and protective qualities. Even if she takes only a few sucks, she is establishing an important link towards her next breastfeed, and you are helping to maintain her wellbeing simply by holding her close against your skin. Some babies also need a while to allow the fluids from birth to clear from their throat and airways before they will settle down to a good feed.

Your baby may, on the other hand, latch on and suck well at your breast straight away. This should not feel sore but if you have not breastfed before it may take a few moments for you to accustom yourself to the sensation of her feeding. You may also notice a cramping sensation in your womb as the oxytocin, the same hormone that controls your "let-down" reflex (*see* p.87) to feed, works on helping your womb to contract. This movement helps to avoid infection or excessive bleeding from the area where your placenta was attached to the wall of your womb, and is one of the ways in which breastfeeding assists your body in remaining healthy after your baby is born.

Encouraging your baby to feed

One side effect of opiate drugs such as diamorphine or pethidine is that they can depress your baby's sucking reflex following birth for as long as 24 hours. This, together with the sleepiness and disorientation that your baby may be experiencing from the medication, can mean that she is slow to take her first feed from the breast. Gently rousing her and offering her your breast frequently during the first 24 hours usually ensures your baby takes in sufficient nourishment, even from small amounts of colostrum, until she is ready to feed effectively. Your postnatal midwife will help you as you wish, and monitor your baby's wellbeing very carefully to make sure that she does not begin to suffer from the symptoms of low blood sugar (hypoglycaemia).

Whether you have chosen breast- or bottle feeding, your midwife should ensure that you have an opportunity to feed your baby before you are transferred out of your labour room, or, if you have had a home birth, before she leaves.

COLOSTRUM – A VERY SPECIAL MILK
Colostrum begins to be made in late pregnancy. Some women notice little yellow beads of colostrum on their nipples or find that they leak colostrum, but even if a woman doesn't notice any signs of it, it will nevertheless be there.

What's so special about colostrum?
Although it is made in smaller amounts, colostrum is high in quality:
• It is high in protein, minerals and vitamins, so it is very nutritious.
• It is also very rich in antibodies – these protect babies from germs. In the first days after birth, when babies are adjusting to life in the world outside, colostrum gives them a unique protection against infection.
• It has laxative properties so it helps babies to get rid of the meconium in their bowels (*see* p.25). This is important, as if the meconium stays put too long it can cause jaundice.
• It is lower in fat than mature milk. This is an advantage, because newborn babies produce very little lipase – the enzyme that digests fat – and so they would have difficulty in digesting large amounts of fat.

Your baby's wellbeing

From the moment your baby is born she will be assessed in different ways to check that she is healthy and to ensure her wellbeing. Your midwife will use a universally recognized tool known as the Apgar Score to assess your baby's condition one minute after birth and then again five minutes afterwards. Both these scores will be documented in your notes.

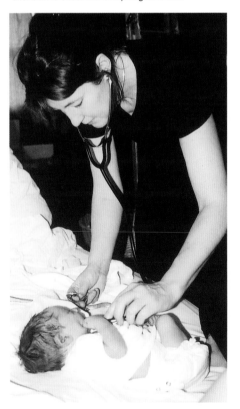

CHECKING YOUR BABY

As well as performing the Apgar Score assessment, the midwife will also gently examine your baby soon after birth to check that everything is normal.

Weighing and measuring your baby

After the Apgar Score (*see* box, opposite), the first assessment is usually to find out what your baby weighs, and this is often one of the questions you will be asked when you tell your friends and family that your baby has been born. A healthy term baby will weigh on average around 3.5kg (7¾lb), although a birthweight between 2.5kg (5½lb) and 4.5kg (10lb) is generally considered within normal limits. If you and your partner are particularly tall and well built, or short and petite, the size of your baby may reflect this, although this is not automatically the case.

The length of your baby may also be measured at this time, using a tape measure. The average length of a newborn is around 50cm (20in). In some hospitals her head circumference will be recorded as well (*see* also pp.76–7).

"Midwife's check"

Your midwife will perform a physical check of your baby at the same time as she weighs her. This is a gentle external examination and causes no discomfort to your baby. Your midwife will talk you through what she is looking at and can answer any questions that you may have, but she is primarily checking to exclude any immediate signs that your baby has been born with a congenital abnormality. You may notice, for example, that she explores your baby's head for any unusual swellings and inside her mouth to exclude a cleft palate or tongue-tie. She will also count your baby's fingers and toes, checking for webbed digits, and examine your baby's spine for any dimples or other signs of possible spinal defects. The midwife's check also includes an overall assessment of your baby's general wellbeing, including her temperature and whether she has passed any urine or stools.

Your baby will be examined again during the next few days, when her eyes, ears, heart, hips, and reflexes will be tested and her internal organs checked. This assessment is often referred to as the "first day check", but is usually performed any time during the first few days, just before you go home from hospital. Increasingly, midwives or advanced neonatal nurse practitioners (ANNPs) may perform this check, as well as paediatricians.

If you have had a home birth, your baby's "first day check" will usually be performed by your GP at around three days. If your GP has not supported your home birth and your care has been backed up by your supervisor of midwives, it is more likely that you will need to take your baby into your local maternity unit or hospital to be checked over by a paediatrician.

Vitamin K

Offered routinely to all newborn babies as protection against Vitamin K Deficiency Bleeding (VKDB), vitamin K is administered either by injection or in an oral preparation, depending on the policy of your maternity unit and on you and your partner's preference (see box, below right). The risk of VKDB occurring in a well, full-term baby is estimated at 1 in 10,000, yet the potential seriousness of the condition has led to a supplement of vitamin K being offered to all newborns.

VKDB is a condition whereby your baby can spontaneously suffer from some internal bleeding. There are two categories of VKDB: "early bleeding", which can occur during the first week of life, and "late bleeding", which may occur when your baby is between 1–12 weeks old. Symptoms include unexplained bruising, nosebleeds, and bleeding from around her cord area, through to invisible haemorrhaging within the area of her brain, which can have serious implications. Jaundice that lasts for more than two to three weeks can be a sign of liver disease, which has also been linked to many babies that develop internal bleeding.

Vitamin K is necessary for your baby's blood to clot effectively but she is born with only a minimal supply: the level of vitamin K is lower in babies than in adults but research has not yet discovered the reason for this. Artificial milk is fortified with vitamin K and therefore the risk of internal bleeding is low in babies who are bottle fed, although research has not yet investigated any possible side effects that might be caused by large doses of vitamin K. However, evidence does suggest that the greater risk of VKDB to breastfed babies is due to insufficient feeding over the first few days rather than to a deficiency in breastmilk.⊙ Breastfeeding well "on demand" from birth will encourage your baby's internal system to begin making vitamin K naturally. If she is not able or keen to feed well from the breast during the first 48 hours it is more likely that she will be at risk of developing VKDB.

SIDE EFFECTS OF VITAMIN K

A small study in the 1980s suggested that there was a link between babies that had been given vitamin K by injection and an increased risk of childhood leukemia. Further research did not confirm such a link, but there was a simultaneous rise in the uptake of the oral preparation. Other side effects include the small degree of pain suffered by your baby and, more rarely, bruising, bleeding, or infection at the injection site, and the wrong dose or drug being administered.

APGAR SCORE
There are five keynotes to assess:
• the rate of your baby's heartbeat
• whether she is making an effort to breathe
• whether she responds to stimulation
• whether she is voluntarily moving her limbs
• what her skin tone is like
Two points are allocated to each keynote so the final score is out of ten. Scores of seven upwards at one minute and nine upwards at five minutes are considered to be healthy Apgar scores. If the score is below seven at any point, it is likely that your baby will have needed some assistance to establish her breathing. A score of ten is usually not allocated at one minute due to the common blueish tinge of the baby's skin, as mentioned on page 18.

VITAMIN K – MAKING AN INFORMED CHOICE
Vitamin K can be given to your baby either by injection or orally. A one-off injection of vitamin K can maintain a store within your baby's system that offers her some protection from late as well as early bleeding. Oral vitamin K is used up by the body more quickly, and, for a breastfed baby, the dose will need to be repeated several times.

You should be provided with all the information necessary with which to make an informed choice regarding vitamin K prior to your baby's birth. If you remain unsure of your options, you can ask to discuss the issue with your midwife or a paediatrician. Whichever route by which your baby is given vitamin K, it is nevertheless creating non-physiological levels of vitamin K in her body. It is not yet known whether artificially boosting these levels is beneficial to all babies. If you decide not to give your baby vitamin K at all, ask your midwife to document this in your notes.

Preparing to leave your birthing room

If you have given birth in hospital then you and your baby will be transferred to the postnatal ward within approximately one hour of birth. If you have opted for an early discharge then you will be able to get ready to go home straight away (*see* box, right).

During the first hour following the birth of your baby your midwife will take your temperature, pulse, and blood pressure, and check that your womb is well contracted by placing her hand gently on your abdomen. She will also observe your lochia (blood loss). This will be red and much like a heavy period during the first 24 hours, although if this is your third or fourth baby it is likely to be more substantial. It is a good idea to try to pass some urine as soon as you can, even if you do not feel like it, as this also helps your womb to contract down.

You will be offered a bath or a shower as it is likely that you will be feeling hot and sweaty from all your efforts during labour. Having the chance to freshen up and change your clothes can boost your self-esteem and energy. Although there is no recent evidence to suggest that any additives to the bath water will encourage your perineum to heal, many women find that a few drops of lavender oil helps them to relax and enjoy their soak.

After your midwife has weighed, measured, and checked your baby, she can prepare a small bath for her if you would like her to be washed. Your partner may enjoy being involved with this, as it provides an opportunity for him to hold and bond with his baby and is also a way he can support the family unit while you may still feel exhausted or unsteady on your feet. Your midwife can help him if he wishes, but bathing his baby can be a positive start to building a father's confidence in participating in her care. However, in order that your baby can enjoy plenty of initial skin-to-skin contact time with you and does not become cold, she will more usually be offered her first bath on the postnatal ward some hours later.

Transfer to the postnatal ward

Once you are settled into your cubicle or room on the postnatal ward it is likely that your care will be transferred to other midwives, although in some maternity units you may benefit from the same carer or another midwife from your team. If your birth midwife hands over to your postnatal midwife, your new carer will check your womb and sanitary pad once more and offer you mild painkillers if you have had stitches. She will also look at your baby's cord area and ensure that her

TIPS FOR YOUR STAY IN HOSPITAL
• Ask for help if you want it (feeding, bathing, changing) – be persistent and remember that it may not be offered automatically.
• Have some thin nightclothes, as it may be hot in the ward.
• If your baby is in special care, ask for a wheelchair so that you can visit.
• Draw the curtains if you want to practise nappy changing in privacy.
• Remember that most other new mothers don't know how to change a nappy either.
• Pack some bath cleaner so that you can clean the bath before use.
• There is usually an area where meals are served, but they can be brought to your bed if you wish – for example soon after birth, or if you are feeding your baby.

gender matches that marked on her name bands. Your baby will be given a cot and will remain with you at your bedside throughout your stay in hospital. If you wish her to sleep in your bed with you, following a normal birth with no opiate drugs, your midwife can help to ensure that your baby is safely tucked in beside you. If it is the middle of the night your partner may be requested to return home at this point, but, if you have had your baby during the day he will be able to stay with you both until evening time, as you wish.

Time with your baby

Many women feel euphoric during the first 24 hours after birth, even a little "spaced out", as the cocktail of hormones (oxytocin, endorphins, and adrenaline) generated during labour still reap their benefit – especially following a natural birth. Although you may feel exhilarated and excited to be cuddling your new baby at last, it is important to try to rest as much as you can – even if you are unable to sleep; this facilitates your healthy postnatal recovery and encourages the production of your breastmilk. The initial 24 hours is a unique time when you can simply "be" with your new baby, hopefully without any other responsibilities. It is a time for taking your first steps along the lifelong path of discovering who your new child is.

If this is your first baby you will be shown how to change her nappy. You will notice (if she has not passed them already) that her first stools are made up of a greenish black sticky substance (meconium). The meconium clears through her system as she begins to feed and will change in colour and consistency within the first two to three days.

You will see that she breathes through her nose and occasionally holds her breath, which, as long as she remains a healthy pink colour rather than turning a dusky blue, is normal – although it is common for new mothers to constantly check their babies to make sure that they are still breathing. You will find out that she can gag and cough if she needs to clear her throat, and sneeze if she needs to clear her nose. She may seem reluctant to settle in her cot and be more content when she is held in your arms. This is no cause for concern. She has been contained within your body for the last nine months and she may feel safer staying close to you where she can smell your skin and hear your heartbeat.

If you have decided to breastfeed then you will already have begun to establish this, allowing her to feed when she indicates she is interested and requesting support if necessary to ensure that she is well positioned when she latches on and suckles.

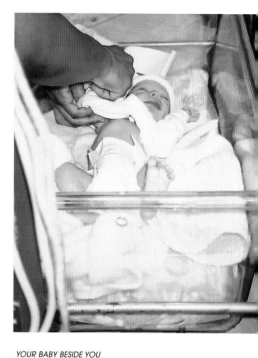

YOUR BABY BESIDE YOU
While you are in hospital your baby will be placed in a cot alongside your bed, so that you can begin to care for her.

DISCHARGE HOME – "SIX HOUR DISCHARGE"
If you have given birth in hospital you may choose to go home as soon as possible. You may leave directly from your birthing room with your partner, or be allocated a cubicle on the postnatal ward until all the formalities have been completed. Your midwife will need to complete the paperwork for your birth and give you the card with which to register your baby (*see* p.50), as well as various postnatal leaflets. A paediatrician will check your baby over before you leave. Once you are home, depending on what time of day or night it is, your community midwife will come to visit you within the next 12 hours or so – but do contact her if you need advice or support sooner than that.

Medical intervention at birth

During your second stage of labour your baby will be nearing the outlet of the birth canal but may not emerge after around two hours of pushing. At this point both you and your baby may still be well and strong. However, if she has begun to show signs of distress, or if you are exhausted, it is likely that your caregivers will offer you some medical help and suggest that you have a ventouse or a forceps birth. If you are having your baby at home, should there be any signs of delay or distress on you or your baby's part your midwife will request your immediate transfer to hospital.

Ventouse or forceps birth – the effects on you and your baby

In the first moments following a ventouse or forceps birth you may simply feel a sense of relief that your baby has been born safely at last. As long as she is healthy, you will be able to hold her against your skin in the same way as you would after a normal birth. Your partner will also be able to participate in those first precious moments with your new baby. It is likely that you will suffer from more severe bruising following a ventouse or a forceps birth, as well as from the effects of having had an episiotomy and stitches in your perineum (an episiotomy is usually inevitable for a ventouse or forceps birth). The doctor will attend to the birth of your placenta and then may need to spend some time suturing your episiotomy and any other

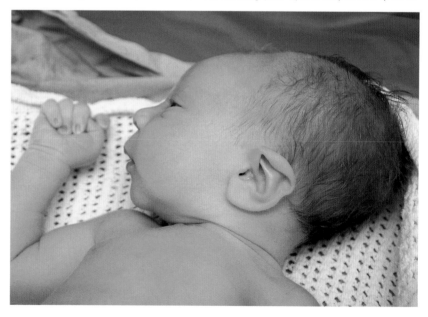

BABY'S APPEARANCE AFTER DELIVERY
If you have had a long labour or a forceps delivery then
your baby's head may appear cone-shaped initially.
This will right itself over the days and months ahead.

tears that you might have suffered during the whole procedure. Your midwife can help you to breastfeed your baby, if you wish to, during this time. Alternatively, you might prefer your partner to cuddle your baby until the doctor has completely finished stitching you up.

The doctor can give you a rectal pessary for pain relief once he or she has completed the repair of your perineum. Your midwife will also offer you some milder analgesia, such as paracetamol, and you may like to continue taking this regularly for at least the first 24–36 hours so that you maintain a steady level of pain relief. Some women like to use homeopathic remedies, such as Arnica tablets and a few drops of Hypercal tincture in the bath for painful wounds. By making sure that you are not feeling constant discomfort you will be better able to rest and enjoy being with your baby, feeding and caring for her.

Keeping your perineum clean encourages your stitches to heal; most hospital bathrooms have a bidet and it is a good idea to wash your vulval area each time you have been to the toilet, ensuring that you carefully pat the area dry after washing. You may also find it uncomfortable or difficult to pass urine at first; if this continues inform your midwife.

You will be transferred to the postnatal ward in the normal way, although if you have lost a lot of blood you may stay on the labour suite until your midwife is satisfied that your bleeding has settled. If you need to have a drip set up to help replace lost body fluids you can still be looked after on the postnatal ward.

You may find that you begin to feel a sense of disappointment at not having had a normal birth, perhaps even of having been cheated of the experience. Some women can feel sad that they were not able to give birth without help, or feel concerned that the instruments may have harmed their baby in some way. Whatever emotions arise for you following a ventouse or forceps birth, it may take time for you to come to terms with what has happened. This is normal. It is important that you feel able to talk through your experience with your midwife and your partner or others around you, should you wish. Your partner may also feel upset or shocked by the experience and it is important for him to be able to express his emotions too.

After an assisted birth it is possible that your baby will suffer from some bruising or soreness around her head and neck area. If you have had a ventouse birth you may notice a round swollen patch of bruising on her head, known as a "chignon", where the cup was attached; occasionally the forceps "arms" can leave a mark on your baby's cheek. These are superficial and will improve within a day or so. You may also find that your baby is particularly sensitive to touch on her head or even irritable when you pick her up or carry her about during the first few days. Try to move her as little as possible and to rest her head on a cushion while she is feeding rather than holding her at the back of the neck.

TREATMENTS FOR BRUISING OR TRAUMA
Some mothers like to give their babies a powder preparation of the homeopathic remedy Arnica, or apply some Arnica cream to help with the immediate bruising. Others later choose to take their babies to a (cranial) osteopath for the treatment of any trauma that they may have suffered during a difficult birth.

If you have a caesarean

Caesarean birth experiences vary hugely, as do women's reactions to them. However well you recover, you are likely to need to accept practical help from others. You may also like to ask about your recovery, mobility, pain relief, and, if you had an unplanned caesarean, about what happened and why. Don't be afraid to talk to health professionals, friends, and relatives about your needs and feelings.

Emotional reactions to a caesarean birth

Caesarean birth experiences vary enormously. If your baby was born by caesarean and you were fully involved and prepared for this you may feel positive about the birth. However, some women who have a caesarean can feel afterwards that matters were taken out of their hands. If they did not feel they were fully informed about the reasons why a caesarean birth was suggested, or they were not able to make choices during the birth, they can feel that they had no control. However, if you felt understood and respected during the birth you can still feel very positive, even if your caesarean was unplanned.

• Women can often be confused following a caesarean, feeling positive and negative at the same time. Women may feel that the birth was emotionally or physically traumatic, but obviously worth it as they or their baby benefited. It can feel confusing if the "mother" in you knows you have done something brave for your baby or yourself, while the "woman" in you feels disappointed or hurt.

• Caesarean birth may also feel surreal. Women have described how odd it can seem to walk into the operating theatre awake, lie down and then, very shortly, to have a baby. Some women can feel that the birth is very passive – a thought that conflicts with the concept of "labour". It is not unusual to feel positive about the birth and yet wonder what vaginal birth is like. However, for many women it is still one of the most amazing events of their lives.

• If your caesarean was unexpected or you felt out of control, you may have more negative feelings towards the caesarean. Some women experience a sense of loss for not having had the birth they planned and can have doubts about whether their caesarean was really necessary. You may feel disappointed or empty, as if you did something wrong. You may also feel that things should have been handled differently.

KEEP YOUR CIRCULATION GOING

If you lie in bed your circulation can become sluggish and both this and surgery increase the risk of a deep vein thrombosis. Many hospitals reduce this risk by giving support stockings to wear until you are up and about; you may also be given a drug to reduce the risk of clots. Your legs may feel a little weak or heavy after the birth; gentle leg and abdominal exercises will speed up your recovery and can help you to feel better. Your midwife or physiotherapist should be able to suggest some easy exercises.

• Some women initially experience little or no feelings towards their baby after a caesarean, and may even feel negative towards her. Women can even feel that they want someone to take the baby away, and blame the baby for their suffering. A caesarean can leave you feeling there is no connection between you and your baby, particularly if you had a general anaesthetic or felt "out of it" during the birth. Photographs of the birth can be really wonderful for filling in the gaps, especially if you have had a general anaesthetic or if you and your baby are separated straightaway afterwards.

• It is sometimes felt by other people that if the baby is okay then the mother should be okay. Perhaps you feel happy and are able to justify your experience because of your baby; however you may feel resentful that other people do not seem to acknowledge what you have been through, or that your caesarean may have been avoidable with better support. You may feel other women who have not had a caesarean will not understand how you are feeling physically or emotionally.

After the operation

What happens after your baby is delivered will depend on the health of your baby and, to some extent, hospital protocol. You can ask for your baby to be passed to you immediately so that you can begin skin-to-skin contact. Alternatively, you may prefer to wait until you are in the recovery room or back on the ward. Unless you request to hold your baby immediately she is born you may find that the midwife will take the baby out of your sight to be checked over and cleaned up before she is handed to you. If your baby needs medical attention you could ask the staff to keep the baby where you can see her; if this is not practical (perhaps your baby needs special care) your partner could go with the baby.

You can offer your baby her first breastfeed as the operation is being finished off or you may prefer to wait until you are in the recovery room or back on the ward. Whenever you decide to feed you are likely to need support from the midwife to help the baby latch on. You may still be numb from the anaesthetic and could feel very shaky. Many women find the most practical position is lying on their side.

After the operation you and your baby will be taken into a recovery room or back to the ward, where you will both be cared for by midwives who will monitor you closely for the next few hours. If you or your baby are very ill then you or she may need to be taken to intensive care, which means that you will be separated. Your partner may find this extremely difficult and feel very torn between staying with you and going with the baby; an additional birth supporter is invaluable in such situations.

POST-CAESAREAN COMFORT
Slippers that you can slip on and off are ideal, as you are unlikely to be able to bend over for a while. A sports bottle or a cup with a straw makes drinking while lying down possible. High-waisted knickers that come above the wound are more comfortable than lower-cut underwear as they keep the pressure off the wound. You will still need maternity pads, nursing bras, and everything else you had planned.

If you have had a general anaesthetic you may feel "chesty". Taking two or three deep breaths every hour should help to clear any phlegm that may have collected in your lungs. Supporting your tummy with one or both hands makes laughing, coughing, or sneezing easier. Also, bending your knees when lying in bed may be more comfortable.

"After I had to have a c-section I felt so deprived. Everyone else could talk about how it all felt, and I felt that I now wasn't qualified to say anything and that people would feel that I had taken the easy way out."

Physical needs

• You will have a catheter to drain your bladder, a drip to give you fluids, and occasionally a wound drain is used. It can be a shock to see all this equipment attached to your body, and it can also make it difficult to hold or feed your baby. You may need a lot of support initially to help you feel comfortable and safe. You will probably want someone to stay with you when you are holding your baby at first. If you do not have a friend or relative with you, ask a member of staff to support you; you should have a bell within easy reach to call for assistance.

• You will usually have a dressing on the wound when you come out of theatre. The midwife may remove this quite early on, as getting air to the wound will promote healing. You will also probably want to freshen up after the birth. As you will be unable to walk unassisted you are likely to be offered a bed bath.

• Women often feel a conflict after their caesarean between being a patient and being a mother. You may feel frustrated because you cannot reach out and hold your baby without getting tangled in tubes or feeling pain. It can be upsetting to hear your baby cry, knowing it will hurt you to reach her. You will probably feel like you need time to cope and come to terms with the operation and the pain.

• When sitting up, you may need to pull yourself up to a sitting position using your arms at first. Using several pillows in bed to prop yourself up may help you get more comfortable and feel more supported. If you know in advance that you will be having a caesarean, you may want to bring in some extra pillows of your own as using bright pillowcases means you can recognize yours easily.

• After the operation you will be offered sips of water, gradually progressing to more fluids and then light food. There is no reason why you can't start eating small amounts as soon as you feel well enough to do so. Food arrangements vary in different hospitals; you may need help getting to a dining room or reaching your food if it is left on your bedside table.

• You should be encouraged to get out of bed as soon as possible, certainly within 24 hours. Doing this may be quite a challenge at first, due to the soreness you will be experiencing. Bending your knees, keeping them together, and then rolling over, keeping your shoulders and hips in line, can make moving easier. Swinging your legs over the side of the bed and sitting up by pushing on your arms may help too. Ask your midwife if it is possible for you to have an adjustable bed, if you do not already have one, as this may help you to feel more comfortable and independent. When standing up, try keeping as upright as possible, as this helps to take the strain off your wound and back. Supporting your tummy with your hands may help you to feel more comfortable and lessen the feeling that the wound may come apart. When sitting down make sure you sit in an upright position, with support in the small of your back. Avoid slumping in a chair as this will put excessive strain on your back.

• Your catheter will usually be removed after about 24 hours. Drinking plenty of fluids, even if you are worried about going to the toilet, will help to prevent you becoming constipated. Make sure you don't wait until you are desperate for the toilet to go – you will need longer to walk to the bathroom and not waiting will cause you less discomfort in the long run.

• It is important to keep your wound clean and dry in order to reduce the risk of infection. Washing with a shower hose and drying with paper towels will prevent towel fibres getting caught in your stitches. Taking a plastic chair into the shower to sit on is a good idea, especially if you tire easily or do not feel steady on your feet.

• If your baby is in special care it is unlikely that you will be able to walk there to visit her and you will probably need to be taken by wheelchair. You may find it frustrating being dependent on other people to see or hold your baby but rest assured it won't be for long. It is a good idea to take a camera in with you to take some photos of your newborn, which you can then place by your bedside.

"I worked with the maternity team to plan how to avoid a second c-section. Although I still ended up having one I felt totally in control. I and the team caring for me had done everything we could to avoid it and I was happy that I'd tried and didn't feel cheated."

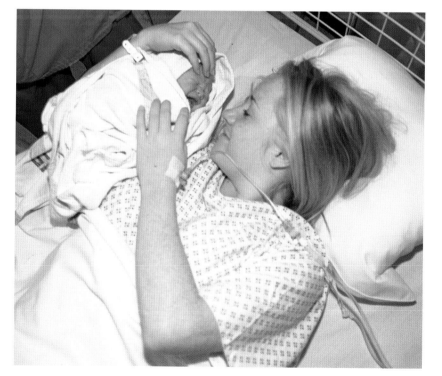

HOLDING YOUR BABY
It may be quite difficult to hold and feed your baby while you are surrounded by equipment (drips, etc) so make sure that you ask for help.

Premature birth

A premature baby is defined as a baby born before 37 completed weeks of pregnancy; an extremely premature baby is a baby born between 24 and 28 weeks in the womb. The moment of premature birth is likely to come as a shock. Whether you have had some warning, or have gone into spontaneous labour, this abrupt entrance into parenthood will not be what you had planned, or hoped, for.

There are many reasons why babies are born prematurely. For example, if you have had twins, triplets, or even more babies, it is likely they will have been born early. In this case you may have had some warning. Or your waters may have broken early, or a highly stressful situation may have started your labour. Alternatively, you may have suffered from pre-eclampsia (symptoms include high blood pressure and headaches), which can become dangerous and can only be stopped by delivering the baby. In a few cases, doctors discover that the baby is not growing well in the womb and decide that it is safer for her outside the womb. However, about a third of all premature births occur for no apparent reason.

Whatever the reason for your baby being born prematurely you can be assured that she will be looked after by experts who deal with premature births on a daily basis. While she will need care for a good few weeks, this may or may not be until her due date or beyond. The care team will carefully monitor her breathing, feeding, etc before making a final decision about when she is ready to be taken home.

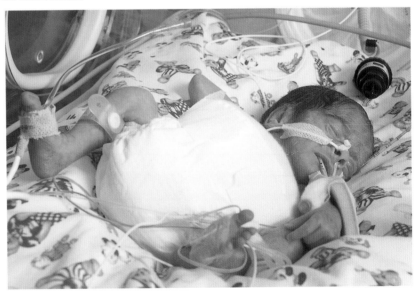

YOUR BABY'S APPEARANCE

Because your baby was born early she will probably appear very thin. She will also be surrounded by lots of equipment, which helps the experts care for her.

Directly after the birth

Your baby will be assessed and then transferred immediately to the neonatal unit. Depending on the kind of care that you need, you may only see your baby briefly before she is transferred. While you will want your baby to be receiving the best care, it will probably feel strange to have her whisked away. However, you should be able to see her whenever you wish over the coming weeks (although neonatal units do vary in practice, and in all units there will be times when parents will not be allowed to see their babies, such as during ward rounds).

Depending on your own condition (for example, you may have had a general anaesthetic), it may be some time before you are well enough to visit the neonatal unit. However, your partner will be able to go to the unit to see your baby and find out about her health, and in most hospitals parents are given a picture of their baby to encourage bonding.

Seeing your baby for the first time

Most parents are shocked when first visiting the neonatal unit. This is hardly surprising as it is full of equipment and strange sounds. However, it is the equipment surrounding each baby that keeps them warm, monitors their bodily functions, and supports their breathing.

The level of care your baby needs will, of course, depend on how early she was born, how she is responding to treatment, how weak she is, and how poorly she is. For example, most babies born before 28 weeks are likely to need mechanical help such as a ventilator, while babies born after 28 weeks may only need oxygen support.

Along with the unfamiliar equipment (*see* box), your baby will probably look different to how you were expecting. This will be because she was born at an earlier stage of development than a full-term baby. Premature babies often appear thin with very little body fat. They may also have a fine covering of dark hair, called lanugo – this will disappear quickly. Your baby may be tiny and her skin may be transparent due to the lack of fat.

Although all the equipment may be distracting, try to focus on your baby. The monitors are there for the staff to check your baby's progress and, while you may feel helpless initially, you are a vital part of their team. It is important that your baby gets to know your and your partner's voice, smell, and touch, and she will be reassured by your presence. Babies often recognize their parents' voices from the moment they are born, and therefore she will find hearing you immediately familiar and reassuring. For more information *see* pp.62–5 for caring for your premature baby for the first six weeks, and BLISS have produced a very useful parent information guide, *Information and support for the families of sick and premature babies* (2004).

EQUIPMENT IN THE NEONATAL UNIT

Here is a list of the equipment your baby may need during her stay at the unit:

• Incubator – this is used to keep babies warm as the temperature inside can be regulated. Some are closed boxes with hand-sized holes in the side – these enable doctors to control the humidity around the baby too. Other incubators have open tops to give doctors easier access to the baby.

• Vital signs monitor – small pads on the baby's chest, connected to a monitor, allow the electrical signals of the heart to be checked. The pads also detect any changes during breathing (a pause may trigger an alarm on the monitor).

• Blood gas monitor – this shines light through the skin to monitor the amount of oxygen in the baby's blood. It is normally strapped loosely to a foot or hand.

• Tubes – a thin plastic tube, in either the arm, leg, or umbilical cord, can be used as an intravenous line to give drugs such as antibiotics straight into the bloodstream. If a baby is too premature or unwell to take food or fluids through her mouth, staff may use very fine tubes into a vein to give nutrition. Sometimes a larger tube is placed into an artery so that doctors can take blood samples.

• Ventilator – this machine drives air through a tube placed in the baby's windpipe.

• CPAP – some babies need gentle help with their breathing, rather than a ventilator. Continuous Positive Airway Pressure (CPAP) helps babies breathe by providing air flow through two fine tubes placed in the nostrils.

Giving birth to twins

With the extensive use of ultrasound scans in the earliest weeks of pregnancy, you will probably have had some months to prepare for the birth of your twins; gone are the days when twins arrived by surprise! However, you may still feel uncertain about what having twins will mean to you and your family. Twins are still relatively uncommon (3 births in every 200), and most information about preparing for birth and coping in the early days is written with single babies in mind. Although you will be able to glean something from this general information, your experience will, in many ways, be quite different. In fact the dual experience of feeling both special and different will be something that you will need to become accustomed to as you give birth to, and bring up, your twin babies.

In the weeks leading up to the birth you will be monitored closely to establish the position of the babies, their rates of growth, and your own health and wellbeing. You may find that medical staff have clear ideas about how twin deliveries should be conducted to minimize risk, and that your late pregnancy and birth will be more actively managed than that of a woman expecting a single baby. Subsequently, you may feel you have less say in terms of a birth plan than parents of single babies. However, it is still worth discussing your preferences with your midwife, so that they can be taken into account as far as possible.

What to expect when you have given birth to twins

• The majority of twins are born at 37 weeks rather than the usual 40, although there is obviously a great deal of variation. Twins are usually smaller than a single baby, but can still weigh around 2kg (4½lb) each.

• About half of all twins are born by caesarean section, the rest are born vaginally. Interestingly, if both babies are well positioned, your labour, especially the second stage, may be less difficult than for a single baby, as each baby is likely to be relatively small. After the vaginal delivery of one twin there may be a pause before the delivery of the second, possibly of up to 20 minutes. During this time you will have the opportunity to welcome your first baby before the other is born.

• Many women find that they experience quite different emotional reactions to each twin in the moments after birth. Some feel an instant connection with one twin and not the other, based on their initial appearance or behaviour. This is perfectly normal. As with all births, emotions are extremely variable and love doesn't always come instantly. Your feelings will change over the course of the days, weeks, and months ahead, so in the first few hours with your babies try not to judge yourself unkindly but make the most of each moment.

• As twin deliveries are relatively uncommon, and because staff are needed to care for each baby, you may find that there are more people in the delivery room than you would expect. You may be asked whether you are happy for trainees to be present to observe. If you would prefer to keep the numbers of people present to a minimum do make this clear to your midwives.

• After birth a paediatrician will check over the babies. As long as they are both well, they will stay with you at all times and be cared for and transferred to the postnatal ward as normal (see p.24). Hold and cuddle your babies, either together or singly, as much as you like, just as you would a single baby.

• About 40 percent of twins will need care in the neonatal unit. This may be because they are very premature or small so will need special care until they have grown a little and are able to maintain their own body temperature and feed independently. Even heavier twins, particularly the second born, can be sent to the unit for a few hours or days if they are experiencing initial breathing difficulties or any other potential difficulty. You will be encouraged to care for them alongside the neonatal nurses as much as you can, and your midwife will support you to express your breastmilk as you wish (see the details on what you can do within the premature babies section, pp.62–5).

Feeding your twins

You can fully breastfeed twins in the same way as you would a single baby. Your body will know to produce the right amounts of milk in accordance with the demand from both your babies. Make sure that midwives or breastfeeding counsellors give you plenty of help to explore different feeding positions to suit all three of you. Learning how to feed both babies at the same time is a useful skill and one that you may need help to master. Handling and positioning two babies at once can be difficult at first so ask for as much help as you need. Feeding both babies at once means that the twins are more likely to settle together afterwards, which means that you will have more time to rest and care for yourself. However, some women prefer to feed their babies separately so that each twin has some individual attention from her mother. Whichever way you start, you can always change later on. Even if you have chosen to bottle feed, while you are in hospital and have the support of your midwife you may want to consider giving your babies the benefits of one or two early breastfeeds (see box on colostrum, p.21).

A CALMING INFLUENCE

Try laying your babies side by side in their cot, which can keep them calmer as they maintain the constant contact that they have had with each other over the past nine months.

2 UP TO SIX WEEKS

- The first six weeks

- Physical recovery after birth

- Your baby's first few weeks

- Naming your baby and registering the birth

- Keeping your baby clean

- What to buy

- Recovery after a caesarean

- Premature babies

- The first six weeks with twins

- If your baby is disabled or is ill after birth

- If your baby has special needs

- Depression and shock

- The six-week check – back to normal?

- *Feature:* Communication

The first six weeks

The first days and weeks after your baby's birth are unlike any other time. The arrival of this new person in your life is a dramatic change and you cannot remain unaffected. Life really will never be the same again. Looking back, some parents remember this time as a collection of blurred images and confusing impressions; however, what most remember, with acute clarity, is a time of heightened emotions, both joyful and anxious. Whatever your experience, remember that it is normal in the early weeks to feel emotional and unsure. You are very early on in your journey as a parent; you won't always know what to do for the best but your confidence will grow as you get to know your new baby and find your own way of being a parent.

The highs and lows

In the first few days after your baby's birth you may feel as though you have arrived in another world where everything feels different – and very intense. This is especially true for first-time mothers. Not only does your post-birth body feel strange and unmanageable, but your emotions are often powerful and extremely changeable. You may find yourself behaving uncharacteristically – one moment glowing with pride, love, and gratitude for your new baby, the next sobbing uncontrollably because you can't persuade him to feed. The only thing that is certain in the first few days is that you will feel very up and down.

Many new parents experience an initial euphoria and excitement after the birth. The waiting is finally over, the new baby is here, and they are at the start of a wonderful adventure. Although this feeling is very strong it may also be fragile, suddenly turning into fear, sadness, or anger following an insensitive remark from a midwife or family member. It can be alarming to be so sensitive and reactive, especially if you are used to being in control of your emotions, but experienced people around you will not be alarmed, as it is an entirely natural and normal response to the new circumstances you find yourself in.

You may feel very emotionally dependent on those caring for you, seeking constant reassurance and advice yet becoming upset if it conflicts with your opinions or seems to ignore the uniqueness of your baby and family. It may seem that there is both too much advice and too little information in the early days. It is a good idea to seek out those people whose advice and support feels helpful, and to ignore, as best you can, anyone whose comments you may find undermining or upsetting.

Feelings of unreality

Becoming a parent starts from before birth of course, but many parents find that their minds and emotions take a while to catch up with their new identity. At birth the baby becomes real and visible and can no longer remain the imaginary, secret baby that you daydreamed about in your head. Medical staff will call you baby's mum and dad from the start and it can feel odd to be addressed in this way for the first few days.

Many parents have feelings of unreality and disbelief to begin with. They may wonder, "Is this really my baby?" Some parents report waking from sleep having briefly "forgotten" that they are parents and may be left with an uneasy feeling of guilt about this, as if they have somehow failed to look after their baby by not thinking about him for a while. This experience is entirely natural and normal. As with any great life event, it can take a while for your new situation and identity to sink in and become real – no matter how prepared you thought you were.

Feelings of responsibility

Most parents feel the responsibility of becoming a parent very keenly. They may fear that they won't be able to meet the challenge. Newborn babies seem so fragile and helpless and their needs so hard to predict. You may actually feel in awe of the midwives and nursery nurses who seem to handle babies with such casual confidence. Some parents fear the prospect of looking after their baby at home without the full back-up of a medical team. If you are feeling this way remember that babies are stronger than they look; they have a drive to live and grow, equal to your drive to protect them. Your baby will make his needs known so do all you can to listen and respond to him as best you can.

Some new parents find that the overwhelming feelings of responsibility affect their ability to rest and find time for themselves. Mothers may worry that they will sleep through their baby's crying or that their baby will need them while they are in the shower or going to the toilet. Enlisting the help of those you trust to watch your baby while you rest or take a shower is important; you need time to look after yourself and recover from the birth, just as your baby does.

Visitors

Birth is an exciting time for everyone and chances are that your family and friends will want to visit you and meet your new baby. In your pride and euphoria you will want to see them too, but you may find entertaining visitors extremely tiring in the early days. It isn't just the practical issues of not being able to sleep while visitors are in the house, or feeling self-conscious about feeding or handling your baby in front of other people, as every visitor will also come with their own feelings and agenda. New grandparents may be full of excitement about their new grandchild, already looking ahead to the fun times they will have and talking

A MIXTURE OF EMOTIONS
In these first few weeks you will probably experience a whole range of emotions, including glowing pride, love, and an intense feeling of responsibility.

about who the new baby resembles and takes after. Friends, meanwhile, may want to catch up with all the recent news. You may find yourself feeling split between giving attention to your visitors and concentrating on your baby. It is not unusual to want to spend time just holding and looking at your baby and starting to get to know him, and having to engage in conversation with visitors can get in the way of this.

Visitors will probably want to hold and cuddle your baby and to say "hello" in a personal way. Some parents find that they have very strong feelings about this – perhaps resenting the fact that their baby is being passed around like a parcel. With your heightened sensitivity as a new parent it may suddenly become very important that only those who have permission touch your baby.

"The craziest thing is everyone says 'take it easy'. You don't listen because you feel fine – until you've overdone it and then it is too late. You're exhausted with no chance of catching up on sleep!"

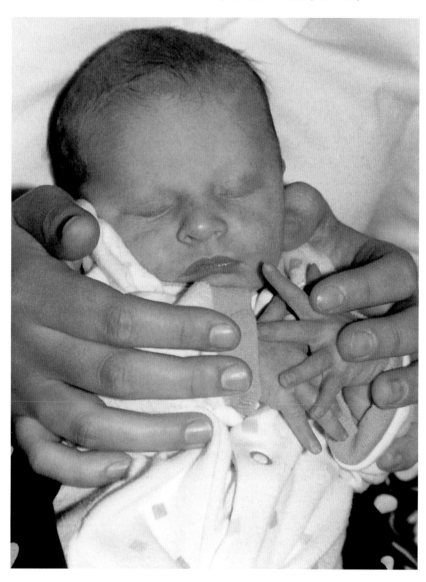

VISITORS

Family and friends will want to come and visit you, but you may have strong feelings about who you want to hold your baby in the early days.

Partners or another close family member may be especially helpful by taking charge and laying down boundaries for visitors. It can be useful to have a set of photographs available for visitors to look at while you find space in another room with your baby. At this early stage your baby's signals that he is ready to feed may be quite subtle and you need to spend as much time as possible focusing on him so that you don't miss early opportunities to get feeding established.

Considerate friends and family will understand that you need your rest and that short visits are better than long, drawn out ones. Visitors should also expect to be asked to help, by making refreshments and bringing in shopping for example. Most people who have had babies will remember their own experiences during this time and will be happy to help in this way.

Becoming mother and father

As you introduce your baby to your family and friends and gradually get to know him over the first few weeks you will experience some strong emotions. Many women feel a new bond with their mothers in a way they haven't experienced before. You may suddenly wonder if your mother loved you as you love your new baby, and the answer you find for yourself may either strengthen you or open up some previously hidden hurts.

You may also become keenly aware of the important people who aren't able to be present to share this new baby's birth. Past bereavements may resurface and you may be filled with longing and sadness for those who will never meet your baby. Friends and family who can listen to how you feel, and comfort and soothe you, will be invaluable at this time. Some new parents, wishing to be strong and capable for their new babies, attempt to bury these difficult feelings; however, they can return more strongly later. If you can accept your greater vulnerability at this time, and make use of any support offered, you are less likely to be taken by surprise by feelings of sadness and depression later.

Taking each day as it comes

In the first few weeks every day may be different from the last. Both you and your baby have a lot of adjusting to do. Very young babies are unpredictable – sleepy one day, feeding voraciously the next. Parents cope with this confusion differently and some may feel that they don't cope with it at all. At this very early stage, try not to let yourself be overcome by concerns and fears that belong in the future. Try to live as your baby does, from hour to hour and day to day, rather than planning weeks or even months ahead. Giving yourself over to responding to your baby's needs and your own, without thinking about what you should be doing next week, will put you in touch with your deep drive to love and care for this baby.

TAKE A BABYMOON

The concept of a honeymoon for newlywed couples is well known and accepted in our society. It is a time when the new couple get away from their daily lives to spend time together, enjoying each other's company and establishing their new relationship, before the responsibilities of daily life take over.

Why not celebrate the birth of your baby by taking a babymoon? You don't need to go away anywhere but you could plan to spend a day or two snuggled together in bed. Babymoons are great for establishing breastfeeding and are good for encouraging both mothers and fathers to slow down and rest after the drama of the birth. Of course lovely food should be eaten and treats enjoyed too!

Physical recovery after birth

Giving birth is a strenuous, physically demanding event – the energy levels that are needed have been compared to running a marathon. It will take time for your body to recover. You may feel there's an expectation to get back to normal as soon as possible after the birth of your baby, but it's important to acknowledge the time your body needs to recover physically. Even if you are not feeling particularly tired at first, it's best to rest when you can. The effects of birth, and the stress of disrupted sleep, may not hit you until a few days or weeks after the birth, at which point the accumulated effect of all these new experiences can kick in.

"When I had my first child I took pre-pregnancy clothes into hospital to wear after the birth and I was quite shocked to find that they didn't fit me and I still looked pregnant."

In the days immediately following the birth expect your body to feel a bit strange. For example, there may be aches in strange places that are related to your labour positions, and you may have bloodshot eyes from pushing.

If you have had a vaginal birth, your perineum will feel sore and bruised even if you did not tear or have an episiotomy. A small episiotomy or tear can take up to ten days to heal; a larger tear may take longer. If your wound has been stitched, a midwife will monitor its comfort daily and she may ask to examine the area – particularly before you leave hospital, if you are experiencing problems, or before you are discharged from midwife care.

To rest your perineum, you might find it easier to lie on your side. Avoid long periods of standing or sitting as this may increase swelling. If you are feeling particularly tender, ask your midwife to help you breastfeed lying on your side. To alleviate perineal pain when you are sitting upright consider using a Valley Cushion; this is a flexibly inflatable cushion and its shape can be adjusted to suit your body. (The enquiries line at the NCT can give details of your local Valley Cushion renting agent – 0870 444 8707.) The Kegel (pelvic floor) exercises that you did during pregnancy will stimulate the circulation in that area, promoting healing. *See* pages 162–3 for more information on suitable exercises to do in the postnatal period.

Sometimes stitches can irritate as they dry and tighten, but if they are causing any discomfort after a week tell your midwife, who may be able to remove them rather than waiting for them to dissolve. In the meantime you might find a cold compress helps. Put some ice cubes in a plastic bag, wrap this in a towel, and hold it against your stitches.

Good hygiene is important in order to avoid infection. Use medical wipes on toilet seats if you're in hospital. When using toilet paper take extra care to wipe

RESTING

Giving birth to your baby will have been extremely strenuous on your body. Try to rest as often as you can – why not take a nap when your baby sleeps?

from front to back only. To keep the whole area clean, stand in the bath and, using either a jug or the shower spray, run warm water between your legs after urinating or defecating and pat dry, working front to back.

When to seek medical help

If any of the following happen while you are recovering at home, you should ring the staff where your baby was born:

• Bleeding that gets much heavier, that is needing more than one sanitary towel per hour

• Prolonged reappearance of bright red blood loss

• Lochia (vaginal bleeding) with a foul odour

• Pain in the lower abdomen

• Raised temperature

• Sharp chest pain

• Localized pain in leg muscles or when you flex your foot, accompanied by redness and swelling

• Localized swelling, redness, heat, or oozing at your caesarean scar

Going to the toilet

After you've given birth your body needs to get rid of the extra fluid you carried during pregnancy, so you will need to urinate a lot during the first few days. For the same reason it's also normal to sweat more than usual at this time. If you don't seem to be passing much water, tell your midwife or doctor as in some cases this can be the first sign of infection. Also be aware of any burning sensation when you urinate, or general lower back pain, as these could indicate a kidney infection. There can be a stinging sensation when passing water while your perineum is tender; pour a jug of warm water between your legs as you urinate to alleviate any stinging. If you are reluctant to go, try sitting on the toilet in earshot of a running tap – it can help.

The thought of having a bowel motion can be alarming after birth. You may not need to go for a while as bowels often evacuate during labour. If your lower intestine has bruised, though, you may feel "churned up", as if you want to go anyway. There is also the psychological fear of pushing while you feel so tender. Do try to go, but don't strain. Take your time sitting on the toilet, relax, and see if anything happens. When opening your bowels, you might find it helps to hold a clean sanitary towel over your stitches to support them.

If nothing seems to be happening, make sure you are eating lots of fibre: fruit, whole grains, dried fruit, and bran. Drink plenty of water too. If you can, try to walk around to get your circulation moving. If you become uncomfortable after a few days, your midwife or GP can give you a gentle laxative to help. If you are feeling gassy, then sipping peppermint tea may help.

Many women have haemorrhoids (piles) after giving birth; these feel like small lumps around your anus. They usually retreat without treatment, but talk to your midwife about them if you are worried and if they are still there at your six-week check-up tell your GP. To help them disappear or reduce, avoid straining heavily when passing a motion; plenty of roughage in your diet will also help.

As your perineal muscles have been under strain giving birth, and may even have been damaged if you tore or had an episiotomy, it is quite usual to have temporary urinary incontinence. Some women may also experience faecal incontinence, depending on where the perineum sustained damage. Practising Kegel exercises will help you regain control of your pelvic floor muscles. If you experience any faecal incontinence tell your midwife, and inform your GP at your six-week check if you are still experiencing urinary incontinence.

Other things to be aware of

• It can come as a bit of shock to find that you still look pregnant after you've given birth. Your bump may be similar in size to how it was at six months gestation, though less firm – more like a half-deflated football. It will shrink and become firmer during the first two weeks after birth; while this is happening you could experience cramps, commonly called "afterpains", as your uterus contracts back to its original size.

• You will bleed after giving birth, even if you have had a caesarean. The bleeding is called lochia and is similar to menstruation. It will probably be heavier and last longer than your usual period. There will also be more clotting than you would experience with normal menstruation. Expect the discharge to eventually turn watery pink, then brown, and then yellow before it ceases. Bleeding may continue off and on for as long as six weeks, but one to two weeks is normal. You may find that the flow varies; for instance it may become heavier or gush when you stand up or move around after having been sitting or lying down. Breastfeeding may bring on heavier flow and cramps, as oxytocin, produced during breastfeeding, also acts on the uterus, making it contract.

• The place where the placenta left the inside wall of the uterus may be vulnerable to infection in the early days after birth. You can help to minimize the risk of infection by taking extra care to wipe from front to back when using the toilet. Similarly, it is also better to use sanitary towels rather than tampons, and to delay sexual intercourse until the site has healed. If your lochia becomes very smelly, this may be a sign of infection in the uterus and can be serious if not treated with antibiotics. Your midwife will ask about the lochia regularly, and may ask to examine your sanitary pad. If you are worried about excessive clotting or any other aspect of the discharge, keep your sanitary towel to show your midwife when she visits. As well as there being a heavy lochia, many women are quite tender following birth and so delaying intercourse until you feel ready is something that would be helpful to discuss with your partner.

• Between two and five days after the birth your milk will "come in"; this happens whether you are breastfeeding or not (*see* pp.86–7). The increased blood supply to the breasts, necessary for making larger volumes of milk, causes the breasts to swell with excess fluid. In some women their breasts become hot, swollen, and uncomfortable (engorged), making it hard for the baby to latch on. This will pass within about 24 hours; in the meantime feeding your baby frequently will help, as will cold compresses.

• While it is important to get plenty of rest during the recovery period, try also to keep active. Get up and walk about a little and change position in bed. This will help your circulation and start the process of letting your bladder and bowels recover from the delivery. If you need to stay in hospital for some time, a physiotherapist may visit who can give you a useful exercise sheet. Start gently working your pelvic floor muscles as soon as you feel able (*see* pp.162–3 for exercises suitable after giving birth).

POSTNATAL CARE

After birth, midwives are responsible for checking both your health and that of your baby. If you're in hospital you'll be looked after by the midwives on the postnatal ward until you leave; at home your care is provided by a community midwife. Ideally she will visit you daily until she feels she can discharge you at around ten days postpartum, but in practice visits may not happen every day. This may be by mutual agreement, but don't hesitate to telephone a midwife or doctor at any time if you are worried about yourself or your baby. If you are taking longer to recover, or if there are worries about the baby, then visits will continue for longer than 10 days (up to 28 days). Eventually, when the midwife is happy that you and your baby are recovering well, she will "sign you off" into the care of your health visitor.

Apart from monitoring stitches and lochia, the midwife will initially check your temperature and blood pressure. She will also check your uterus is returning to its normal size by feeling your stomach. She will ask about your bowels and your mobility, and how you are feeling generally. Your psychological health is also important, so don't hesitate to tell her if you feel you are struggling. This is not failure; it is quite normal after such a life-changing experience that can be physically exhausting.

The midwife will also want to know how well the baby is feeding and can help with both breast- and bottle feeding. She will check your baby's general wellbeing, including skin, eyes (they often become sticky, *see* Common Illnesses, pp. 232–5), and how your baby's cord stump is healing. Discuss any worries or concerns you have; you might want to write down questions beforehand so you don't forget to ask.

Your baby's first few weeks

You may have an idealized image of a baby in your mind before you meet your own, but newborn babies can look very different to how you may expect. The baby commonly seen in popular images is several months old – chubby, sturdy, smiling, with clear skin. Your baby will look like that eventually, but for now he may seem skinny and his head may look too big for his body. You need time to get used to this new person's appearance.

HEEL-PRICK TEST

At about day six, usually when you are at home, you will be offered a series of screening tests for your baby, to pick up any rare metabolic disorders. Your midwife will take several small samples of blood by pricking his heel. Disorders tested for include cystic fibrosis, phenylketonuria (PKU), low thyroid function, and haemoglobinopathies. None of these conditions are curable but they can be treated. For instance sufferers of PKU will need special diets, while children with cystic fibrosis benefit from physiotherapy. Babies usually get distressed during the sample taking. To facilitate the tests, keep your baby's foot warm before the midwife comes. Some women breastfeed during the heel prick to comfort their baby; others find it upsetting and prefer to leave the room. Do what feels right for you.

If your baby is born on time, or early, he will probably be covered with what looks like a white cream. This is called vernix and helped protect your baby's skin from the effects of being submerged in water in the womb (*see* p.18). If your baby is born late the vernix will have worn off, and his skin may look dry and flaky.

Initially your baby will hold his body in a foetal position, but this will gradually straighten over a few months. If your baby was born vaginally his head may seem a bit misshapen – it may appear elongated, a bit like an egg. This is normal and will right itself over a few days. If you had a forceps or ventouse delivery this will leave bruising and marks as well. On the top of your baby's head you will see a fontanelle. This is a soft area where the bones of the skull have not yet fused together; this allowed the baby's head to mould so he could negotiate the birth canal. Although it may look vulnerable, the fontanelle is covered with a very tough membrane so you can't do it any damage. You can sometimes see a pulse beating under the skin. Normally the fontanelle is flat or very slightly sunken, but if there is a visible dip it could be a sign of dehydration. If your baby is crying, lying down, or vomiting, the fontanelle may look like it is bulging but it should return to normal when the baby is in a calm, head-up position. If ever the fontanelle bulges outwards see a doctor, as this can be a sign that your baby has an infection. You will be aware of the fontanelle for several months until your baby's hair grows over it and you no longer notice it. It can take up to 18 months to close completely.

Your baby's eyes may be swollen, puffy, or show broken veins after the birth – they will clear up soon afterwards. It is quite normal for your baby to look as if he has an occasional squint. One eye may wander while the other is looking at something. This usually stops in a few months but if the squint appears fixed, in other words if the eyes are always out of alignment, you should report this to your doctor – as early treatment is essential to ensure the eyes develop normally.

It is normal for babies to have waxy ears, but you should report any other discharge to a doctor. Don't attempt to clean inside the ears as this can damage

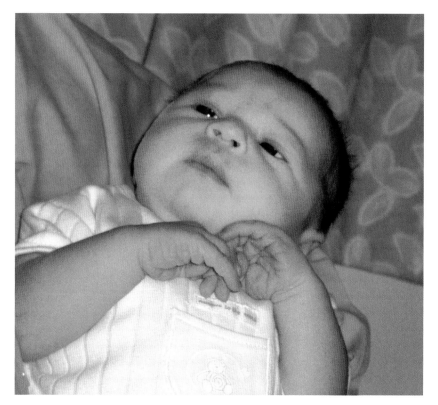

YOUR BABY'S APPEARANCE

Initially your newborn baby may look different to how you were expecting, but gradually his appearance will settle down into a more familiar "baby look".

the eardrum, although you can clean around the folds and creases. Many parents think their babies have sticking out ears, but that's only because he has such fine hair at this stage. The ears will become less noticeable as the hair grows.

Young babies' tongues often look white all over, which is fine, but watch out for patches of white on an otherwise pink tongue as this could be a sign of thrush (see p.103).

Your baby's skin may look blotchy and wrinkled at first, and sometimes there are darker areas (so-called strawberry birthmarks) on the forehead, eyelids, or around the back of neck. These are sometimes called "stork bites" and they usually fade over the months to follow. A "port wine stain" is darker, may be slightly raised, and will normally require some treatment to eliminate. In white babies birthmarks appear as pink or purple, in darker-skinned babies these patches of pigmentation look blueish.

Some babies get spots. Small white spots are called "milk rash" and they clear up with time. If the spots are red with a yellow centre, more like pimples, they are called neo-natal urticaria and are a sign that your baby's skin pores are not yet working efficiently; again these don't need treatment as they will clear up in time, but don't be tempted to squeeze them as you will leave scars.

Once a baby is born he needs to develop new blood cells and destroy the ones containing foetal haemoglobin. In breaking down, the old red blood cells

"At birth, the plates of my son's skull were really visible, but within a day they had settled back and I didn't think about it anymore."

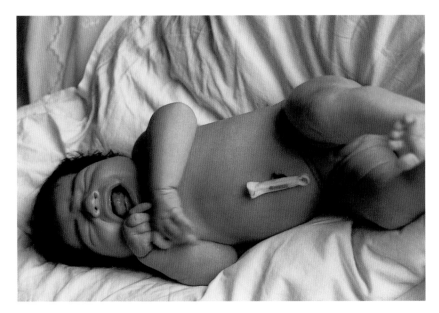

produce bilirubin (the main pigment in bile). If this is not cleared quite quickly enough from the bloodstream the baby may become yellow, or jaundiced, around the third day after birth. This is common and normal, especially in breastfed babies, although bottle-fed babies also get jaundiced. This "physiological" jaundice will normally peak at around five days and then start to decrease. Frequent breast-feeding will clear bilirubin from your baby's blood, so try to feed him every two hours until it passes. As long as your baby is alert when awake and feeding well and regularly, there is rarely any need to worry. However, if he becomes lethargic and too sleepy to feed, contact your midwife straight away, as high levels of bilirubin can be dangerous. If your midwife is concerned she will ask to take a blood sample from your baby's heel to check his bilirubin levels.

It is normal for your baby to have slightly enlarged breasts after birth, and for the genitals to be swollen. Girls may also have a vaginal discharge of mucus or blood. These are all due to hormones picked up from you in the womb and will soon fade after birth.

Some babies are born with quite a lot of body hair, especially if they were born prematurely. This will fall out, as in fact will the hair on their heads. When the mature hair grows in, it may well be a different colour.

Your baby's skin might seem to go through the mill in these early weeks. Up until now he has been in a sterile environment; emerging into the world his skin is the first line of defence against dirt, germs, and pollution. It is quite normal, therefore, for your baby to get rashes and skin complaints. However some rashes can be symptomatic of illness, so call your doctor if your baby has any other symptoms such as a raised temperature or listlessness (*see* Common illnesses, pp.232–5).

CORD CARE

After birth your baby's umbilical cord will be clamped with a plastic clip. This is removed after a few days. The cord stump itself will dry up and fall off in about a week. Until it does, your midwife will check it on her visits. There is no need to do anything special to the area or to clean it in a particular way. If you have any worries, talk them through with your midwife.

Your baby doesn't really need any particular creams or lotions, just warm water. A mild barrier cream is useful for preventing nappy rash, but don't use it unless your baby's bottom seems to need it. (If your baby's bottom looks at all red, treat it as nappy rash.) Nappy rash is caused by urine being left in contact with your baby's skin. To help alleviate the condition, rinse your baby's bottom and then leave his nappy off for a short while each day so that he has time without a urine-soaked nappy next to his skin.

Detergents can contain fairly strong chemicals, so you might want to swap to a milder variety and not use fabric conditioner. Be careful too about chemicals around the house – furniture polish or surface cleaners may leave things clean and sparkly, but there will be residues. ⊙

Babies often get blocked noses because the nasal tubes and throat are all very small so it is easy for them to get obstructed. If your baby seems to have difficulty breathing when feeding, your GP can prescribe some drops to apply in his nose just before you feed him.

Midwife or health visitor – what's the difference?

A midwife is someone who is trained to assist women and babies during pregnancy, childbirth, and the early postnatal period. She may have trained originally as a nurse, but many midwives now train directly for this specialized role. They are independent practitioners who are competent to help assist women in normal birth without other medical supervision.

A health visitor focuses on public health, and works in the community with a focus on preventative healthcare. She is a registered nurse who has had extra training in assessing the health needs of people in the community.

Your involvement with a midwife will probably be from about ten weeks of pregnancy until about ten days after the birth, but you will work with your health visitor until your child starts school, and possibly even beyond that. She is there to give you advice on the general health and wellbeing of your family. For instance, she may discuss diet, vitamins, formula, and breastfeeding. She will also visit you at particular times to assess formally your child's development.

Midwives and health visitors should offer you support and advice based on good evidence and also from experience. Don't hesitate to discuss things with them if you feel the advice is not appropriate for you. Build a relationship with them if you can, as they want to help both you and your baby throughout the pregnancy and early years of motherhood.

THE MIDWIFE CHECK OF THE BABY

In the first few days after the birth the midwife will be keeping an eye on you and your baby. In particular if the paediatrician had any concerns during his initial check, the midwife will want to follow these up. Ideally she will visit every day for the first ten days after the birth, but in practice this may not always be possible.

• Feeding – the midwife will ask you how the feeding is going, and should be able to help you with any positioning problems you experience if breastfeeding. It is worth talking to a breastfeeding counsellor, though, if you need further information or support (*see* box, p.82). Your midwife can also offer advice about bottle feeding, including sterilization.

• Weight – your baby is weighed after birth, again five or six days later, and a third time at around ten to twelve days of age. There is much discussion among professionals about "normal" weight gain or weight loss at this stage, but it is viewed as acceptable for a baby to lose up to ten percent of his birth weight at five or six days, and to have regained it, or nearly regained it, by the ten to twelve day mark.

• Another measure of progress will be your baby's nappies. The midwife will want to ensure that you are changing plenty of wet and dirty nappies (*see* pp.52–3).

• Jaundice – the midwife will be keeping an eye on the progress of any jaundice, ensuring that it improves before she discharges the baby.

• Cord – your midwife will check your baby's cord to ensure it is healing well. Do ask the midwife if you have any other worries at all about you or your baby.

Naming your baby and registering the birth

Once your baby has arrived, one of your first responsibilities is to name him and to register his birth. This is at once both a very personal decision and a very public event, through which you introduce a new individual to family, friends, and society at large.

INFORMATION REQUIRED FOR REGISTRATION

When you register your baby's birth, the registrar will ask for the following details:

Baby
• When and where your baby was born; if he is one of twins, or more; the registrar will also want to know the time of his birth.
• Your baby's sex.
• Your baby's full name.

Mother
• Your full name.
• Your maiden name if you are, or have been, married.
• Your date and place of birth.
• Your occupation at the time of your baby's birth or, if not employed at that time, your last occupation.
• Your usual address at the time of your baby's birth.
• Your date of marriage, if you were married to the baby's father at the time of his birth.
• The number of previous children you have.

Father (if his details are to be entered)
• His full name.
• His date and place of birth.
• His occupation at the time of your baby's birth or, if not employed, his last occupation.

Choosing a name for your baby is very exciting but can be overwhelming thanks to the enormous number of names available to choose from, the many books and websites of baby names, and the contributions of friends and family. When choosing your baby's name it is worth considering a few basic principles:
• A name that is currently very popular will probably be shared by at least one other child in your child's class at school.
• Say the name you are thinking of out loud with the surname to make sure you have not chosen something like "Mark Spencer". The same is true of nicknames and abbreviations – look for trouble.
• Double check that the initials of the names do not form an unfortunate acronym, such as M.A.D. or A.S.S.
• Once you have a fairly good idea of the name you like, try it out on friends and family to be sure that they can spell and pronounce it – never underestimate the eccentricities of spelling and pronunciation.

Registering your baby's birth

Once you have chosen your baby's name you will be able to register his birth (*see* box, left), apply for child benefit and his passport, and sign him on with your family doctor. In England, Wales, and Northern Ireland, your baby's birth must be registered within 42 days (in Scotland within 21 days) at the register office in the district where he was born, or in the district where his mother lived at the time of his birth. (The register office is often located in the local town hall but the hospital will be able to inform you where your local one is.) In some rural areas the registrar visits the local maternity hospital.

If you and your partner are married, then either one of you can register your baby's birth. However, if you are not married, your baby's father's name can only be recorded on the birth certificate:
• If you both attend and sign the registration together.

• If one of you is unable to go to the register office with the other, then you may make a statutory declaration acknowledging that you are the biological mother or father, which the other must produce to the registrar (this form may be obtained from any register office).

• Where you have both made a parental responsibility agreement (a standard legal form that you can get drawn up by a solicitor), or either of you has obtained an appropriate court order; the agreement or order should be produced to the registrar by either one of you.

If you are an unmarried father and your name is recorded on your baby's birth certificate, you will have parental responsibility for your baby (see box, right). If your name is not recorded you will not have parental responsibility.

If you and your partner are unable to register the birth of your baby, the registrar will arrange for the registration by one of the following people:

• The hospital or occupier of the house where your baby was born.

• A person who was present at his birth.

• A person who is responsible for your baby.

If your baby was born in Scotland, you should also take the card issued by the hospital where he was born and your marriage certificate, if applicable.

It is important that all the information that is recorded in the birth register is completely correct, as mistakes can take quite a bit of time and trouble to put right. This is why the person registering your baby's birth should check all the information very carefully before signing the register.

If your baby is born overseas and you are a British citizen you can register his birth at your nearest British Embassy or High Commission office. You do not have to register your baby's birth at such places, but it can often be useful for him to have a British birth certificate and for his birth to be recorded in the UK. The Embassy or High Commission Office will need to see certain documents to prove the nationality of your baby, including the following: your baby's local birth certificate, full birth certificates for both you and your partner or other evidence of British nationality, your marriage certificate (when applicable), and the British passport of either the baby's father or mother.

WHAT IS PARENTAL RESPONSIBILITY?

Parental responsibility is a legally defined term that means being responsible for:

• Your baby's wellbeing – looking after, feeding, and clothing him.

• Making decisions about his schooling.

• Deciding whether to consent to medical treatment when appropriate.

• Representing him in legal proceedings.

• Making decisions about his religious upbringing.

The law sets out who has parental responsibility for a baby. You have it automatically if you are:

• Your baby's biological mother.

• Your baby's biological father and were married to his mother at the time of his conception or birth, or you married your baby's mother after his birth.

• An adoptive parent once an adoption order has been made.

Even if the marriage breaks down, both the baby's father and mother will continue to have parental responsibility.

Previously, unmarried fathers did not have the same rights and responsibilities as married fathers. However, the law has changed and it now gives an unmarried father parental responsibility where he and the mother have both their names on the birth certificate. The new law is not retrospective, so unmarried fathers whose children were born before 1 December 2003 can still only get parental responsibility for their children by:

• Making an agreement with their child's mother.

• Applying to the court for a parental responsibility order.

• Marrying their child's mother.

Keeping your baby clean

Many parents are anxious about bathing their babies, and many babies don't like being bathed either, but you don't need to bathe your baby every day. However, it is a good idea to "top and tail" him (to wash his face and bottom regularly). A young baby will wee a lot – up to as many as 20–30 times in 24 hours – but you will not normally be aware of this except for when you change his nappy, which will probably be wet or heavy. As your baby matures he gradually gains control over his bowel and bladder, so that the frequency of wetting and dirtying his nappy will decrease.

STEP-BY-STEP GUIDE TO BATHING YOUR BABY
- Get the room as warm as you can before you start – babies chill quickly (see box, right).
- Run the bath to body temperature – test it with your elbow – it should feel neither hot nor cold but neutral.
- Undress your baby except for his nappy. Wrap him in a towel on the changing mat next to the bath. Wash his face.
- Take off his nappy last and clean his bottom.
- Lift your baby into the water with one arm behind his shoulders and neck, holding his outside arm with your hand. Place your other hand under his bottom. Once his bottom is resting on the floor of the bath, you can free that hand to wash him.
- Scoop some water up onto the back of his head to wash his hair. You don't need to use shampoo, as warm water is enough for a young baby.
- Splash water onto his tummy and over his legs. Many babies enjoy this sensation, especially if you sing and chat as well.
- When you are both ready, slip your free arm back under his bottom and hold his legs as he will now be slippery, then lift him out onto the towel.
- Dry, paying particular attention to skin folds.

Changing your baby's nappy

Your baby's first bowel motion will be of meconium – a sticky black poo, like tar, which is difficult to clean. Occasionally you may also see blood in these early stools; this comes from maternal blood swallowed during delivery. The very early urine may contain a substance called urates, which is red and can be mistaken for blood – although it looks more like brick dust in the nappy. If you are at all concerned, speak to your midwife, health visitor, or GP.

After the meconium has cleared, which can take from 24 hours to several days depending on how often your baby feeds, breastfed babies will have a mustardy colour, sweet-smelling poo the consistency of scrambled eggs. (If your baby is not producing yellow motions by day five it may indicate that he is not getting enough milk and can be a cause for concern.) Bottle-fed babies will have poo more like an adult's, but it should be soft. If your baby's motion is hard or dry then he may be constipated, so talk to your midwife or doctor. Breastfeeding your baby colostrum helps meconium pass through his system more quickly. If the meconium is not excreted quickly, then he is more likely to get jaundice as bilirubin is reabsorbed from the gut.

A doctor should see any baby who has been dry for 24 hours. Your baby will also move his bowels frequently, though irregularly. A baby who is not moving his bowels at least once a day in the first few weeks needs to be monitored. After a couple of months he may not be wet every time you change him, and you may begin to see a more regular pattern to his bowel movements.

It is safest to change your baby's nappy on a changing mat on the floor. Be aware that when you take off the nappy, your baby will often wee – so have a small cloth ready to fend off the spray from a boy's genitals, and lay a girl on a towel to soak up any spills, otherwise you will find her whole back gets wet.

Take off the dirty nappy and clean your baby's bottom, just cleaning what you can see. Don't try to clean inside the vagina or pull back the foreskin. Girls need to be wiped front to back, to keep soil away from the genitals. Then hold the ankles, lift your baby's bottom into the air and slide a fresh nappy underneath. Bring the nappy up between the legs and fasten the tabs.

If your baby has nappy rash use a barrier cream and, if possible, let him go without a nappy by laying him on some towels to have a kick around.

Topping and tailing

If you can cope with kneeling, it's easiest to work on a changing mat on the floor, as you won't need to worry about your baby rolling off as he gets bigger. As you work, you can make eye contact and talk to your baby, so choose a time when he is alert and ready to interact.

You need to avoid spreading any infection, so cotton wool balls are useful for washing with as you can throw them away after use. Immerse each one in a bowl of warm water and squeeze it out so it's just damp. Start by wiping each eye with a separate ball, working from the inner corner outwards. Use another ball to wipe around his mouth and nose. Finally take another ball and clean his ears, neck, and face, paying attention to the neck creases where milk and fluff get trapped. Never put anything like a cotton bud in his ears or nose; just wipe what you can see. You can then wash his hands and feet, looking out for sharp fingernails. Babies often scratch themselves with these so remove any scraggy ends – either with tiny scissors or you could chew them off. Finally you can "tail" him – take off his nappy and wash his bottom and genitals. If he has a dirty nappy and you want to start with the "tailing", then change the water before you "top".

Giving your baby a bath

You don't need to buy a special baby bath – when your baby is tiny he could probably fit in the sink, but very soon he will need to go in the main bath, either with you or supported by you. A rubber mat might be useful, as babies can feel slippery. It is probably not safe to buy a baby bath chair – the temptation to leave your baby propped in it or to turn away for a minute to grab something will always be there, and could be dangerous.

Some babies dislike being unwrapped as they feel unsupported and unsafe. In this case you could keep him swaddled in a towel until the last minute. Lower him slowly into the water so he does not feel he is falling. It might also help to hold his arms by his sides while you lower him.

Dads are often better at bathing a baby that seems insecure, as their bigger hands feel more supportive. You could also co-bathe, but make sure there is someone in your home to pass your baby to when you want to get out as it is difficult, and potentially dangerous, to get yourself and your baby out together.

KEEP YOUR BABY AT THE RIGHT TEMPERATURE
Be aware that babies are not very good at maintaining their body temperature. The best way to check is by feeling your baby's abdomen, as his hands and feet may feel cold even when his body is warm.

If your baby is naked, air temperature lower than 29°C (85°F) will mean he is using up energy to keep warm. Obviously you will not keep your home at that temperature, but it is worth thinking about when you are bathing him, because if the bathroom is chilly he will cool off very quickly.

Unless your baby is outside a lot, or you have a particularly draughty home, your baby is more likely to overheat, often because of too many clothes. Think about how many layers you need and be guided by this – your baby won't need a lot more.

Even in hot summer babies can cope quite well with the heat, as long as they are not too wrapped up. Keep your baby out of direct sun, as his skin is vulnerable to burning.

EXPERIMENT WITH BATHTIME

Some babies take to baths well, while others dislike them, so you may have to experiment to find a way you both enjoy the experience – such as co-bathing.

What to buy

Before your baby arrives it can be tempting to buy lots of equipment, toys, and clothes. But children are expensive, and they get more expensive as time goes on. So you should try and limit yourself to only buying what you really need.

Traditionally, people buy clothes, teddies, or toys as presents for a new baby, so you are unlikely to need to buy these in the early months. You may want to start with just a set of babygros for the first few days. Look for clothes with poppers so that you can easily get to the nappy area, and avoid clothes that have to be pulled on and off over your baby's head as many babies don't like this sensation. If your baby is born at term and is of an average weight, you might want to buy clothes for the three months age group rather than newborn, as baggy feet won't matter and you'll get more wear out of them. Clothes for premature or very small babies are available from the large chain stores. Remember, too, that you can get hold of baby clothes cheaply in charity shops, car boot sales, or NCT nearly-new sales.

Think about waiting until you actually need something before you buy it, and then choose according to your family's developing lifestyle. There is not very much that is essential to buy, but most parents will take their baby in a car at some point so it's vital to buy an appropriate car seat for your baby's age (see pp.56–7).

Nappies

Probably one of your biggest expenses over the first two years of your baby's life will be nappies, so it's worth thinking carefully about which type of nappy you're going to use. There are basically two types – those that are washed and reused, and those that are disposable (see box, p.56).

Washable nappies are easier to fit than the terries that previous generations had to use. They are now shaped to fit your baby's bottom, usually have Velcro fastenings, and are less bulky – as well as less likely to leak. You line them with a thin liner so that you can flush away the worst of the mess and then put the nappy to soak in a bucket before washing it at your convenience.

Nappy laundering services are also available. They take away your bucket of dirty nappies once a week and leave a clean supply in exchange. You don't buy these nappies – they are on hire, but are washed at high temperatures in hospital laundries so are hygienic to use. Using this service should work out at about the same cost as using disposables.

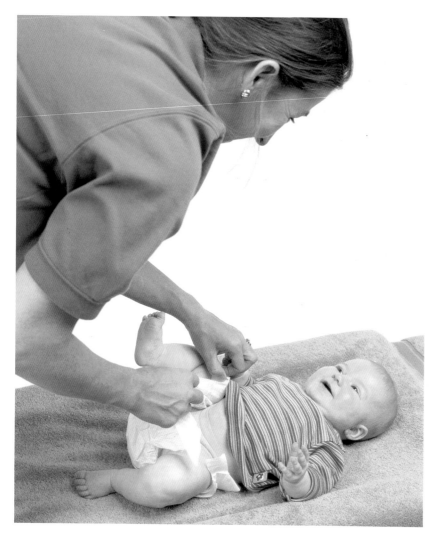

There are a range of nappies available nowadays. You can choose from reusable or disposable, or you might want to use a combination of both.

Before you make your decision as to which type of nappies to use, you will probably find it useful to ask other mothers what they've done. You can often buy cloth nappies second-hand at NCT nearly-new sales or car boot (garage) sales. Weigh up the various costs. Cloth nappies are usually cheaper, especially if you have more than one child, though the initial outlay is quite high.

If you are intending to wash nappies yourself, think about the amount of space you have for drying them; a large airing cupboard would be useful, but you may not have one. If you have to tumble dry, factor in the cost of the extra electricity. Be aware that you will be doing lots more washing anyway now with a baby.

Other items to consider

• There is a range of expensive baby-changing furniture on the market, but in fact all you really need is a plastic mat. Some people choose to allocate a particular area in their home for changing their baby's nappy, perhaps near a sink, where they can keep the mat and a supply of nappies. Other people prefer to be portable and take the items they need to whichever room they are using. Think about which way works best for you. It is useful to have a changing bag packed ready to go out by the front door containing a few nappies, some wipes or cotton wool and water, plastic bags for soiled nappies, and a fold-up change mat or towel. It is also best to have a complete change of clothes in case your baby has a really messy nappy when you're out. You might also want sun cream and a hat in the summer, and a woolly hat and coat in winter. The changing bag can also double up as a downstairs nappy-changing station to save you going upstairs.

• If you have a baby who dislikes being put down, you are probably going to want a good-quality sling. These vary in price tremendously, but your baby is heavy and is going to get heavier so you want one that's supportive and allows you to change your baby's position as he gets older. If you travel on public transport a sling is ideal. Look at several different models and ask for advice before you decide. If possible, borrow one from a friend and see how you and your baby like it.

• You may want to wait until you have your baby and have thought about what would best suit your lifestyle before buying a pram or pushchair. A small foldaway pushchair is cheaper, and easier to take on and off public transport or to stow in the boot of a car, but may not be suitable for a tiny baby who needs to lie down rather than be more upright. A sturdier and more expensive pushchair allows you to take your baby in it from birth, and usually has a luggage rack for a changing bag and shopping, but being bigger and heavier it will take up a lot of space in the boot of a car, and may clutter up your hallway. You may also want to think about whether the baby will face towards you or away from you. Some pushchairs are adaptable so that you can choose either position. Prams are expensive, but last for years so any relatives or friends with older babies could probably lend you one. Be wary about buying a secondhand one from someone you don't know though.

• If you are in and out of your car a lot, you might want a car seat that straps onto a set of wheels to double up as a pushchair. If you walk everywhere you might want a more robust pushchair – perhaps even an off-road one, but think about how much rough terrain you will really be crossing before purchasing this type.

• There are so many car seats available that you need to be careful that the one you select will suit your car. Some garages will check your baby seat for you to check that it is properly fitted (ask your local council's road safety department for the nearest garage offering this service). Check the label to make sure that it conforms to government safety standards. Look for the British Standard Kitemark or European Regulations Mark (EUR 44.03). It is not safe to buy a secondhand car seat.

• Read the section on where your baby should sleep before you buy a cot (*see* Where to sleep, pp.124–7.) You might decide to bed-share or you might want to buy a cot that slots onto the side of your bed. Moses baskets are cute, but unless your baby is premature you may not get much use from one as babies can grow out of them in a few weeks.

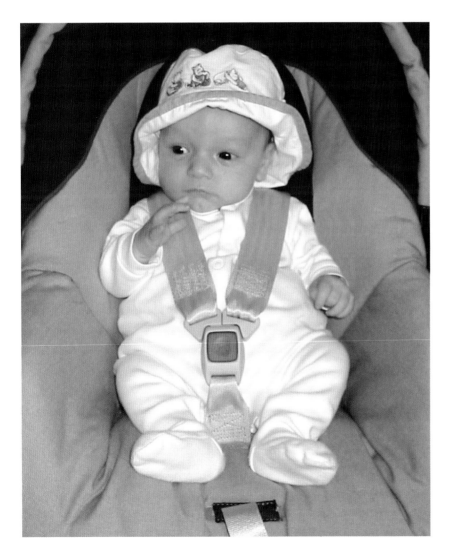

CAR SEAT SAFETY

It is vital that you ensure you have the right car seat for your baby's age, as well as for your make of car, and that it is correctly fitted.

Recovery after a caesarean

You are likely to be in hospital for three or four days after your caesarean, although your stay may be longer if you or your baby need extra care. Some women go home sooner; discuss what you feel is best for you with the hospital.

On the way home you may find the car journey quite uncomfortable, as you will probably feel every bump. Pillows placed across your stomach or behind your back can help to make you feel more comfortable. Relaxation or breathing exercises may be helpful too.

Once you get home you should be able to do most things for your baby – change his nappies, bathe him, and so on – although you will probably need help with tasks such as filling the baby bath, if you use one. Although you will probably be able to take care of yourself on a personal level, you may feel you need someone to help with the domestic side of life. Taking gentle exercise, resting as much as you can, and listening to your body will help your recovery. Remember that you have had major surgery so don't expect to be able to do everything you normally do straightaway.

You may find that you feel more emotional once you get home and have time to reflect on the birth. If your caesarean was unexpected you may be particularly affected. Many of the feelings discussed on pages 28–9 will be just as relevant now as immediately following the birth. At what point the events and feelings around the birth catch up with you will vary from woman to woman and from birth to birth.

Recovering from surgery

The stitches in your wound will usually be removed before you leave hospital (although the community midwife can do this if necessary). Try to relax when your stitches are removed; breathing out slowly can help you to stay feeling calm.

You will be advised to avoid lifting anything heavier than your baby for approximately the first six weeks. Most women can cope with carrying their baby (using a sling can be helpful), although some women find the baby's feet "kick" against the wound. When sitting down, you may feel more comfortable if you place cushions or pillows behind your back or over your stomach to ensure you are well supported. A footrest can also help to make you feel more comfortable, especially while breastfeeding.

If possible, let the fresh air reach your wound, as this can help the healing process. Some women like to look at their scar, others don't. You may find a mirror helpful, particularly if you still have quite a "pregnancy tummy" that overlaps your scar. Your wound may also itch or be numb in patches but this is normal as the wound heals – the regrowth of shaved hair can be very itchy too.

You will still have lochia (vaginal bleeding) following a caesarean. If it is very heavy, smelly, or you are worried about the blood loss, speak to your midwife. Postpartum infection is more common following a caesarean so it is important to check with your midwife if you feel the bleeding is abnormal in any way.

After a caesarean some women complain of abdominal pain radiating into the shoulder. This is usually trapped wind. Sipping peppermint cordial or tea can help to relieve this wind pain; the midwife may recommend using peppermint oil.

You will gradually be able to come off your painkillers. How quickly is down to the individual, but most women are in less pain after about two weeks.

Practical tips for when you get home

If you have had a caesarean, your needs may be different from many women who have experienced a vaginal birth. You are likely to need help from people, so that you can look after your baby.

Lining up help from your friends and family, and getting your visitors working, can ease your load. Guests who can help prepare meals, put out washing, do vacuuming, or bring some shopping can be a great help. If you can afford it, you may wish to think about paying someone to do your cleaning, ironing, or other jobs for the first few weeks (see box, right). Asking people for help allows you to spend as much of your time and energy as possible looking after yourself and your baby, rather than the home. If you've been used to being independent, or you do not like asking for help, you may find this difficult. However, many women acknowledge that accepting help when recovering from any birth helps to speed their recovery. Try not to see "asking for help" as a failure to cope but as a necessary part of being a new parent.

Carrying your baby up and down stairs can be very tiring. Setting up baby-changing units upstairs and downstairs can avoid this inconvenience. You might want to think about setting up a bed for you and your baby downstairs, if you think this would be helpful. You could rest on the sofa; however it is recommended that you never fall asleep with your baby on a sofa, as this increases the risk of cot death. Having a kettle upstairs is useful for preparing a hot drink for you, or for warming bottles for night feeds if you are bottle feeding.

If you have a toddler or older child they will often be keen to "help" you with simple tasks. Explain to them that you cannot lift anything heavy, as this can help them understand why you can't pick them up as you did before. Having "picnics" together on the floor reduces the need for lifting toddlers into high chairs and can be fun for all your children. You will still be able to cuddle your children, providing you are sitting down and you use lots of pillows around your stomach for protection.

DAY-TO-DAY HELP

Help can be invaluable, even if it is only short term. Day-to-day help can include:

- Doula, nanny, or nurse
- Domestic or home help
- Nappy delivery/washing services
- Laundry and ironing services
- Mobile hairdresser
- Mobile library
- Milk or grocery delivery
- Online shopping
- Equipment hire – baby equipment or mobility aids

Making a "staircase" of steps, books, chairs, or other household items can be a good way to help a toddler climb into a high chair, bath, or cot.

Going out for walks is good exercise, but don't be too ambitious at first. If you have got steps leading to your front door, a ramp will help you to get the pram in and out of the house.

You are likely to be advised to avoid driving, although there is a difference of opinion as for exactly how long. If you intend to drive before your six-week post-natal check, you will need to confirm that you are insured. You also need to be confident you can stop in an emergency, and can drive comfortably without putting too much strain on your abdominal muscles – especially when steering and operating the pedals. However, most women do not feel up to driving for the first few weeks, and therefore need help with transport.

When making love you may feel anxious about the wound and be worried about putting any pressure on it. You may find it helpful to discuss your fears with your partner, as he may also be frightened of hurting you. Taking things slowly will allow both of you to regain confidence in your body. The wound is normally strong and well healed in less than a month, but you may feel more comfortable if you try making love in different positions that do not put it under strain.

Where to get help

Following a caesarean birth you may need extra support. If it is necessary, the community midwife can continue to visit for as long as you both feel she needs to do so. Your health visitor should also visit you at home initially and may also be

SUPPORT AT HOME

A community midwife or health visitor should be able to continue visiting you at home until you both feel it is no longer necessary. Make the most of this support by chatting over any concerns that you may have.

able to continue to visit until you can get to the clinic, if you wish. If you are worried about your health you can also speak to your GP, who can make home visits if appropriate.

In some circumstances you may receive some of your postnatal care from the hospital. Some women have their six-week check from their obstetrician, but this varies from hospital to hospital (*see* pp.76–7). However, women can ask for an appointment with their obstetrician at any time, if they want one. Indeed this may be particularly useful for women with unanswered questions about the birth or their recovery. If you have had any complications you may see other health professionals, such as obstetric physiotherapists.

You can approach your local council for extra help as it may be possible to get some help around the house or for your other children. Voluntary drivers, hospital transport, school taxis, and "dial-a-ride" may be available to you, especially if you need to get to the hospital for appointments, or if your baby is in special care. Services are means-tested and availability varies from area to area but, if you feel you could do with extra help, it is worth investigating what is available, especially if you are on your own or your partner is unable to help support you for any reason.

Talking it over

Emotions after a caesarean section can be complicated and confusing. Although many women are quite happy, others find themselves on an emotional rollercoaster with loss, joy, grief, happiness, relief, and anger happening one after another. How expected your caesarean section was, and how sympathetically you were treated – along with the amount of control you were able to retain over events – can all affect your feelings.

Finding others who understand what you have been through and how you are feeling, can make your emotional recovery much easier. In some areas it is possible to find caesarean birth groups, where you will be able to meet other mothers. Many women find that Internet groups can provide really good support as well. Some women also benefit from professional help in coming to terms with what has happened to them; this can be found from a variety of people such as trained volunteers, midwives, counsellors, and doctors.

Many women can feel that they have unanswered questions about the birth; this can make coming to terms with the experience more difficult. You have a right to a copy of your notes; ask to see them or ask someone to go through them with you. Many women find that they have new questions when approaching another birth and wish to have questions answered at this point – do not be afraid to speak up if you feel this way.

Premature babies

The first days after a premature birth are a difficult time; many parents feel that they have been through a birth, but do not really have a baby yet. Anxiety over the baby will be intense, and you may be unwell too. Your partner will need to be very supportive at this time. However, once you have seen your baby (*see* p.32) staff will encourage you to become actively involved in his care over the coming days and weeks.

It is natural to want to find out as much as you can about your baby's condition. The staff on the neonatal unit will be able to tell you how your baby is doing and what to expect. BLISS, the premature baby charity, publishes a *Parent Information Guide*, which is available free of charge to all parents with a baby in neonatal care. If you are not given a copy, ask for one, or call BLISS on either 0500 618140 or 020 7820 9471.

You will come to know the routines on the neonatal unit, for example washing and sterilizing your hands and forearms each time you visit, the quiet times in the unit when the babies are left undisturbed, and when the doctor's rounds take place. Even so, the atmosphere on a neonatal unit can be intense and may seem uninviting. If the staff are busy, ask for some time to talk when they are free. Remember you are not being a nuisance by wanting to know something, though sometimes it may not be possible to deal with your query immediately. If you do not understand what you are told, say so.

Always speak up if you think your baby is in difficulty or if you have any questions. It may be a good idea to write down questions as you think of them, and also to record the answers you are given. Some doctors are even happy for you to tape-record appointments regarding your baby's development, and this can be an invaluable way of keeping yourself well informed.

What you can do

Talking to staff in order to understand the care your baby is receiving, getting into a routine, and being involved in his care will help both you and him. The staff have to carry out many medical procedures and some will cause your baby a little discomfort. It is best that you as parents comfort and support him through daily contact. The times that you interact with your baby are precious; not only are they a huge step forward in the bonding process, but they aid his physical and emotional development too.

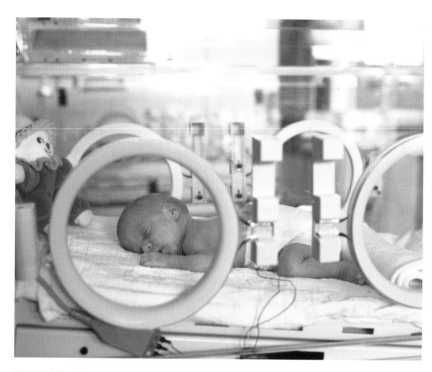

INCUBATOR CARE

An incubator will keep your baby warm. You will still be able to touch your baby while he is in there, which is comforting for both you and him.

POSITIVE TOUCH

Feeling your touch will be very reassuring to your baby. There may be days when he is extremely tired so staff will suggest you keep contact to a minimum, but as he grows stronger these will become less frequent and there will rarely be a day when you can't hold his hand.

Your baby may sometimes be best left in his incubator, but you can touch him through a still hold, rather than stroking and patting (these can be too stimulating). To hold him, place one hand firmly but gently on his head and the other on his middle. However, you should always check with medical staff that your baby is medically stable enough to be touched before doing so.

KANGAROO CARE

As your baby becomes more stable you may be able to lift him right out of the incubator and snuggle him next to your skin (known as "kangaroo care"). However, it is very important that you do not try kangaroo care, or attempt to pick up your baby, without the support and guidance of the medical staff on the neonatal unit.

Kangaroo care provides a wonderful feeling of attachment for both you and the baby, and can have a very positive effect on his health as it is very comforting. You will need to be careful not to disturb any of the equipment that is attached to your baby, but the staff should be there to help you to lift him out of the incubator.

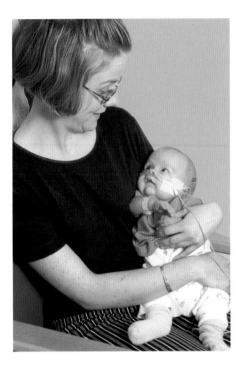

GETTING TO KNOW YOUR BABY

As your baby progresses, you will be able to hold

him outside of the incubator. This intimate contact

can have a very positive effect on his health.

NAPPY CHANGING

Over time the staff will show you how to do some of the routine tasks such as nappy changing. With such a tiny baby you may feel all fingers and thumbs to start with, but it is good to get involved with such day-to-day activities and your baby will be reassured by your touch.

BATHING

The staff may be reluctant to let you bathe your baby initially. This is because washing, even with warm water, could cool the baby down. It is best to avoid bathing at this stage. However, once your baby is stronger you should be able to help with bathing. The staff will help you to begin with but you should quickly be confident enough to do this yourself. Communication over the timing of care is important, though, so tell the staff if you are expecting to visit for a specific reason, such as giving him a bath.

FEEDING

How to feed your baby will be a question that arises early on. Human breastmilk is enriched with fats and nutrients, so there is good reason to consider breast-feeding. However, your own and your baby's circumstances may make it a difficult choice. If your baby is very premature or ill he may need to be fed via tubes initially. Even when he is stronger, he may not be able to suck from you for some time, which means you will have to express your milk using an electric or hand pump. Staff will give you help and support with this. The NCT has specialist breastfeeding counsellors who can also offer support through the Breastfeeding Helpline – 0870 444 8708 (*see* box on p.82).

If you do try and express, not being able to be with your baby, to touch and smell him, may make getting a let-down reflex (*see* p.87) especially hard. Having photographs, or tiny baby clothes with you, may work. You may find it helpful to put a (clean) favourite scarf in with your baby and then take it home with you, as the baby's scent can help stimulate the let-down reflex. Once you can hold your baby and he can root (seek out the nipple) and try to suck, getting a let-down reflex may become easier, as you can focus on those moments – even when you are not with him. Your baby can have modified formula milk for premature babies if you decide not to breastfeed, or you can combine formula with expressed breastmilk. The staff will support you with your decision and you can still be actively involved with feeding your baby.

Looking after yourself and the rest of the family

It is only natural for you to want to be at the neonatal unit as much as possible. However, you should not feel you have to keep a vigil beside the incubator. Taking care of yourself may seem unimportant, but it is vital. If you have other children you will need to spend time with them too. They will have picked up a sense of the stress you are under but may not be old enough to understand what is going on. They will need the reassurance that you still love them. It is also important to explain to any older children what is happening. Siblings should be encouraged to see and get to know the new baby as soon as possible. It is also a nice idea to suggest they make cards and pictures that can be hung next to their baby brother's incubator.

Once you have been discharged from hospital, travelling to visit your baby may be an issue, especially if you cannot drive after a caesarean section. Some hospitals have accommodation for parents, but availability is limited and arrangements vary. You may need to accept help in the form of lifts to hospital, care of older children, and doing the shopping. Keeping a sense of control when you are preoccupied with your baby's wellbeing can be difficult.

Your feelings

There is a huge amount of new information to deal with in the early days. Emotionally, the trauma and shock of the birth will still be very immediate. Some mothers speak of feeling guilty at not having had a natural birth, and not being able to hold or see their baby once he is born. Others may feel anger or confusion about what has happened. It may be hard to know what you are feeling amid the exhaustion and upset, and feelings may also come back years later. For example, your emotions may be stirred easily if you watch a television programme on premature babies. All these emotions, whenever they arise, are normal, but do seek out counselling if you feel you would benefit from it. (The Birth Trauma Association can be contacted at PO Box 1996, or via email at enquiries@birthtraumaassociation.org.uk.)

During the initial weeks it is important that you find people you are able to talk to. Often parents who have babies in the same unit find a great deal of emotional support from talking to one another. Many neonatal units actually run groups where parents can meet to share their experiences over a coffee. For information call the BLISS Freephone Helpline on 0500 618140 and ask about the BLISS Shared Experience Register, which has 16 parent volunteers who are available to listen to and talk with other parents of premature babies.

Your thoughts are likely to be taken up with your baby's wellbeing at this early stage. Many parents speak of "living on auto-pilot" or of feeling "numb", burying feelings of shock and guilt in the effort to be with and care for their baby. Keeping name tags, incubator labels, and photographs will help you to remember this time later on. Keeping a diary is a short-term means of recording information, and in the long term will allow you to reflect and come to terms with what has happened.

At first work commitments may not be a concern but this will eventually be an added strain, particularly if you and/or your partner are travelling a distance each day to get to the hospital. However, amid the anxiety you will find moments to cherish as you watch your baby grow. Undoubtedly, yours is a very special baby.

The first six weeks with twins

Twins are special, and having twins is a very different experience to having a single baby. Parents of twins often describe their situation as being both lucky and unlucky, and in the early weeks the workload of caring for two babies for 24 hours a day can feel overwhelming. However, during the first year the times when having twins is a double delight will become increasingly frequent as they become less dependent and the relationship that they share becomes a source of pleasure for the whole family.

SUPPORT FOR PARENTS OF TWINS AND MULTIPLES

Getting in touch with other parents of twins and multiples can be both reassuring and helpful. Parents who share your experiences can offer you the understanding that comes from "being in the same boat". Some areas have twins/triplets clubs where you and your children can go to socialize. Even if you are not the club-joining kind, the TAMBA (Twins and Multiple Births Association) website, www.tamba.org.uk, is full of practical information that can help you to make the most of family life, from the best double and triple buggies on the market to issues such as finding childcare for twins.

Your feelings about having twins

Your twins may be identical or non-identical, the same gender or different, and, although you may find identifying them as individuals worrying at first, many mothers find that they instinctively recognize each baby's individual characteristics after a while. On the rare occasions when the babies are extremely similar you will be helped initially by hospital name bands and will develop your own strategies later.

Your early identification with one twin or the other may persist in the early weeks, or you may find that you switch your focus from twin to twin. Some mothers find the sharing of love and attention between two babies difficult, feeling that while loving and attending to one they are depriving the other – even if it is just for the space of a few minutes.

Some parents find that they always attend to one twin first, usually the one who demands most attention, and then feel guilty about the other "coming second". Alternatively, they find that they fall into a pattern of one twin becoming dad's responsibility while the other "belongs to mum". You may feel concerned that you haven't time to get to know them well, such is the pressure of constant baby care.

All of these feelings and experiences are entirely normal. Don't be too hard on yourselves but congratulate each other on the commitment and care that you are both giving. Most parents have their hands full with just one baby so it is important to remember that there really is only so much you can do; comparing yourself with parents of single babies is best avoided. Reassure yourself that the best parents are "good enough", not perfect, and that there is plenty of time over the coming months for your situation to change and for relationships to grow and develop.

All new mothers find that their emotions are very changeable in the first few weeks after birth and you may find that your feelings about having twins, and the sheer amount of work you need to undertake, makes you especially vulnerable. It is quite likely that those closest to you will not have had personal experience of a multiple birth and you may feel misunderstood, as other people's expectations

ATTENTION GRABBERS

People often find twins fascinating, and you may find yourself and your babies the focus of a lot of attention when you're out and about.

don't fit with your experience. You may feel very special and the focus of a lot of attention, but you may also find that attention overwhelming, and even intrusive at times. Many parents of twins have to deal with strange questions, comments, and odd advice given by those who have no personal experience of their situation. You may be irritated or amused, but keeping your sense of humour where possible is a good way of reducing the stress.

Practical ways of coping with twins in the early weeks

While all new parents find the early weeks a challenge, parents of twins can feel overwhelmed. Recovering from a twin pregnancy and possibly a caesarean birth, as well as looking after two babies, can seem like an impossible task. Prioritizing, asking for plenty of practical help, and making a point of caring for your own health are the best strategies.

In the first few weeks feeding, sleeping, and keeping the babies comfortable and warm are the only things you should expect yourself to deal with. Others can also help you with some of these tasks, as well as bringing you meals, doing some shopping, and cleaning the house.

Some mothers find that retreating to a comfortable room where everything is close to hand and the babies can be kept calm and quiet is especially helpful. Make sure there are plenty of nutritious snacks, such as nuts, cheese, and fruit, to hand, as well as plenty to drink. Keep yourself and your babies as calm and rested as possible, with plenty of cuddling up together. You may find that the babies are especially comforted by being placed close together in a cot or Moses basket.

As the weeks pass you will probably find that establishing some sort of a routine for feeding and sleeping becomes necessary. Starting with your babies' natural patterns but giving activities some framework may help you to make your days more predictable and manageable.

VENTURING OUT

Getting out and about after a twin birth can feel like a monumental undertaking, and you may find that your ability to get any further than the immediate neighbourhood is challenged for a while. However, a short walk in the fresh air will do you all good and can combat feelings of "cabin fever".

In the first six-week period you may not have the energy or inclination to venture out much but it is worth getting used to managing outings whenever you can. You will find that the attention and congratulations of neighbours and acquaintances, as well as strangers, can be a real boost.

If your baby is disabled or is ill after birth

People often say that the important thing about birth is that the baby is alright, but what if this isn't the case? According to the website of Contact a Family, the umbrella group for parents, "every day over 75 children in the UK are born or diagnosed with a serious disability or rare syndrome". Even if parents know in advance that there may be a problem, it can still be distressing when this is actually confirmed after the birth and they face a future that is going to be different from the one they had hoped for.

Immediate practical arrangements

Whether your baby is ill at birth or becomes ill soon afterwards, maternity staff should be able to help you with information about practical arrangements. If your baby is being transferred to a specialist hospital, you will probably want to stay near him. Most hospitals have accommodation for parents (if the hospital is far from your home), although precise arrangements vary; staff arranging the transfer should be able to help you with questions about where you can stay. Most children's hospitals also have websites with pages for parents, which can be reassuring in answering the most common questions. If you and your baby are likely to be separated, staff usually take a photo of the baby for you to keep beside you.

Your baby may be unable to breastfeed directly from you, but you may want to consider expressing your milk in order to start building up your supply. Hospitals are expected to encourage and facilitate breastfeeding, so some hospitals provide a breastpump and ready-sterilized bottles, although others expect parents to use their own pump. If you do need to provide your own pump the NCT hires them out. You can find details of your local breastpump agent by phoning the enquiries line on 0870 444 8707. Breastfeeding counsellors can also offer support and information. They can be contacted on 0870 444 8708.

Care for mother and baby

Midwives will continue to care for you as normal, either in hospital or back at home. If your baby has been transferred to another hospital and you decide to go as well, the hospital should be able to arrange for a local community midwife to see you. However, you may need time to recover from the birth before being able to rejoin your baby.

Your baby may look fragile surrounded by unfamiliar medical equipment. This can be reassuring in some ways – the best is being done for your baby – but can be intimidating for parents who want to do something, however small, to care for their own baby. You may want to discuss with the nursing staff what it might be possible for you to do for your child (see pp.62–5 for further information on the care given to both ill and premature babies by both staff and parents).

Telling others

Telling others, especially if they are expecting "good news", can be daunting, and one parent may feel able to tackle this better than the other. Family and friends may want reassuring that everything will be alright, or may try to say something to "make it better". It can be a strain coping with other people's emotions at a time when you are anxious and worried as well. It can be very stressful leaving hospital without your baby, as some people, either embarrassed or over-interested in your situation, may avoid you or ask intrusive questions.

If you do find it overwhelming, you could inform a small number of family or friends who could then pass on the news to others. Some parents find it helpful to ask a close friend or relative to manage a calendar for family and friends who want to visit the new baby in hospital. This can be a good way of taking pressure off yourselves. If you have other children they will need extra consideration, but they can often be very matter-of-fact about such situations if they have been given an explanation they can understand.

Keeping informed

When you first discover your baby is ill, it's normal to have a lot of questions about the condition and its treatment. You may find it helpful to write down any concerns and to talk to medical staff together, rather than one parent trying to report everything back to the other.

There is a lot of information available on the Internet, but it's worth giving some thought to how much information you really want; while some sites are excellent, others may give prominence to unhappy outcomes or rare complications. Hospital staff generally understand that parents do try to find out more about their baby's condition and treatment, so if you come across anything on the Internet that gives you cause for concern discuss this with a sympathetic member of staff.

Further practicalities

As time passes, some of the arrangements will become almost routine. However, if your baby is likely to be in hospital for a longer period of time, you may begin to find changes are needed. Spending all day, every day, away from home with a sick baby can be lonely, boring, and dispiriting. Your partner may have to go back to work, possibly unable to see the baby regularly. You may feel you should stay with the baby, but at the same time feel you would benefit from getting back into normal surroundings. You may also have other children who need you and your partner as well, so it's not uncommon to feel torn in all directions.

HELP AND SUPPORT

In the hospital both staff and the new PALS (Patient Advice and Liaison Service) may be able to provide information about sources of help and support, including financial support if your baby is some distance away.

Many parents gain a lot of informal support from talking to other parents with children in hospital at the same time, who are probably dealing with similar stresses – even if the babies have different conditions. Contact a Family is the umbrella group for organizations supporting parents of children with disabilities, who can provide information on specific support groups. The NCT Experiences register may also be able to put parents in touch with others who have shared similar experiences.

During such an emotional period, it can be hard for parents to find the space to look after each other. It can be especially difficult to discuss fears for the baby and, longer term, there may be a shadow over future pregnancies. The midwife or health visitor may be able to offer a listening ear or arrange counselling for either or both of you if you wish.

If your baby has special needs

Whether you find that your baby has a condition before his birth, at birth, or in the weeks or months afterwards, it is devastating to be told that your baby has special needs. The news will be earth-shattering and you will need some time to take it, and the implications, in. Whatever the condition your baby has, be it congenital, such as Trisomy 21 (Down's syndrome) and spina bifida, or caused by problems at birth, as in many cases of cerebral palsy, there are likely to be medical implications. The first priority will be for doctors to assess the health of your baby and the likelihood of whether he will need medical intervention now or some time in the future.

FEELINGS FOR YOUR BABY

Finding out that your baby has special needs is likely to lead to a range of emotions. Remember that your baby is still special to you, and that you can feel proud of him.

Getting the news

After what is in many cases a tense wait for the test results to assess your baby's condition, your emotions will be running at a high level. Grief, anger, disappointment, fear, and sadness are likely to be at the forefront of your feelings. Remember, no one can tell you how you ought to feel or react to your baby – the most important thing to hold on to is he is still yours; you carried him and looked forward to his arrival before he was born and, despite everything, you are still allowed to feel pleased that he is now here. Your feelings, whether they are positive, negative, or swinging rapidly from one place to another, are entirely valid.

Your partner will be hurtling along the same rollercoaster as you, as you both work towards coming to terms with this new and unexpected situation. As with the arrival of any new baby, there are a variety of ways in which parents, and couples, can react. For some, adversity can bring them closer than they have ever been; for others it may drive them apart while each person tries to deal with their feelings privately and in their own way. It is perhaps worth remembering that mums and dads parent their children, special needs or not, together, and that a united front, where couples communicate honestly, is the best way to a happy family.

It is normal and natural for parents of a baby with special needs to ask "Why me?" But a question that might be more helpful is "Why not me?" Your baby has come to you, not in order to open your eyes, but because he needs a mum and a dad just like you, and to be in a family just like yours, which will help him to find his place and to make his way in the world.

Telling other people

It can be very hard to tell other people that the baby you have waited so long for, and looked forward to with such joy, has special needs – partly because in the telling, the news becomes real. Waiting for test results can delay the inevitable, but at some point you will have to explain to family and friends what has happened. Some people find the fact that your baby is different difficult or frightening and, together with the concerns of doctors and midwives, it can feel as if you have given birth to a monster. However, despite being surrounded by normal people with their normal babies, you may find it surprising how many people either know, or are related to, someone with special needs, and how many of them have been through similar, or worse, experiences of their own. It is by talking about what has happened that you are able, firstly, to try and make sense of your situation and, secondly, to begin to realize that, despite appearances, you are not alone.

Things you can do to help come to terms with your new situation

• Do not isolate yourself from the friends you made at antenatal classes, or indeed those you have known for many years. At a time when you feel as if everything is in a state of flux, these are the very people who will help you to remain in touch with the person you were before you had your baby. Others with babies of the same age are invaluable in helping you to grasp the normality of your situation. Sleepless nights, feeling like you are constantly feeding the baby, wondering when you are ever going to eat again, and what on earth was in that nappy, are common to all new parents. Although you may be apprehensive, terrified even, of first meeting your friends with their new babies, when you meet the babies that were bumps you realize that they are different in every way you can imagine – size, shape, personality, tastes – and that special needs or disabilities are just one other part of that difference.

• Get in touch with others who are in the same situation. Your health visitor, community social worker, and paediatrician can all be invaluable in helping you contact other people who understand both what you are going through and your own special needs. How little or much you become involved in the various support groups is up to you.

• Gather information – the amount you will find useful is a matter of personal taste. Some people like to know as much as possible; others prefer to find things out as they go along, as and when they need to. Knowledge about your child's condition can bring a certain sense of control back into your life that you may feel has been lost. There are times when your baby seems to be public property rather than yours alone, thanks to the visits by a seemingly huge number of professionals. Knowledge and understanding of his condition can help restore balance.

DRAWING NEW HORIZONS

It is during the first few weeks and months at home with your baby that, like every other new parent, you will be rapidly readjusting how you see the future for you and your child in the light of what you now know about him. You will have been bombarded with information regarding everything from the best way to feed your baby through to his potential life expectancy, and it can feel as if there is no point in making any plans or having any dreams for your child, as his life is already mapped out according to his condition.

However, hold on to the fact that no one has a crystal ball and that the delight in seeing your child achieve milestones such as his first smile, his first solid meal, the day you find him in a different position in his cot to where you left him, are still yours. In fact, your pride in his achievements may even be heightened by your knowledge of what he has overcome.

Depression and shock

Having a baby is usually a positive experience for mothers and fathers; society expects us to feel happy and fulfilled as we welcome a new life into our world. Yet parents have a major readjustment to deal with – these include the loss of independence, changes in financial status or security, and sometimes changes in relationships with those in different circumstances. Although you may feel prepared for these changes, having a baby can still be a shock for many people.

A MIXTURE OF EMOTIONS

After birth you may be surprised that you feel a whole range of emotions – some of them may be negative. This is absolutely normal; after all, you've just been through an exhausting experience.

It is perfectly normal to feel emotional, vulnerable, and sensitive after your baby is born. Some mothers may feel confused about their feelings – believing that they should be overjoyed and instantly fall in love with their baby. This is not always the case and there are understandable reasons why you may not feel like that. For example, you may have had a difficult labour or a traumatic delivery, which has left you feeling exhausted and possibly unfulfilled of the expectations you may have had. Don't forget that we are not taught how to be mothers; it is something we need to learn for ourselves, and at this time of our lives we sometimes need to be mothered ourselves.

Baby blues

The baby blues are extremely common. They typically occur between three to five days after the birth. One theory is that they coincide with the hormonal changes that occur as the breastmilk starts to come in. Other theories are that the baby blues are due to the "come down" after the effects of endorphins (*see* p.25), or that they are a sort of physical shock reaction after the upheaval of birth. You may feel weepy, irritable, have a low mood, and feel you lack confidence in caring for your baby. This is quite normal, and these feelings usually subside after a week or so. It is perfectly acceptable to have a good cry and to talk to someone about how you are feeling.

Postnatal depression

Postnatal depression (PND) is a recognized and treatable condition that affects approximately 10–15 percent of mothers and it can affect anyone, irrespective of background. Although it can occur straight after the birth it often does not get acknowledged or recognized until later on. For some women it may come on later in the year – some women get depressed after a few months. The most common signs and symptoms of postnatal depression are low mood, anxiety, an inability to look forward to anything, lack of motivation, and extreme tiredness. Some mothers may not actually feel depressed but may feel far more anxious or agitated than normal – this is a common symptom of PND. They may not know what they are feeling anxious about and may experience panic attacks due to their anxiety. These feelings can be very frightening; however they are normal and symptomatic of PND and will decrease and eventually disappear with recovery. Obviously many new mothers feel extremely tired but, when combined with other symptoms that are causing distress or problems, this may be a sign of postnatal depression.

Getting help

There are a number of things that can be done to help, whatever postpartum condition you may suffer from. It is important to contact your GP or health visitor to find out about the options and choices available. Remember that different options suit different people and their varying symptoms and circumstances.

THE HEALTH VISITOR

Your health visitor can be extremely helpful in getting you to acknowledge and seek treatment for your postnatal depression, initially by using a tool known as the Edinburgh Postnatal Depression Scale. This is a questionnaire designed to focus solely on the mother, not the baby. It is a self-report questionnaire that the mother fills in on her own while the health visitor is present. It should be used routinely with all new mothers, not just the women that health visitors think might be suffering from postnatal depression. It consists of ten short statements about how she has been feeling in the last seven days, which the mother has to grade herself. It is usually used between six and eight weeks after the baby's birth and gives the mother an opportunity to talk about her feelings. Some women may feel assessed or judged by this tool, but it should not be seen as threatening – rather it is a useful tool to identify how a new mother is feeling. Health visitors can offer support to mothers, for example by visiting them in their own home on a regular basis, and allowing them to talk about their feelings.

Some women may not feel comfortable talking to health professionals about their negative feelings and thoughts, and may mistakenly believe that their child might be taken away from them if they do share how they are really feeling. This is not the case; health professionals are there to help.

YOUR GP

If you think you have postnatal depression, it is important to speak to your GP. For some women, just the consultation and the acknowledgement between the GP and the woman that there is a depressive illness, possibly mild, is enough and they may not require any other treatment. However, your GP may suggest that you try anti-depressants, which can be extremely useful in aiding recovery. Some women

PUERPERAL PSYCHOSIS

This is a totally different condition to postnatal depression. It affects approximately one in five hundred to a thousand new mothers and usually occurs within the first six weeks after birth. The mother may experience delusions, hallucinations, and erratic behaviour; family members commonly notice these first. This condition is considered a medical emergency so it is very important for family members or friends to contact the woman's GP if they are concerned. Usually puerperal psychosis is treated in hospital, preferably in a mother and baby unit, where, if appropriate, the mother can have her baby with her.

Even if you do not feel like it, talking to a professional, such as your GP, will help enormously. For some women, this is all the "treatment" they need.

may be anxious about taking medication while breastfeeding; however, there are some anti-depressants that are considered safe for use by breastfeeding mothers. It is important to discuss this with your GP.

Your GP may suggest counselling or a referral to the Community Mental Health team, who should have expertize in this area. Postnatal depression support groups can also be extremely helpful as you will be with other mothers experiencing similar feelings. Your GP or health visitor should know of such support groups in your area. These can help to reduce feelings of isolation, as being aware that other women have had similar thoughts and feelings can be hugely reassuring.

Helping yourself

Having postnatal depression can be frightening and distressing; sometimes you may feel like you are going mad and will never feel normal again. It is important to remember that, with the right support and treatment, you will recover and enjoy life again.

• If possible try to rest, as tiredness may make your symptoms worse. Don't feel that you have to get the housework done first; you are more important.

• Try to eat small, regular meals, especially if your appetite is poor. This helps to keep the blood sugar level constant (if it isn't this makes the depression worse).

• If you are feeling up to it, try to take some exercise. This doesn't need to be as vigorous as a workout; a steady walk in the fresh air every day can do a lot to ease irritability and tension.

- It may help to keep a diary of your feelings so that you can look at your progress.
- Don't force yourself to do things you don't want to do, and try to avoid the things that cause extra stress.
- Try to confide in someone you trust who won't pass opinion or judge you.

Advice for those supporting women with postnatal depression

It is very important to remember that a woman experiencing postnatal depression is unable to pull herself out of it. If she could she would, as no one wants to feel as dreadful as she does. The following tips may make it easier for you to understand how she is feeling, therefore helping you both through her recovery.

- She will have good and bad days, times when she will feel more like her old self that will be better for both of you, but this doesn't mean that she is totally recovered. The good days will become more frequent as the bad days decrease but this does take time, and she will need constant reassurance that she will get better. During the bad days it may be hard for her to remember her good days and she may even feel that the bad ones are the real her. This is not so; it's the depression that makes her feel like this.
- It will help her enormously if you can accept these good and bad days, support her when she is feeling low, and encourage her on her good days. She will go through periods of being well and then may experience times of feeling low again; this is totally normal and is always the case with postnatal depression. However, this can be frustrating for both you and her – to see her feeling well for a time may lead you to believe that she has recovered, but recovery from postnatal depression is gradual.
- The woman may find her new role as a mother boring, with frustrating endless chores to be done without having much adult company during the day. Even when she meets up with others for coffee, she may not be able to have a conversation without being interrupted, needing to change a nappy, breastfeed, and so on. All these demands will be made worse by her postnatal depression. She may begin to resent the fact that you can go out to work, get on with your job, and eat your lunch without being interrupted. Try and understand her feelings.
- You may not necessarily be able to see how she is really feeling by her behaviour (many women are great at covering it up), so asking how she is feeling will give you a better indication and allow her an opportunity to tell you.
- Finally, remember that this is an illness that takes time to recover from. She will be her old self again and things will get better for you both. With the right support and treatment all mothers will eventually recover.

"No matter how badly you feel about yourself or your capabilities, your baby knows you as the most wonderful person he could ever wish for, and you are."

The six-week check – back to normal?

The six-week check can feel like a milestone. You should have your postnatal check about six weeks after your baby's birth and you can go to your own GP or you might be asked to return to the hospital. Your GP's surgery will probably arrange for your baby's six-week check to be done at the same time as your postnatal check, although if you go to the hospital the baby's check will usually need to be arranged separately.

CHECKING YOUR BABY

As well as your own six-week check, your baby will also have a check-up. During this his head circumference will be measured (see box, right). .

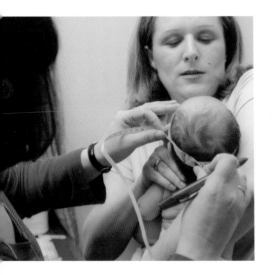

At the check, your GP will have specific things to discuss and examine. It is worth writing down any questions beforehand as they occur to you, as it is hard to remember everything at the time. For instance, if you have had a caesarean section you may like to ask if another one will be needed if you have another baby.

You may be weighed, your blood pressure will be taken, and you might have your breasts checked. Your urine may be tested to make sure your kidneys are working properly and that there is no infection. The doctor will also give you a pelvic examination; this means checking any stitches, and giving you an internal examination to make sure the cervix has closed and the uterus has contracted to pre-pregnancy size. The doctor will also be checking that your vagina has regained its muscle tone. He or she may remind you if you have not had a smear for a few years that you need to do so, though it is usually at least three months after delivery before this is done.

If you have haemorrhoids (piles) or varicose veins, these will be examined. If you are feeling very tired the doctor may want to take a blood sample to check your iron levels. If you were anaemic during pregnancy this will be particularly important. Do tell your GP if you are still having problems with incontinence.

In addition the GP will ask you about contraception, and ask if sex feels okay. Many couples may not have attempted sex by then anyway, so don't worry if you don't know the answer. However, you will need to make sure that you have contraception in place, even if you don't yet feel ready for sex:

• If you had a diaphragm beforehand it will need to be refitted as your size may have changed.

• Some doctors may not want to fit a coil yet for fear of introducing infection.

• It is not known if there are any long-term effects on babies, particularly boys, of exposure to female hormones in the Pill. Oestrogen suppresses lactation, and so the combined pill would reduce your milk supply. The progesterone-only (mini) pill is usually offered to breastfeeding mothers, although this also briefly reduces supply.

• Breastfeeding can be an effective method of birth control, but only if certain conditions are met, and these are rarely met in the West. Like all contraception, it is not foolproof. Breastfeeding delays the return of your periods; however, the first time you ovulate after giving birth will be before your first period, and you have a ten percent risk of falling pregnant if you rely solely on your period returning as a warning that you are fertile. Scientists have defined LAM (Lactational Amenorrhoea Method, ie relying on absence of periods while breastfeeding) as 98–9 percent effective only if: a) you are breastfeeding your baby on demand, night and day, without using any supplements (usually meaning at least ten short or six long breastfeeds within 24 hours with no interval between feeds of more than six hours and no use of dummies); b) your baby is less than six months old.

By six weeks you may not have felt any need for sex, but what about your partner? He may want to resume sex but have no idea how to approach the subject. However, it may be that he feels traumatized by watching the birth, or tired by the broken nights, and is not that bothered. Try to talk about how you both feel, so that it does not become an issue.

Until menstruation returns, your hormones will not be geared to sex, which means that if you are breastfeeding it may be quite a long time before your body, at least, is thinking about sex.

For most couples, a "normal" sex life takes much longer to come back – and perhaps it will never be the same again. This does not mean it will be worse, but it may be different. Respect and good communication are vital. Practically speaking, if intercourse is uncomfortable you may need to vary positions, slow things down, and perhaps use extra lubrication for a while until your hormone levels are back to their pre-pregnancy state.

In addition, there will be a baby who has his own demands, and sex may need to be booked in advance around your baby's resting times. Most people find that spontaneity ceases when they become parents.

Perhaps the answer is to start out with cuddles rather than explicitly trying to have sex, and see what happens. Be patient with each other, and talk about it – don't panic but give yourselves time. For some women giving birth gives them an extra confidence in their own body and for them sex is more pleasurable, although probably less frequent, than before.

YOUR BABY'S CHECK-UP

Checks on your baby are similar to those carried out immediately after the birth (*see* p.23). His eyes, muscle tone, ears, limbs, heart, and lungs are all examined. His weight is taken and his length and head circumference measured. Again his hips will be checked for displacement.

Immunizations are discussed, but not actually begun. The first immunization usually happens at three months, but this is a good time to discuss any worries or concerns, as there is not always a doctor available at the time of the vaccination itself. *See* pages 194–5 for more about immunizations.

This is also your time to discuss any niggling worries you may have, so don't be afraid to ask, no matter how trivial they may seem. However, do remember that you can call on the doctor at other times if you need to. Most GPs are sympathetic to the new mother syndrome, where you continually need to seek reassurance until your own instincts and experience take over. GPs are usually very responsive to the needs of new parents, as they recognize how vulnerable this time of life can be.

Communication

What sets us apart from other animals is our intelligence, our adaptability, and our sophisticated language. Your baby is born with these faculties ready and waiting to go. He's already capable of an enormous amount, and during the early months he develops at a pace that he'll never achieve again in his life.

Although babies are born very capable, they depend on involvement from parents to grow and develop. The most important gift they have is to be flexible – they can adapt to any language, and any environment. This flexibility has made human beings the dominant creature on the planet. Babies fit into this by being good at learning, excellent imitators, and taking many years to mature. The only resource they need is adults around them who want to help them learn. The good news is that your baby will guide you in what he needs. He loves to learn, and will complain if he gets bored. Learning is as natural to him as feeding or breathing. In addition, adults instinctively change their behaviour to provide what a baby needs. So don't get too concerned about what you do; just give him your love and your time.

Physical skills – he's not completely helpless

Newborn babies delivered onto their mothers' stomachs, if left to their own devices, use their limbs in a slow but coordinated way to crawl up until they reach the breast, where they then latch on and feed, unaided. So newborn babies are born with lots of physical skills to help them survive. Other reflexes also involve complicated, coordinated body movements. If he is held upright with his feet in contact with a hard surface he walks purposefully, although the weight of his head and torso is too much for his legs to bear unsupported. If he is startled by a loud noise or feels the sensation of falling, the Moro (startle) reflex makes him throw his head back, extend his arms, legs, and fingers, and then bring them all together as if grasping. A sensible strategy if falling out of a tree, but with his heavy limbs he would not be able to hang on for long.

So it is not that your baby is physically incapable, it is just that his muscles are not yet strong enough to support his heavy body. You can see how well he can do things when he doesn't have this weight to contend with – for example, look at him extending and flexing his fingers and toes, and feel his strong and sustained grip on your finger. He can also coordinate and control the hundreds of muscles in his face when he cries, opens his eyes, or smiles.

Communication skills – that first smile

Your baby is born to smile. His earliest, "reflex" smile may happen in the first few days, usually when he is dropping off to sleep, or hears your voice. By four to six weeks you will see a different, more definitely social smile.

He's still unselective at this age, so will smile at most things. By four months, though, only faces will do, and he will reserve his best smiles for you. His whole face lights up, his eyes twinkle, and his shoulders rise with pleasure.

Did you know?

• Babies can't cry tears for at least three weeks, sometimes not until they reach four or five months of age. Tears contain stress hormones and so crying is a way of calming down after a fright. No other animals cry stress tears, so perhaps our tears are a signal, showing up against our skin. Mothers instinctively feel the need to clean up their children, so we cuddle them and dry their eyes.

• At first your breastfeeding baby will close his eyes, unable to concentrate on two things at once, but by his third month he will feed with his eyes open, gazing at you.

• Kissing has origins in primitive weaning. Originally we would chew our baby's food and then pass it from our mouth to his, like a kiss. "Kissing it better" is an old tradition that symbolizes sucking out evil forces that cause pain.

• When a baby is full he turns his head away – the origin of shaking our head "no".

• Sticking out your tongue is seen as rude because it symbolizes the way babies reject food.

• Babies like being rocked and we instinctively rock them at heartbeat pace.

• Psychologists have found that even newborn babies have an elementary grasp of maths and physics. They can tell the difference between one, two, three, and more objects, and also can add up and take away. They may not have an abstract concept of numbers, but they know how many apples should remain, for instance, if one is taken away, and express surprise if it is wrong. Five- and six-month-old babies express surprise if objects seem to pass through solid walls, float, or roll the wrong way.

• During his first six months of life your baby can distinguish more sounds than he will be able to later. This is so that he could adapt to any human language, but as time passes he will become "tuned" to his native tongue.

• Babies love to learn, and get immense satisfaction from solving problems. Newborn babies love being able to switch a light off and on by turning their head; two-month-old babies giggle with delight when they find that they can make their cot mobile dance about.

• Babies become self-aware sooner than we might think, although psychologists still can't agree when this happens. Very young babies love looking at themselves in mirrors, but they may not realize who they are looking at for quite some time. If you pop some lipstick on your baby's nose and then show him his reflection, it is not until about 15 months that he will touch his own nose when he sees it.

INDIVIDUAL PERSONALITY
Even when your baby is first born he is by no means a blank sheet. He is born with a variety of skills just waiting to be nurtured and developed.

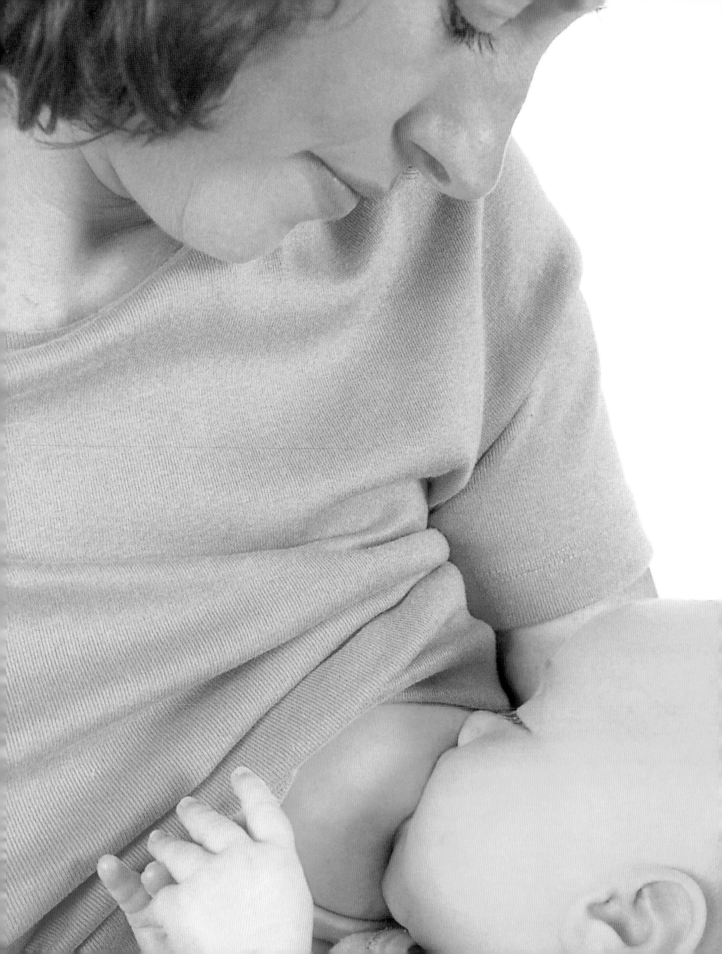

3 FEEDING

- Feeding and feelings

- How breastfeeding works

- How formula feeding works

- Getting enough to eat

- Expressing and storing your breastmilk

- Breastfeeding – potential problems

- *Feature:* Are routines right for you?

Feeding and feelings

Looking after a baby is an awesome responsibility; this tiny human being is totally dependent on you for survival. It is little wonder, therefore, that you spend so much time worrying if she's getting enough to eat. These feelings of anxiety about your baby's diet are all part of being a parent, and they don't go away. Even when your children eventually grow up and leave home, you'll probably still be anxious about what they're eating!

Worrying about whether your baby is thriving is completely normal. It can be reassuring to know that most healthy children will not starve without putting up a fight, and that if your baby isn't getting enough to eat you will usually soon know about it. For some parents, breastfeeding seems to exacerbate these worries; after all you can't see how much your baby is taking at each feed. But parents who bottle feed worry, too, so try not to let these normal fears sway you into choosing one type of feeding method over another.

Breastfeeding and your feelings

If you are not really sure whether to breast- or bottle feed, then the safest option is to start with breastfeeding and see how you feel. It is always easier to change to formula feeding if you want to, but it is difficult to change from formula to breast. It can also be satisfying to know that even if you only breastfeed your baby for a short time, you are giving her the healthiest start you can.

Although only a very tiny proportion of women are physically unable to breastfeed, there are other reasons why women might decide not to. Whether breastfeeding goes well is mainly down to how much skilled help you receive at the beginning – and unfortunately such help is not always readily available. Some mothers who want to breastfeed end up bottle feeding due to this lack of support and practical help. In the end they feel as if they were unable to breastfeed.

The health advantages of breastfeeding are well known, but what about the emotional feelings associated with breastfeeding? Seeing your baby grow, and knowing that it is your body that is providing the means for your baby to develop, generates a sense of pride and achievement for many women; it seems like a continuation of the nurturing role your body took on while you were pregnant. After the initial full and uncomfortable feeling in your breasts, they gradually settle back to feeling normal, while at the same time being able to produce milk for your baby wherever and whenever it is needed.

GETTING SUPPORT
National Childbirth Trust (NCT) breastfeeding counsellors are there for you to talk through feelings about any aspect of breastfeeding – they are not just there for problems such as mastitis or sore nipples, though they are able to help with these too. If you need support to carry on breastfeeding, or to stop breast-feeding, or if you feel unsupported in your choices whatever these may be, pick up the phone and talk to someone. They won't advise or judge, but will listen and understand. They can be contacted on 0870 444 8708.

The sheer convenience of breastfeeding comes as a surprise too. Once you have mastered latching your baby on quickly and easily, you can move from noticing the first signs of restlessness that indicate an interest in food to the baby happily feeding without her even having the chance to whimper. Being able to prevent your baby's cries in an instant gives many women a sense of power and fulfilment. The actions involved can become so automatic that you may put your baby to your breast without needing to break off conversation with another person.

Babies do wake at night and an unexpected benefit of breastfeeding is that the feeding makes you and your baby feel sleepy. This means that, although you may wake several times, you wake less fully because your baby does not need to wait long to be fed, and once she is full you both drift back to sleep quickly. Some mothers even report waking with breasts that feel as though they have been fed from but having no memory of feeding their baby during the night.

Despite the pleasure and pride associated with breastfeeding it can, on occasions, still feel like hard work. It may also be needed at a moment when it is difficult for you to meet the need. While there is much a dad or grandparent can do to care for and nurture your baby, you may want to give them the opportunity to feed the baby too. Being able to express some milk to give you the flexibility to be away from your baby, if that suits you, can be very useful. It is also lovely to know that although you are not there your baby smells and tastes you. She therefore has some of the experience of being with you while being fed in the arms of someone else. Breastfeeding can also become an instant cure for fright, pain, and a comfort during illness. If you choose to respond to needs other than hunger with

THE CONVENIENCE OF BREASTFEEDING
Once both you and your baby are used to her latching on, breastfeeding is such a convenient way to feed her that you can continue a conversation without having to stop to concentrate on the feed.

It is great to know that your body provides all the nourishment your baby needs. This also means you can easily stop and feed her while you are out and about.

the offer of a feed then you have the means to help your baby deal with difficult circumstances while she develops the resources she needs to cope by herself.

Bottle feeding and your feelings

Even though we know that breastmilk is much better for babies (*see* p.21), bottle feeding is often seen as quite normal. Breastfeeding is sometimes presented as something that takes effort and is problematic – and any woman who does breastfeed is seen as quite courageous. The downside of this is that women who bottle feed can feel as if they have failed to live up to the heroic standards of those who breastfeed. Whatever you decide, no one should pressurize you to breastfeed or formula feed. All that is reasonable is that you are given the information and are then supported in whatever decision you make.

Whatever the outcome for you, try to remember that feeding needs support, and no one should make you feel guilty, or disapprove of your decision. There are only two important people in this situation, you and your baby, and what your baby will remember is the love and care that you gave her in those early years, however she was fed.

Getting close to your bottle-fed baby

One way of staying in tune with your baby and fulfilling her needs is to bottle feed on demand. Be guided by the manufacturer's recommended amounts within a 24-hour period, but within that timespan you can go with the flow. Cuddle your baby skin-to-skin, your bare skin next to hers. This will help your baby bond with you, as well as fulfilling her needs for contact.

Other people

There are no shortages of opinions on offer about feeding, whether with the breast or bottle. Anyone who has had a baby themselves will have strong feelings about how it went for them. They will want to offer their opinion, mostly because they want to be helpful, but it can feel undermining if people don't seem to support you in your choices, preferring to try to push you into what they think is best.

On top of this, breastfeeding can be considered unusual or strange in some places and in some families. It's not surprising that many people feel ambivalent about breastfeeding – breasts are often seen as purely sexual in our society. So how is it for the baby's father? He is meant to push this to the back of his mind and support his partner in her choices. Most men do this really well, but some will find that it is extremely hard for them to be completely at ease with their partner breastfeeding the baby.

For the majority of people, breastfeeding is acceptable while your baby is really tiny but what about feeding her as she gets older? Seeing a baby older than one being breastfed is rare in our culture, though biologically our species can probably breastfeed children until they are 2½–6 years old. In the UK many people do breastfeed older babies and toddlers but because older babies breastfeed less often, and toddlers often only in the morning and evening, it is rarely seen in public. In fact breastmilk should be the most important source of nutrients for your baby until she's at least one year of age. If you decide to carry on feeding for as long as both you and your baby want to, you might find yourself doing it in private and keeping quiet about it because it feels unusual in our society, but do remember that there are others who are doing the same and you might like to search out another woman so that you can share the joys and difficulties together.

Remember that however old your child is, she will still be benefiting from breastmilk, and it is fine to keep going until one or both of you want to stop. The World Health Organization recommends that babies are breastfed for up to two years or beyond. Eventually there will come a time when either you or your child wants to stop breastfeeding. It can be hard for you if your child is ready to stop when you are happy to continue. If you want to stop and your child is keen to carry on do talk to a breastfeeding counsellor about the different ways there are of bringing breastfeeding to an end.

How breastfeeding works

Breastfeeding is a natural, biological process governed by your hormones and physiology, as well as your baby's own automatic instincts. However, in our society it is not always easy – some mothers are uncomfortable doing it in public while others may never have seen friends and relatives doing it. Many mothers and babies struggle with breastfeeding as a result, especially in the early weeks. Understanding how it works will help to make it easier.

Many women doubt their ability to sustain their babies purely on breastmilk, but in fact your body has nurtured your baby throughout pregnancy amazingly well. After the birth, your breasts are designed to take over the role of the placenta in feeding and protecting your baby.

Why breastfeed?

Breastmilk is more than just nutrition; it is a living fluid that protects your baby from the world around her. It also stimulates her own immune system, which will take more than a year to fully develop – in the meantime she will receive copies of your own antibodies from your milk. Breastmilk is also perfectly digestible, so even her nappies won't smell unpleasant!

Breastfeeding develops your baby's jaw in preparation for chewing and talking. The pauses and eye contact, as well as the interaction that takes place when you are breastfeeding, all prepare her for conversing later. Through your breastmilk she will also be able faintly to taste the food you have eaten, thus preparing her to join her family at mealtimes as she will remember those tastes. Breastfed babies' teeth tend to be better aligned than bottle-fed babies',[⊙] and as their palates are not distorted by anything hard, like a bottle, they may be less likely to snore as adults.[⊙]

Finally, breastfeeding is intimate and enjoyable, a way of bringing you closer together. What more could a baby want?

The mechanics of breastfeeding

As with pregnancy, breastfeeding is controlled by hormones. These work to keep the volume of milk at the right level to nourish your baby, and to let the milk out when your baby wants it. Prolactin is the hormone responsible for producing milk. During pregnancy it stimulates your breasts to develop milk-producing cells and to produce a small amount of milk. Levels are kept low by the hormone progesterone.[⊙] This initial, low-volume milk is called colostrum and is there ready

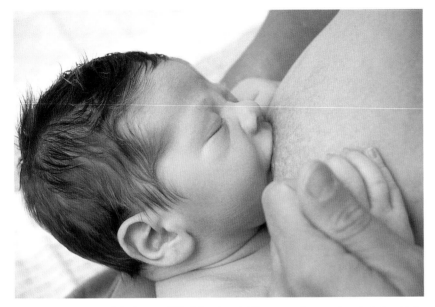

SKIN-TO-SKIN
It can be a lovely feeling to hold your baby naked
next to your skin, and it can help to encourage
breastfeeding as well.

for your baby at birth (see p.21). After her birth progesterone levels fall, which allows the milk levels to rise – referred to as milk "coming in". Your milk then gradually changes from colostrum to mature milk.

Whenever your baby stimulates your nipples prolactin is released to create more milk, so the volume of milk you produce is decided by your baby's feeding pattern. This is why putting your baby to your breast whenever she wants to feed is particularly important initially, to get your milk supply established. Prolactin levels are higher at night, so it is vital that you allow your baby to breastfeed at night in order to fully establish your milk supply. If milk is not removed from the breasts, prolactin levels fall and milk production will eventually cease.

Oxytocin is the other main hormone involved in breastfeeding, and is responsible for ejecting milk from the breasts – the "let-down" reflex. Muscles high up in your breasts contract, squeezing milk down towards your nipples where your baby can get it. Some women are unaware of this; others find it a strange, almost tickly feeling. A few find it slightly painful. Oxytocin also helps your uterus contract, so when you feed your baby in the early days you may feel "afterpains". These are usually stronger for second or subsequent babies.

Oxytocin can be switched on by different stimuli. Feeding your baby raises oxytocin levels, but just holding your baby also works – as does thinking about her when she's not there. That's why it's possible to express breastmilk without your baby present. This hormone is also produced when you make love so you may find you leak milk during sex, especially at orgasm. It's best to feed your baby just beforehand if possible and have a towel handy.

Your baby can get quite a lot of milk from what is released by oxytocin. However, she also needs to play an active part in removing the milk, thus stimulating prolactin to produce enough milk for the next feed. Milk left in the breasts contains an inhibiting factor that stops further milk being produced, so even if your baby feeds often, if she cannot get the milk out effectively then your milk supply will fall.

The first, thirst-quenching milk is often referred to as "foremilk", which means "the milk that comes before". If this is all your baby drinks then she will need to feed more frequently as she will not be getting the levels of fat that she needs to grow. She may also get colicky if she is drinking mostly foremilk, as this passes through the gut quickly and may reach the lower intestine before all the lactose is absorbed. If this happens it will ferment and cause discomfort – as well as green, explosive nappies! (*See* the feature spread on colic on p.152.)[⊙]

Holding your baby so that she can get at the milk effectively is very important, not only in building and maintaining the milk supply but also in extracting the fat-rich hindmilk. There are three things to consider: your posture – how you are sitting or lying; your position – how you hold your baby's body so she can reach your breast; and attachment – the relationship between your baby's mouth and your breast.

Your posture

As you will be in one place for quite some time, try to get comfortable before you begin. An upright chair might be useful, one that supports a straight back. If you are leaning back, for instance on a sofa or against bed pillows, your breasts flatten and it is harder for your baby to get a good mouthful (although some babies can manage like this – especially when they are older, stronger, and more used to breastfeeding). Some women can feed sitting cross-legged on a floor cushion.

FEEDING WHILE LYING DOWN

You can feed successfully while lying down. This is a useful position as it allows you to rest at the same time. If you have had a caesarean it also ensures your baby does not lie on your wound.

You can also feed lying down. This is a useful position as you can have a doze during the day while you are feeding or you can feed your baby at night in your bed. (This position is also useful if you have had a caesarean as it ensures that your baby does not lie on your wound.) However, if you are likely to fall asleep when feeding make sure that it's a safe environment for your baby. Don't sleep on a couch or armchair with your baby as there is an increased risk of cot death, and if she is in your bed make sure she can't fall out or get covered by bedding – *see pp.124–7 for more information on safe bed-sharing.*

Position of you and the baby

You need to hold your baby so that her body is turned towards your body (remember: "tummy to mummy"). Do not hold her in the position you would hold her in if you were bottle feeding. If you do, she will have to turn her head towards your breast and it will be difficult for her to swallow (try it and see). Once your baby is facing towards you her nose needs to be next to your nipple to begin with so that when she opens her mouth she will be reaching out a little to latch on. If you tuck her bottom in close and leave her neck and head relatively clear, you will find this allows her to extend her neck better. Avoid holding the back of her head as this will force her chin down and most babies don't like it. Also, if her chin is too close to her chest it will be awkward for her to feed and swallow comfortably. The size of your breasts and the position of your nipples will affect how high up or down your body your baby lies. For example, if you have smaller breasts you will be holding your baby higher up your body than if you have larger breasts.

Lying across the mum's tummy, as described above, is the most common position for a baby to lie in when breastfeeding. In this position you can support your baby's body using the arm on the same side as the breast (supporting her with your left arm while she feeds from your left breast and vice versa) and support the back of her head somewhere on your forearm (not in the crook of your arm as this will constrict her neck and chin). Alternatively you can hold her with the arm opposite to the breast she's feeding from, supporting her shoulders and neck cradled in your hand. This position gives you quite a lot of freedom to move her body in relation to your breast ready for latching on.

Once you have your baby attached to your breast, if you need to support your arm you can tuck a pillow or cushion under it. This then leaves the other hand free to hold a drink, a book, the phone, or television remote control! You can also hold her under arm – this is a useful position after a caesarean because it keeps the baby away from the scar. Support her lying along your forearm, cradling her shoulders and neck in your hand. Her feet will extend out behind you so you'll need to sit quite far forward with cushions or pillows behind you. This can be a useful position if you are having problems at the beginning, as you can see what is happening. It is also useful for mothers with twins, if you feed both babies at once.

Feeding your baby whenever she is hungry means that your breasts will match the supply of milk to your baby's needs. As your baby takes milk, more is made to meet her needs. So when she is hungrier, she will take more from your breasts and they will make more milk in response.

"For the first few weeks I had to be in a comfortable position in a certain chair to be sure I was getting it right. After that it became easier to do it anywhere, any time."

To latch on successfully, your baby's chin should make contact with your breast first.

Your baby's natural rooting reflex should ensure that she opens her mouth very wide.

Your nipple needs to go right to the back of your baby's mouth.

To position her when lying down, lie on your side and support your head and shoulders with pillows. It may help to have a pillow behind your back so that you have something to relax against. Your lower arm can extend out and round the top of your baby's head. Use your upper arm to position your baby and draw her onto your lower breast. Your baby should lie on her side, facing you, again so that she has to reach up for the breast. As is the same when sitting up, if you tuck her bottom in close and leave her neck and head relatively clear you will find this allows her to extend her neck better.

Attachment or "latching on"

The final part of the jigsaw is how your baby takes the breast. It is important that she has a good mouthful, with her chin making contact with your breast first. She will need to open her mouth really wide, which she will usually do instinctively. This is part of the rooting reflex, an automatic response that enables her to turn towards whatever is touching her mouth or cheek and then open her mouth. So when you see her rooting get ready, and as soon as she opens her mouth wide – gaping as if she were about to bite on an apple – draw her onto your breast (*see* picture sequence, left).

Your nipple needs to go right back to make contact with your baby's soft palate – this is the smooth bit of the roof of the mouth. If your nipple is in contact with the hard palate – the ridge of bones at the front of the mouth – it will chaff and get sore. Stimulating the soft palate triggers the baby's feeding reflex.

Your baby's jaw then uses a chomping action, working with a rolling action of her tongue, to squeeze milk out of the breast. A good mouthful, with her chin in contact with your breast, is important as it allows the baby to reach the milk that lies behind the nipple and areola.

Your baby will show you that she has had enough milk from your breast by coming off it of her own accord, looking satisfied. Now is the time to offer her the second breast. This gives her the opportunity to have more milk if she is still hungry. Some mothers find that their baby often wants the second breast, others that their baby rarely wants it. It doesn't matter as long as your baby has the chance to have more if she wants it. Either way, start with the "second breast" the next time you feed, to balance out the milk supply.

Breastfeeding a baby with special needs

Having a baby with special needs (*see* p.70) can seriously dent your image of yourself as a mother and as a woman, and to know that you are able to feed your baby from your breast is an enormously affirming and reassuring experience. Emotion aside, the health benefits of breastfeeding are magnified for your baby, who will generally be more vulnerable due to her condition. Even so, it is essential that you seek advice as, although breastfeeding is usually less stressful for babies than bottle feeding, for some babies it takes an immense amount of effort – especially at the beginning. If you want to feed her yourself you may need to engage in some lateral thinking.

Your baby may find it hard to coordinate the actions of sucking, swallowing, and breathing all at the same time. Some are simply too weak to breastfeed successfully and fall asleep before they come to the richer, more nutritious hindmilk. It is possible to express some of the foremilk before you start to feed, stimulating the let-down reflex so that your baby reaches the hindmilk straight away. You can store your milk in the fridge (see pp.98–100 for how to express, and storage times). Expressing has the added advantage of stimulating your milk supply to an extent that your baby may not yet be able to do. Don't wait until your baby is ravenous before feeding her, as by this time she may already be weak with hunger. Look out for other signs that she is starting to get hungry (smacking her lips or rooting are dead giveaways), and feed her while she is alert when possible.

Exercises to encourage the sucking reflex are useful, such as rubbing your baby's gums with a clean finger or popping your finger in and out of her mouth. Drawing your finger firmly over her top lip in the direction you want her to turn helps her to latch on. Having your baby in a good position and keeping her well supported means that she does not have to work too hard, and will make sure that you don't get sore. You will need to be prepared to spend longer feeding your baby, especially at first. Undressing your baby and placing her next to your skin, tickling her feet, or gently rubbing her ear will help to keep her awake while she feeds.

If your baby has medical problems that make breastfeeding impossible, then expressing your milk so that you can still feed her yourself (even if she is being tube-fed) is certainly a viable option. Seek medical advice and work out a regime that works for you and your baby.

Remember, your baby will not always be as weak as she is in the first few weeks, or even months. Do not despair; all your hard work will be repaid in terms of the health benefits for your baby, the confidence it gives you, and the close bond that will be forged between the two of you through your shared experience.

Breastfeeding counsellors are excellent in providing information and support for you when you are breastfeeding. Books and the Internet can also be good sources of information, but the most important person in supporting you is your partner. If the going gets tough it can be very easy to throw in the towel, so to have two of you believing you are doing the right thing, working together, and supporting each other is invaluable. It is possible to breastfeed a baby with special needs and, when everything else feels as if it is upside down, it can be a welcome injection of normality into a crazy world.

BENEFITS OF BREASTFEEDING FOR YOUR BABY

• Children who have breastmilk for eight months or more have higher average IQ scores and do better at school than babies who have formula milk.

• There is some evidence that children who were breastfed are less likely to develop cancer before the age of 15. The longer they were breastfed, the less likely they are to have insulin-dependent diabetes or obesity.

• Premature breastfed babies are protected against the potentially fatal bowel disorder called necrotising entercolitis.

• Adults who were breastfed have lower average blood pressure and risk of cardiovascular illness.

• Formula-fed babies have more respiratory, urinary tract, ear, and gastro-intestinal infections, diarrhoea, prolonged colds, more allergic illnesses such as eczema, asthma and wheeze, and may have poorer eyesight.

BENEFITS OF BREASTFEEDING FOR YOU

• Mothers who breastfeed lessen their risk of breast cancer, ovarian cancer, and hip fractures when older. In fact the longer you breastfeed, the lower your average risk of breast cancer.

• Breastfeeding is free, and you don't have to mix up formula or sterilize bottles.

• Breastfeeding is designed to use up the body fat you store in pregnancy.

How formula feeding works

Breastfeeding is the healthiest option, but there are many reasons why women decide to use formula milk, or a mixture of both. If you are planning to formula feed your baby you will still need lots of support and help. You may find it helps to be clear in your own mind about your reasons for deciding to bottle feed, in case people question your decision.

BOTTLE FEEDING YOUR BABY

Lay your baby across your lap and support her neck in the crook of your arm. Hold the bottle at an angle as she feeds to avoid air bubbles.

Most health professionals will support you in your choices, but some hospitals may not have supplies of formula or bottles on the ward. If you are having a hospital birth make sure you know what you need to take with you. Your breasts will produce milk after the birth whether you breastfeed or not. You will need a good, supportive bra for comfort, and may need painkillers for a few days.

It is important that you use only formula milk, which is modified cows' milk and mostly comes in cans or packets in granular or powder form. Hospitals may prefer you to use ready-made formula, but this is very expensive, so when you get home you will probably want to revert to dried formula. Ordinary pasteurized cows' milk is not suitable for babies to drink until they reach one year old, although you can use it in your child's food from six months.

Cows' milk formula is either whey- or casein-dominant. Whey-based formulas are more easily digested and are marketed for newborns, though they are suitable for your baby up to one year and beyond. Casein formulas, also called "stage two" milks, are sold for "hungrier" babies, although there is little evidence to show that one or the other will make your baby less hungry. If you are unsure which formula to use, your health visitor may be able to advise, though the brand you choose is mostly down to personal preference as there is little difference in reality.

Your midwife or health visitor should give you one-to-one tuition on safely mixing feeds – do ask for this if it isn't offered. It is important that you get this right. Never be tempted to make the feed a bit thicker or stronger to encourage your baby to sleep for longer. This is more likely to dehydrate your baby and make her ill.

Bottle feeding equipment

You will need to buy:

- Several 200ml (6¾fl oz) bottles, teats, and bottle covers (around six)
- Formula milk
- Bottle brush and teat brush
- Sterilizing equipment

You will need to sterilize the bottles and teats every time you use them, using either heat or chemicals. You can boil them in a large pan on the stove, in which case they must be completely submerged in boiling water and boiled vigorously for at least ten minutes. This works well in a small kitchen where you might not have space to store specialized sterilizing equipment.

Alternatively, you could buy a sterilizing unit to use in a microwave, or a free-standing steam sterilizer that you plug into the mains. Both use the same principle of heating to destroy germs and will take less time than boiling.

Chemical sterilizing involves submerging bottles and teats for at least 30 minutes in a container filled with sterilizing solution (you make this up with tablets following the manufacturer's instructions). Change the sterilizing fluid every 24 hours. You will then need to rinse the bottles and teats in cooled, boiled water before using.

Formula-fed babies can be fed when they seem to be hungry, or according to a schedule. If you are feeding to your baby's pattern you will need to keep a note of how much she consumes in 24 hours, as it can be tempting to feed her every time she cries and it is possible to overfeed a formula-fed baby. You also need to throw away unfinished feeds. This can feel wasteful, but you cannot reuse partially drunk milk or reheat feeds as formula milk is not sterile. Also, contact with your baby's mouth can encourage bacteria to grow in the milk.

Babies do not need feeds to be heated; they may be just as happy with a bottle straight from the fridge or at room temperature. This makes it easier to feed your baby when she is hungry, especially at night, as you will not need to warm the feed up. If you do want to give your baby warm feeds, heat a bottle of milk by placing it in a jug of hot water. Test the temperature by shaking a few drops onto the skin in the crook of your arm or the inside of your forearm. Never heat milk in a microwave as babies can be scalded by the milk.

How to bottle feed

Sit comfortably, in a chair with good back support, and lay your baby across your lap, supporting her neck in the crook of your arm so that her head is higher than her tummy, but tipped back so that her throat is open. Hold the bottle in her mouth, keeping it at an angle so that the teat stays full of milk to avoid air bubbles. Allow plenty of time, as your baby will need to pause for rests. When she has finished, wash and rinse the bottle and teat, using the brushes to clean into all the corners.

If you are formula feeding you may want to offer your baby water in hot weather as she will probably be thirstier but you don't want to overfeed her on formula.

If you are going out with your baby, you need to keep her milk cool until just before you need it, so carry it in an insulated bag padded with ice blocks. If the milk no longer feels cool when you take it out of the bag, it's probably not safe to use it. Most restaurants will heat a baby's bottle on request if you need them to, and some mother and baby changing rooms also have places to heat bottles.

BOTTLE FEEDING AT NIGHT
The easiest way to feed your baby at night is to boil some fresh water, let it cool to just above body temperature, and put the required amount in a sterilized thermos flask. Put a measure of formula in another feeding bottle without adding the water and seal it. You can then add the water to the formula when your baby wakes at night and shake it up to create instantly ready milk. What you must not do is keep prepared formula warm or reuse heated formula when she wakes again. Formula milk is an ideal breeding ground for bacteria.

MIXING UP BOTTLES – STEP-BY-STEP GUIDE
1 It will save time if you make up all the bottles you need each day in one go, so get everything ready beforehand.
2 Boil a kettle with more fresh water than you need and allow it to cool.
3 Make sure everything you're going to use has been sterilized. Wash your hands and then rinse the bottles and teats in cooled, boiled water if you've used chemical sterilizing.
4 Fill each bottle to the correct level with the cooled, boiled water.
5 Using the spoon provided in the tin, take a scoop of formula, and level it with a knife. Don't pat it down or compress it.
6 Add the right number of scoops to the bottle, put the top on, and shake thoroughly until all the powder has dissolved.
7 Store the bottles in the fridge.

Getting enough to eat

One of the biggest concerns parents have is about their child's diet. Is she getting enough to eat? Is it the right quality – is it healthy? And perhaps these worries are most prominent when the child is tiny – when she is entirely dependent on milk to supply all her nutritional needs.

BREAST TISSUE AFTER SIX WEEKS

Around six weeks after birth you may notice that your breasts become much softer and are not noticeably different before and after a feed. This can seem worrying – as if you have less milk. However, much of the fullness you experienced in the early days was in fact tissue swelling. Now that your breasts have settled down to milk production this no longer occurs, but your breasts will go on making milk as long as your baby goes on feeding from them.

Breastfeeding – getting enough

As we saw on page 89, thanks to prolactin your body will make the right amount of milk for your baby if you let her feed whenever she seems to want it. If you try to impose a feeding schedule from the beginning, your body will produce the amount of milk you tell it to, which may not be the same as the amount your baby needs.[*] Only your baby knows how hungry she is and how much breastmilk she needs in order to grow properly.

You will soon come to recognize your baby's hunger signals: she will become restless, her head will turn from side to side as if looking for something, her mouth will open, and her tongue extend. If she can't find your breast she will cry after a while, but it's easier to latch her on before she starts crying as crying is tiring and therefore she won't feed as effectively. When you see your baby feeding with big, slow jaw movements, and swallowing milk for much of the time she is on the breast, then you will know that she is well attached.

It's easy to make comparisons and feel that your baby can't be feeding properly because she is faster or slower than someone else's baby. However, breastfed babies vary greatly in how long they take to have a breastfeed, because some mothers let down milk faster than others and babies vary in how quickly they feed. The most important things to look for are whether your baby is feeding effectively and is satisfied after a feed. The gap between feeds will also vary. Sometimes your baby may "cluster feed", wanting several feeds in a few hours and then having a longer gap. This is absolutely normal.

To begin with, she will feed little and often. Her tummy is, after all, only the size of a walnut and will empty quickly. Breastfeeding can feel tiring for both of you when your baby is tiny, and while you are both still getting used to it.

In the early weeks expect to spend long periods of time feeding; you are investing in your milk supply. After about six weeks this will be well established. Your baby will be older and stronger, and feeding should gradually become much less time consuming. At this stage you will reap the rewards of ease and convenience that breastfeeding brings.

MAKING PLENTY OF MILK
If your baby is comfortably attached and feeding well, and you are feeding her when she asks for it rather than sticking to a strict routine, then you will make plenty of milk.

Breastfeeding should be comfortable for you. If you experience more than a slight twinge as your baby starts to feed, it is probable that she is not correctly attached. (*See* pp.102–5 for breastfeeding problems.) If feeding does seem to take a long time, and your baby seems unsettled afterwards, talk it through with a breastfeeding counsellor. It might be that your baby is not attached to your breast in the best way, making feeding harder work than it should be.

Many women stop breastfeeding because they think that they don't have enough milk. It is worth remembering that even women who are starving or severely malnourished keep their babies alive purely on breastmilk. Your body can nearly always produce enough milk to feed your baby if you allow her access to your breast as often as she wants.

Sometimes your baby, having seemed settled and content in a feeding pattern, suddenly enters a phase where she seems to want to feed all the time. This could be because she is having a growth spurt and wants to increase your milk supply. If she's ill or teething she may also want to feed a lot. Sometimes she will feed all the time for a day or so before she develops an illness. Trust your baby's instincts and be led by them, as when she's ill breastmilk is the best thing for her.

Bottle feeding – getting enough

If you are bottle feeding, it is easier to assess how much your baby is getting to eat as you can see the empty bottles. There is a recommended amount that your baby should take at a particular age or weight and you should try to stick roughly to that (details will be given in the manufacturer's instructions).

Formula-fed babies are more likely to grow up to be overweight adults, and one of the reasons for this may be because parents can ignore a baby's signals that she's had enough, wanting her to finish the bottle each time, whereas breast-feeding mothers have to be governed by their baby's cues. If babies' tummies are constantly overfilled, past the point of feeling replete, then in time they may learn to ignore that signal. When they are older and in control of how much to eat, they will continue to eat past the point of repletion.

Babies will often feed even when they're not hungry, as feeding is comforting. If your baby has fed recently but is crying, it is worth trying to comfort her in other ways – see the sleep chapter starting on page 110 for more suggestions.

If your formula-fed baby is putting on what appears to be too much or too little weight, it is important to discuss possible reasons with your health visitor. Do not be tempted to alter the instructions for making up formula to make it more dilute or stronger – this is very dangerous for your baby.

Your baby's weight gain

In the early days it's easy to get obsessed by your baby's weight, but this is only one part of the picture. It's important to look at the overall pattern. Babies normally lose a small amount of weight in the first few days after birth. If your baby lost more than ten percent of her birth weight in the beginning, for instance, it will take her longer to catch up. If she put on a lot of weight for a couple of weeks, then the weight gain may well slow down in the following weeks. Also consider whether your baby is generally alert, healthy, and interacting with you.

Nappies are also a good indicator of whether your baby is getting enough milk. If you are using disposables, they should feel heavier when you change them (which will probably be about four to six times a day). With reusables, she will probably have six to eight wet nappies in 24 hours. Nappies should not smell strongly of urine, as it should be fairly dilute. If your baby is breastfed then bowel motions will be mustardy yellow, sweet smelling, and the consistency of scrambled

HOW TO INCREASE YOUR MILK SUPPLY

If you are worried about your milk supply and feel that you want to increase it, then cut right down on everything you are doing over a 48-hour period. Feed your baby as often as possible, rest as much as you can (spend time in bed during the day with your baby ideally), and eat plenty of nutritious meals and snacks.

eggs. If she is bottle fed, her bowel motions will be regular, sizeable, and shouldn't cause her too much discomfort. After the first few days a breastfed baby should be producing several bowel motions a day. After five or six weeks, the number of motions per day may decrease – a few breastfed babies may only produce two bowel motions a week. Provided the baby is otherwise healthy, this is not a cause for concern. It does not mean that the baby is constipated.

It is important to look at growth in length and head circumference too, since these are far more accurate and positive signs of normal development than just focusing on weight, which is partly about body fat. There is no need to have your baby weighed every week or even every fortnight. Sometimes your baby's weight will fluctuate because she is weighed with different scales, or with or without clothes or a nappy, or because she did a bowel motion just before being weighed the last time. Do not worry about slight changes in the readings.

Weight charts

Formula-fed babies are known to put on weight in a different pattern compared to breastfed babies. This difference is most marked after two to three months, when formula-fed babies gain weight slightly faster than breastfed babies on average. If it seems that your breastfed baby is crossing the centile lines downwards on the chart that you have, check that the growth chart is based on breastfed babies' normal growth patterns. (It is important to remember that breastfed babies are the biological norm.)

Breastfed babies typically gain weight more slowly after the first three months. They tend to be slightly leaner at a year old than formula-fed babies, and this may be related to a continued healthy weight in childhood.

Expressing and storing your breastmilk

There are lots of reasons for learning how to express breastmilk and how to store it safely. If you do express, you will also need to persuade your baby to take milk from a bottle or cup.

If you are returning to work, or leaving your baby for periods of time for any other reason, then you may need to express your breastmilk. If your baby is premature or otherwise separated from you, expressing your milk will maintain your supply as well as providing the most nutritiously valuable substance possible to nourish your baby during this difficult time. Some women manage to feed their babies entirely on expressed breastmilk, but this does involve quite a lot of time and effort.

How to hand-express

Expressing by hand is actually quite efficient, so it's worth learning this technique. It can be useful in many situations, perhaps if you are a bit engorged and want to relieve that feeling, or to soften your breast in order to make it easier for your baby to latch on. Later on you might want to express some milk to mix with your baby's first solids. If you are away from your baby, hand expressing will also maintain your milk supply.

• It is a good idea to massage your breasts first to release the hormones.

• Hold your breast, with your thumb on top and your fingers underneath, so that your little finger is against your ribcage, and your first finger and thumb are opposite each other, making a big "C" shape around your breast (see the picture on p.100).

• Your milk comes from deep within your breast, so your finger and thumb need to be well away from your nipple, back behind your areola.

• Squeeze your thumb and first finger gently together, hold and release, and keep doing this without changing the position of your fingers, until you see some drops of milk appearing. This may take a few minutes. Some women find this method of expressing more effective if they push their whole hand back towards the ribcage before they squeeze.

• Once the flow of milk slows, move your hand round, keeping that "C", so that you are milking a different section of your breast.⊙

Specialized cups

If your baby is not finding it easy to breastfeed in the early days, you may want to use another method to give her your breastmilk. Instead of a bottle, you could use a teaspoon or a specialized small cup. Some hospitals prefer to use cups as there

USING CUPS

If your baby is having trouble latching on initially you can express some milk and use a special cup, such as those shown below, to give it to her.

is an indication that if a baby is given breastmilk in this way she may be more likely to be able to revert to breastfeeding than if she had been given it in a bottle.

Babies need to be supported so that they are upright, and may need to be wrapped so that their hands do not knock the cup. The cup should be held gently against the baby's bottom lip, tilted so that she can lap or sip the milk. It should not be tipped into her mouth; the key is for the baby, rather than the parent or carer, to control the rate at which milk is taken.

Using a breast pump

If you know you will be expressing frequently, perhaps because you are returning to work within the first few months after giving birth, then you might want to use a breast pump. Alternatively, if your baby is premature and not able to breastfeed at first, pumping regularly will help maintain your milk supply as well as providing the nourishment your baby needs.

All pumps work by drawing the milk through your nipple and into a sterilized container. Handheld pumps are relatively cheap, portable, and quiet, which might be a consideration if you have to express when you are out and about, but they are generally less effective. Cylinder or lever mechanisms work well. Any pump that requires you to squeeze something will be tiring after a while.

Battery- or mains-operated electric pumps are also available. These are quicker and easier than hand-held pumps but are noisy and more expensive. It is best to shop around or ask friends for personal recommendations. You can hire electric pumps from the NCT on a daily rate.

If you are finding expressing with a pump difficult, you could try a flexishield. This is a soft insert that moulds around your breast to emulate your baby sucking. These are also available from NCT breast-pump agents.

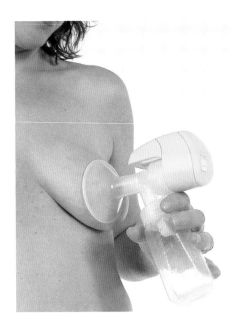

BREAST PUMPS

These work by drawing milk into a sterilized container. As well as the hand-held one shown above there are pumps with cylinder or lever mechanisms and others that are battery- or mains-operated.

When to express

As previously stated, your breastmilk supply is generally well established by six weeks under normal circumstances. This is a good time, therefore, to start experimenting with expressing, if you want to. Before this you will be spending quite a lot of time feeding your baby anyway.

Think about when would be the easiest time for you to express. For example, if your baby only feeds from one side at a time, it might work if you express from the other breast while she's feeding. If she has long gaps between feeds (three hours or so) you could try expressing in-between feeds. Alternatively, you can express what is left after your baby has finished a feed.

Storing breastmilk

Expressed breastmilk (EBM) keeps very well, but needs to be handled safely. It is important to sterilize all containers (*see* p.93). Many components in fresh,

Hand expressing can be a useful skill to utilize in a variety of different situations when you are away from your baby – especially if you are feeling engorged.

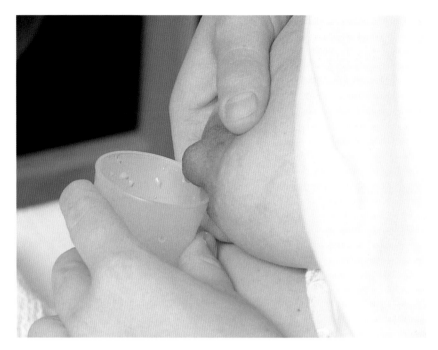

untreated breastmilk actually inhibit bacterial growth, so even at room temperature it will be fine for several hours. If you are storing breastmilk in a fridge, it will be safe for up to five days stored in the coldest part of the fridge (at or below 4°C/39°F, usually the back or the bottom, not the door). If it is not possible to maintain your fridge's temperature at this rate – perhaps because it is old, has a lot of food stored in it, or the door is opened a lot – then you will need to use the milk more quickly.

Freezing causes only minor changes to the nutrients and anti-infective properties of breastmilk. Frozen EBM stored in a freezer or chest freezer should be safe for up to six months if the temperature is maintained at 0°F (-20°C). An ice-cube compartment within a fridge is not as cold as a separate freezer, so if you are storing in one of these you should only keep it there for two to four weeks before using. Once EBM has been defrosted, use it within a couple of hours as freezing compromises the anti-bacterial properties.

You will need to freeze EBM in sterile containers and date them. You can buy special EBM bags into which you pour the milk straight from the pump container. After defrosting, simply pour the milk into your baby's bottle or cup just before use.

Chilled expressed milk can be added to milk that is already frozen, as long as you don't add more than half as much again. Remember that milk will expand on freezing, so don't fill containers right to the top.

Introducing bottles

The majority of parents give their babies a bottle at some time, although whether you put formula or breastmilk into it will depend on your situation. Being able to use a bottle can be a useful option, as you can go out knowing that someone else can feed your baby. You will almost certainly need to introduce bottles if you are returning to work early. If you replace the occasional breastfeed with a bottle, you will need to express some milk otherwise you may become engorged.

If you do plan to give your breastfed baby some bottle feeds, around six weeks of age can be a good time to start. Most babies at this time are very used to breastfeeding and will not get confused – they will simply see a bottle as some-thing different. At six weeks they are well able to master two different feeding techniques. However, if your baby won't take a bottle:

• Get someone else to give it, while you leave the room completely.
• Try a different temperature – some babies will only take it when it is the same temperature as breastmilk, while others will take a bottle of cool milk.
• Experiment with different teats, and try warming them with hot water first.
• Leave it for a few weeks, if there is no rush to introduce bottles.

If you are going back to work, or planning to change to formula milk when your baby is more than six months, you may be able to leave out bottles altogether. Babies of this age should be capable of taking drinks of water or milk from a beaker or cup.

"I thought it would be easy to switch from breast to bottle feeding. We tried everything – different bottles, different teats, different people. Finally I found a type of teat that he approved of."

BABY DRINKS
Water can be offered in a beaker after six months, but be wary of giving juice – babies don't need it and it can be bad for their teeth.

Breastfeeding – potential problems

When breastfeeding is going well it's an enjoyable experience for you and your baby, but if you encounter difficulties it can be disheartening. Here are some of the most common problems and how to overcome them. The main thing to remember is to always ask for help when you feel you need it.

Many women who choose to breastfeed do manage to get going with it and enjoy this special time with their babies. For others, difficulties with breastfeeding make the experience feel like a chore. As with anything new, breastfeeding needs to be learned, and you and your baby will need to practise to learn this skill. Most women, though, say they're glad they persevered.

Understanding what the common problems are and how to avoid them will help. The best approach is not to ignore difficulties hoping they will go away, but to tackle them as soon as they arise, asking for help as soon as you need it.

The majority of breastfeeding problems stem from not getting your baby latched on to your breast in a way that is comfortable for you or allows your baby to reach all the milk she needs. This is understandable; holding your baby exactly right is hard when you're both novices. Make sure you ask for help from your midwife in the crucial early days, and have another look at page 90 to remind yourself how to latch your baby on. Also, if you can put your baby to your breast as soon as possible after birth, that can help you both get off to a really good start.

Sore nipples

Many women have sensitive nipple skin for the first week after birth. You will also not be used to the strong sensation of your baby's feeding action, so it can feel uncomfortable to start with. There is a difference, though, between discomfort from something you are not used to, and pain that is warning you that you are actually damaging your nipples.

If you are not sure what type of pain you are experiencing, when your baby latches on wait for 30 seconds. If you still feel uncomfortable, take her off and start again. If you are finding it particularly painful, practise relaxation at the beginning of the feed and try to latch your baby on when she is just waking up, before she gets really hungry. The most important consideration, though, is that when your baby comes off your breast, your nipples should not look chaffed or distorted. If they do, then revisit how you are positioning and attaching your baby, because your nipples may become damaged if you continue to feed like this.

"Savoy cabbage leaves inside my bra did really help with early breast tenderness."

It is miserable if you have sore nipples. Nipple skin is very like the skin on your lips – easily cracked and painful when damaged. Try to hang on to the fact that once you have tackled the cause of the problem, your nipples will get better very quickly. If your nipples have become damaged to the extent that the skin is broken, then you can spread a little hindmilk over your nipples at the end of a feed to moisturize them. Allow your skin to dry before putting a bra or breast pad on. Some women have found that a pure lanolin cream can soothe the pain and help the cracks heal. It is best not to let cracks dry out and form scabs, as these will keep reopening when your baby feeds.

Another less common reason for sore nipples is thrush, which can occur if you have had thrush during pregnancy, are prone to thrush, or if you or your baby have recently taken antibiotics. Thrush causes severe nipple pain, and sometimes deep breast pain. Your nipple skin may look lighter than usual and be shiny, and your baby may have white flecks in her mouth. Women usually report that the pain continues throughout the feed and between feeds, and simple tasks like taking a shower can be painful as the water touches the nipples. If you think you have thrush it is important that both you and your baby are treated by your GP, even if your baby shows no symptoms, in order to avoid cross-infection. ⊙ Ask a breastfeeding counsellor about current topical applications for thrush.

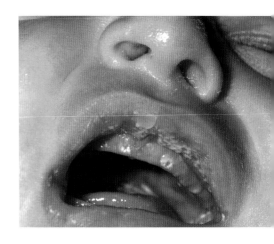

CHECKING FOR THRUSH

If you are suffering from thrush check the inside of your baby's mouth. If she has white spots it means she has picked up the infection too.

Sore breasts

Two to five days after the birth your milk "comes in", replacing the initial colostrum. This happens whether you are breastfeeding or not. Your breasts become engorged, hot, swollen, and uncomfortable, and it can be hard for your baby to latch on. As well as containing milk your breasts are also swollen with excess fluid due to an increased blood supply. This will pass within 24 hours. In the meantime, feeding your baby frequently will help. Some women find ice-cold flannels bring relief. Cabbage leaves can help too, especially Savoy cabbages; hold a chilled leaf against your breast. ⊙

Once breastfeeding is established, engorgement usually only happens if you go for too long between feeds, or miss feeds, and you will have some prior warning that it is coming on. If you start to feel a bit full, then put your baby to your breast, or express some milk. Leaving milk in your breast when you feel uncomfortable can lead to blocked ducts. You can feel these as painful lumps, and they can also occur if your bra doesn't fit well or if you have something restricting your milk flow during a feed – such as your hand or your baby's hand pressing against your breast.

If you develop a blocked duct, feeding your baby is the best cure and you should gently massage the lump towards your nipple during the feed. Pressing something hot or cold, such as a flannel, against your breasts can also help to alleviate the discomfort.

SIGNS THAT YOUR BABY HAS THRUSH:
• Pulling away and crying while feeding.
• White spots in the mouth that look like drops of milk but that don't go away.
• Sometimes your baby will also have thrush on her bottom, which manifests as a nappy rash of paler, shiny skin.

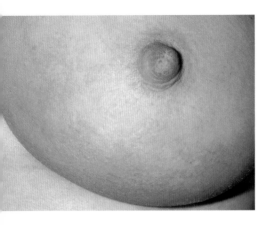

MASTITIS

It's important to keep breastfeeding if you develop mastitis, as you will need to clear the blocked duct. Feed from the sore breast first.

If you keep getting blocked ducts think about where in your breasts the blocks occur, and whether something is pressing into your breasts during feeding. It helps if you can get your baby's chin nearest to the lump when feeding, so, if it occurs on the outer side of your breast, try feeding underarm on that side, for instance.

MASTITIS

If untreated, blocked ducts or engorgement can lead to mastitis. This is caused by milk that is trapped in the breasts overflowing from the ducts into the surrounding breast tissue, where the body treats it as a foreign substance and rallies the immune system to fight.

If you are unfortunate enough to develop mastitis you will feel fluey, may develop a temperature, and your breasts will be sore. Try to rest and drink plenty of fluids. It is important to keep feeding your baby, as stopping breastfeeding will make the problem worse. Usually, if you clear the blocked duct or engorgement the mastitis will ease.

Your GP may prescribe antibiotics, but most cases of mastitis are not caused by infection and so antibiotics are purely precautionary. It's better if your GP can prescribe an anti-inflammatory drug to reduce the inflammation.$^{\odot}$ Neither of these drugs will harm your baby, though antibiotics may upset her tummy and you need to watch out for thrush – *see* previous page.

It is important to treat mastitis promptly, as, if left, you could go on to develop a breast abscess that will have to be drained in hospital. If you can identify why you got mastitis in the first place you can hopefully prevent it from happening in the future, so why not talk it through with a breastfeeding counsellor or your health visitor?

Do I need to buy anything special for breastfeeding?

Despite the abundance of nipple creams, sprays, and lotions available in the shops, you do not need to buy anything special for breastfeeding. Your skin may even react to some of these products, making sore nipples worse. Skin creams are really only necessary if you have thrush, in which case you should be using prescribed medication.

Breastfeeding breasts, like pregnancy breasts, are fuller and heavier, and you will probably want to wear a comfortable, supportive bra to minimize discomfort. A proper breastfeeding bra will be best as they are specially designed both for comfort and practicality. Underwired bras are not recommended as they may press on ducts, causing blocks or even mastitis.

Breast pads are useful if you leak a lot, but try to avoid using any that have a plastic backing as this keeps heat and moisture next to your skin – a perfect breeding ground for thrush. Washable, cotton pads are best.

Perseverance will be rewarded

It may sound like breastfeeding is problematic, but many women encounter few, if any, difficulties. The main thing is to always ask for help, and keep asking for help until breastfeeding is a pain-free, pleasurable experience for both you and your baby.

"The help I received from a breastfeeding counsellor was invaluable, and I know if it wasn't for her knowledge, help, and support I would have given up feeding my son."

WEARING THE RIGHT BRA
A good breastfeeding bra will help to make you feel comfortable and supported when feeding your baby.

Are routines right for you?

The idea of getting babies into a routine has gained in popularity in recent years. But is this the right thing for you and your baby? And how does it actually work with a baby who has never seen a clock before?

There is no shortage of advice available to new parents. The problem is that there is no one, right way to bring up a baby, and part of the process of becoming a parent is learning which way is best for you and your new family. How your day pans out is one of these considerations. Some people suggest trying to get into a routine, by which they mean doing things by the clock, while others suggest going with the flow.

Perhaps the place to start is with you. Are you already a routine person – do you watch the clock? Do you have a list of things you want to do and tick them

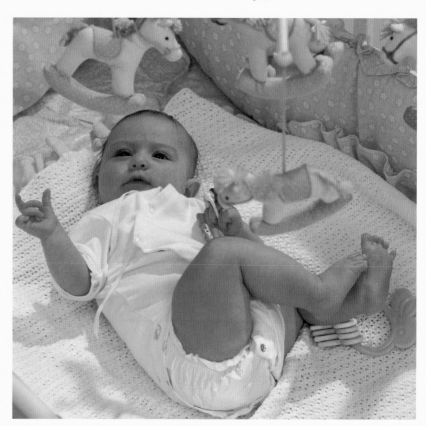

LEARNING TO NEGOTIATE

While the idea of getting into a routine with your baby may be appealing, you need to remember that she is an individual with her own preferences. You will probably have to learn to give and take, at least initially, rather than imposing a routine that isn't natural to her.

off as they happen? Or do you take each day as it comes? Both approaches have something to recommend them, and in fact both ways will eventually end up in the same place. It's just that each way represents a different outlook on life, and a different pattern.

When your baby arrives there is another human being to consider and she may have her own preferred approach to the day. She is unlikely to want to clock watch, but may be happy to fall into a predictable pattern. On the other hand, she may struggle with this; she may find the world a confusing, frightening place and want to be held, carried, and fed constantly until she gets used to it all.

If you and your baby have different needs then you need to negotiate. The main thing to bear in mind is that how your pattern evolves must be something on which you both agree, otherwise one of you is going to be unhappy.

Feeding in a routine

It is possible to feed in a routine, and this is probably going to be desirable later on, when your baby is old enough to feed with the family. You won't want to be supplying meals to everyone whenever they want them; you will probably want to have at least three meals a day at approximately the same time.

However, in your baby's first six weeks of life she needs to feed a lot. Her tummy is extremely small and will need to be topped up frequently. She is not particularly skilled at extracting milk quickly from the breast or bottle, so feeding will take her some time.

If you are bottle feeding it may be easier to get into a clock-watching routine earlier if you want to, but often mothers like to have those early weeks to relax and get to know their baby. If you're breastfeeding, your baby will need to feed frequently to build up your milk supply (see p.87).

Your baby also needs to grow. She will double her weight in the first few months of life – never again will she need to grow so quickly. If you had to double your weight in six months, what would you do? Eat often and eat for a long time!

By about six weeks many women find that a pattern begins to emerge naturally. This makes sense, as it is about the time that your baby's diurnal rhythms start maturing (this is how your baby recognizes the difference between night and day).[*] If breastfeeding, your milk supply should be well established by six weeks. If no pattern has emerged, and you are feeling the need to get some control over your life, then maybe it is time to start negotiations.

Firstly, keep a diary over the next few days. Write down what happens when, and try to see if there is a pattern emerging that you could build on. You can try gradually to extend gaps between feeds, and perhaps also to keep your baby awake for longer during a feed so that she will take in more. Perhaps you would like her to feed a little longer in the afternoon and early evening so that she may go longer between feeds at night.

The important thing to note with breastfeeding is that the pattern has to suit you and your baby, as your milk supply and her appetite are unique to the pair of you. Biologically it is not possible to say that all babies can feed at 7am, 10am, 1pm, and 4pm. Each baby could feed at regular intervals, but how long these intervals will be, and how long each feed will take, is not something that can be set in stone.

If you try to impose arbitrary time limits on when and how long your baby feeds for, you will either diminish your milk supply or you will have a baby that does not get enough hindmilk, and who then wants to feed more frequently. Evidence shows that when this happens many women give up breastfeeding.⊙

Sleeping in a routine

While daytime feeding patterns are something that you might work towards gradually, you may be quite keen to have a routine at night – longer stretches of time asleep, with as few disruptions as possible. Pages 110–35 cover sleep in some detail, but one of the earliest routines that might prove useful to you and your family is the routine of bedtime.

There are various things you can do to help your baby sleep longer at night, such as emphasizing the difference between day and night⊙ (*see* p.122), and establishing a bedtime routine. The aim of this routine is to help your baby fall asleep on her own in the evenings. Bedtime routines can also be helpful if your baby is fretful in the evenings; a predictable pattern may be soothing. You can also try to pre-empt the crying time by settling her to sleep before it starts. What you do is down to you, but here are some ideas.

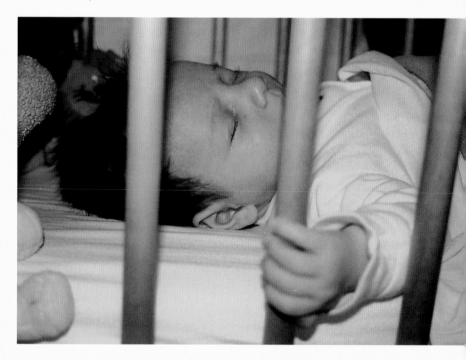

ESTABLISHING A BEDTIME ROUTINE

To help your baby sleep for as long as possible at night it's a good idea to emphasize the difference between day and night, for instance by not turning on the light or stimulating your baby if she wakes at night.

- A warm bath – with you or on her own.
- A song or nursery rhyme, which could later turn into storytime.
- A milky drink (breast or bottle).
- Plenty of cuddles and kisses.
- Lying her down in her cot with some soothing words.

You will probably also eventually want to establish a pattern of daytime naps, so that your baby has definite times for being asleep and being awake, rather than drifting between states as she will do in her early weeks. These could evolve alongside the bedtime routines, perhaps with some different cues so that she knows it is not "bedtime" – such as leaving the curtains open, playing a soothing tape, and having a few toys or teddies for her to play with in the cot.

Other routines

As your baby gets older, it may be fun to start living your life to a predictable routine – Monday swimming, Tuesday going to the park, Wednesday postnatal group, and so on. Or perhaps predictability bores you to tears, and you and your baby will treat each day as it comes, deciding on the spur of the moment to go to the zoo or take a train ride. However you live your life, make sure it is the one you want to live, not one where someone else tells you what to do.

4 SLEEPING

- "I've never been so tired..."
- How sleep works
- Soothing and comforting your new baby
- Self-soothing: helping him to help himself
- Sleep routines
- Where to sleep
- Coping with broken nights
- Daytime naps
- Sleep and older babies

"I've never been so tired…"

Sleep is definitely a hot topic for new parents. Who is getting it? Who isn't? Couples may even find themselves arguing about who is the most tired! For new parents sleep often becomes a major fixation. However, it needn't be this way; understanding your need for rest and making changes in your approach can reduce the stress and beat the obsession.

"The best advice I had was to forget the concept of day and night for the first two weeks, so not worrying what time it was, and sleeping, eating, and showering when we could."

Why are new parents so tired?

New parents are probably the most tired group in the population. There are many reasons for this. Not only do they have to care for a highly dependent newborn baby, there is also the immense change and upheaval that new parents have to accommodate in their daily lives.

Most people will remember how starting a new job leaves them feeling exhausted at the end of the day. This is because constant learning is tiring. In a new job we have to develop new skills and keep open to the various different ways of doing things in our new workplace. New parents experience something very similar except that they can't go home at the end of the day and have an early night! In fact they have to stay on duty for a full 24 hours a day with no holiday in sight. Learning to care for a new baby is a demanding task physically, emotionally, and intellectually.

New mothers will also be dealing with the physical aftermath of the birth process. Even a normal vaginal birth is a big physical challenge and mothers' bodies need time to recover. Women who have had a caesarean operation will have the additional challenge of recovery from major abdominal surgery. Usually when our bodies have been through this sort of upheaval we are given bed rest and are cared for intensively by others. After birth the situation is very different; unless you are in a high dependency unit you will be expected to care for your baby yourself from day one.

The importance of rest

Early discharge from hospital and "rooming in" (where babies are kept with mothers after birth rather than being cared for in a nursery) on postnatal wards have had a positive impact as parents spend more time with their babies, experiencing the intimacy that begins their life-long relationship in the best way. Home births also mean that new mothers stay in constant contact with their new babies and their families. The fact that mothers are no longer treated as hospital "patients" beyond the first few hours or days (if at all) does not mean that they don't need special care, attention, and rest in the early days. However, some families interpret the hospital discharge as an opportunity to "get back to normal".

While the initial euphoria that many women experience after birth can carry you through the early days, getting on with daily life too soon can lead to stress and exhaustion later. It is extremely important that new mothers take care of themselves as much as possible in the first weeks after birth. Traditional cultures understand this, and women and babies are given special treatment – usually involving lots of rest, special foods, and no work for the mother in the first 40 days. Western women, by contrast, are expected to accommodate a stream of visitors, keep up appearances, and return to normal activities as soon as possible. No wonder women report being exhausted! In the first few weeks it is important to rest whenever possible. Some women find it helpful to stay in their dressing gowns for the first ten days at least, as a signal to others that they're not up to their usual activities.

Slow down for the first few weeks

In Western industrial societies success is not only measured in terms of material wealth; increasingly people's status is related to how "busy" they are. Important people are busy because their skills are needed. In our culture of long working hours, having extended periods of time with no planned activities is seen as acceptable only for the very young, the very old, and those who cannot contribute to society for other reasons. We are accustomed to filling our days and evidence suggests that on average adults sleep fewer hours each night than even a generation ago.[⊙] Adults in our society expect to work hard, play hard, and sleep in short concentrated bursts at night-time.

Caring for a baby requires a very different approach. Parenting, especially in the early months, requires a much slower and gentler pace. Concentrated bursts of deep sleep, waking refreshed, and getting on with a timetable of activities are a thing of the past for the time being. Parents who are least stressed accommodate this and "go with the flow". However, it is not always possible to put life on hold in this way and on pages 128–9 we will examine ways to cope effectively with loss of sleep.

It's not forever

Becoming a parent will change the way you sleep, especially in the early months and years. Lying in at the weekend will become a treat rather than an expectation. However, as in all areas of becoming a parent, the situation will change over time. What seems like forever now may be a distant memory in six months. As parents you need to adjust to the needs of your baby and then gradually your baby can be encouraged to adjust to your needs. Parenting is about relationships and negotiation – and negotiation over sleep is especially important.

EXCESSIVE FATIGUE

Feeling extremely tired is common among women in the postnatal period. Up to 60 percent of women report extreme fatigue at the six-week check and beyond.[⊙] As well as lack of sleep other factors may be to blame – such as recovery from a long labour and/or difficult birth, blood loss at delivery, hormonal shifts, ongoing anaemia, and discomfort or pain.

In the busy postnatal period it is common for new mothers to overlook their own healthcare as so much concern is focused on the new baby. If you are feeling excessively tired or exhausted do discuss this with your GP, midwife, or health visitor. Effective, timely treatment for anaemia or pain, for example, could make all the difference to your enjoyment of the early weeks with your baby.

see also

coping with broken nights   128–9

How sleep works

Understanding what sleep is and how it works, both for yourself as an adult and for your baby, is vital. Armed with this basic knowledge you can work with what is actually happening rather than spending fruitless time and energy pushing for what can never be. Understanding how sleep develops in your baby will help you to change what can be changed and stop worrying about what can't, which means less stress all round.

What is sleep?

The human need for sleep remains somewhat mysterious and is the subject of ongoing research. However, we do know that we need to sleep for our bodies to recover physically from the stresses of the day and to allow our brains to process information. Sleep is regulated by our endocrine (hormonal) system, which regulates our metabolism throughout the 24-hour day. We are influenced both by a circadian rhythm, which is linked to daylight (and means that we tend to find it easier to sleep during the night than during the day), and an ultradian rhythm, which is linked to many biological processes (the most obvious one being that the longer we are awake the more we acquire a sleep debt that increases our need for sleep). These two rhythms acting together make us ready for sleep at the end of the day.

When adults sleep they move between a number of sleep states. These different sleep states are reflected in different brain activity. Arguably the two most important sleep states are deep sleep and REM (rapid eye movement) sleep. Deep sleep is important for physical recovery and helps us to wake feeling refreshed. REM sleep is important for processing information, learning, and possibly emotional recovery. When woken in REM sleep, people report having been dreaming. Getting insufficient REM sleep is associated with increased stress and emotional vulnerability.

Adults move through the different sleep states in cycles that last about 90 minutes. During each sleep cycle an adult will move from light sleep into deeper sleep and then progress to a period of REM sleep. During the early part of the night adults tend to spend more time in deep sleep while towards the morning there is more REM sleep. Because REM sleep tends to come at the end of a sleep cycle, frequent waking can mean that adults don't get enough REM sleep.

How do babies sleep?

Young babies have sleep cycles that are much shorter than those of adults, and they are not capable of maintaining deep sleep for as long. They also have much more REM sleep than adults (as much as 50 percent of their sleep time is REM) although we don't know whether they are "dreaming" as such.[⊙] Even foetuses have been found to experience REM sleep.

Babies tend to drift in and out of sleep states in unpredictable ways and spend far more time than adults in light sleep (*see* pp.143–5). In the early weeks, especially, their circadian rhythm is less well developed (so that they sleep just as well during the day as at night) and sleep tends to be organized around feeding times. These patterns change over the first months of life as the baby matures.

Sleep is important for a baby's normal growth, development, and health, therefore it is important to help your baby get as much sleep as he needs. Babies who become over-tired are often miserable and irritable, and while very young babies cannot stay awake at will, they can have difficulty being calm enough to drift off to sleep. Having effective ways of soothing and comforting your baby is important for both of you.

How much should my baby be sleeping?

Newborn babies normally sleep for between 16 and 18 hours a day. Of course in this case "normal" simply means "most usual", so any individual baby may sleep much more or much less than this amount. The longest continuous sleep period is generally from two and a half to four hours. Very young babies are more "inefficient" sleepers than older babies, which means that they are prone to waking often and may sleep for unpredictable and irregular periods of time.

By around two to three months of age a circadian rhythm of responding to light and dark starts to emerge and there is some responsiveness to social cues. Babies start to sleep longer at night than during the day so that an average six-month old will be able to sleep for an unbroken stretch of about six hours at night. So, during the first year after birth even an older baby will probably wake at some point in the night-time or early morning before going to sleep again. This is why parents are often confused when reading about "sleeping through the night". What health professionals mean by this is that a baby will sleep for at least five hours without waking, say from midnight to five o'clock, rather than for twelve hours at a stretch. In fact the statistic that 85 percent of babies sleep through the night by six months (which is often quoted) actually means that those babies sleep for a period of about five or six hours during the night.

Parents may wish their babies to sleep for ten to twelve hours a night but it is an unrealistic aim for at least the first year after birth. However, babies can be helped to sleep at times that fit in with family life; although there are no guarantees that this will always happen. A more realistic aim is to focus on reducing the disturbance to the rest of the family. What most parents find helpful is to develop a sleep pattern that causes least stress to both your family and your baby (*see* pp.122–3 for some useful strategies).

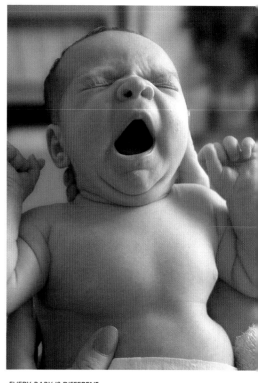

EVERY BABY IS DIFFERENT

Babies have very different sleep requirements and patterns to adults. Understanding and working with those of your own particular baby is the best way forward in the early weeks.

see also

Soothing and comforting your new baby

Just like adults, babies need to feel relaxed and comfortable to fall asleep. As adults we have learned what calms us down and makes sleep possible. Babies need our help, especially in the early days when life outside the womb may feel strange and unsafe. There are many techniques for calming and soothing your baby, and different babies like different things. Discovering what your baby prefers is an important part of getting to know him.

Recreating the womb

It is helpful when thinking about soothing a very young baby to think about what the baby was used to in the womb. During your pregnancy your baby was: held at a constant temperature; in a confined space; listening to the muffled sounds of your heartbeat, digestion, and the voices of family and friends; and rocked at a steady pace as you walked about. This explains why most newborn babies like to be warm, well wrapped, close to their parents, and rocked. Most prefer the background noise of normal family life rather than silence. Most soothing techniques are based on recreating aspects of the womb environment.

Holding, touching, and carrying

Human infants are extremely vulnerable and physically immature, and need constant care and protection, so much of their instinctive behaviour is driven by a need to keep adults close by. Babies thrive on close physical contact with a small number of responsive adults who care about them. They love to be held, stroked, and carried. Luckily, holding, stroking, and cuddling babies is pleasurable for parents as well as babies. Nothing can beat the feeling of a contented sleepy baby snuggling in your arms. Do take time to enjoy holding your baby; too much cuddling cannot spoil babies and won't increase their need or create a "bad habit".

"When Niamh was first born she loved to be held, almost constantly. She had been so close to me for nine months already, I suppose it was a hard habit to break."

Holding your baby close mimics womb conditions such as warmth, containment, and perhaps movement if you walk about. Your arms help him to feel contained and, lying close to your chest, he may be able to hear and feel your heartbeat. Skin-to-skin contact is especially comforting for new babies.

Babies tend to differ in the way that they like to be held. Some enjoy being cradled in your arms so that they can look at your face and make eye contact. Others like to be held upright against your shoulder. Newborn babies' heads are very large in comparison with the rest of their bodies and their neck muscles are weak, so when holding your young baby upright give good support to his head and upper back and put the other hand under his bottom. Some babies jerk or bump their heads away from your shoulder so keeping a hand to the back of their necks keeps them safe.

Baby slings and carriers are useful ways of holding your baby when you need your hands free or when you wish to carry your baby for a long time, such as during an outing and while travelling. There are myriad of slings and baby carriers available and it is well worth doing some research and even trying out a few before you buy one (see box, right, and p.56).

Sometimes a baby's wish to be held, carried, and cuddled exceeds the parent's ability to respond. There may be other demands on a parent's time or a parent may simply need a break to recharge his/her batteries. Once again, as in so many areas of parenting, the key to this situation is negotiation. It may be that your baby can be comforted by other means, at least some of the time, or you could enlist the help of someone else to hold and carry your baby while you have a rest.

Attachment parenting

This is a particular approach to parenting that arose from a study by Jean Liedloff, an anthropologist working with South American tribal people. Liedloff argued that human infants are designed to be close to their carers at all times. She described how in these traditional societies babies are always carried, often in slings tied to their mothers' bodies. At night they sleep in their mothers' beds. She noticed that babies in this environment cried and fussed far less

WHAT TO LOOK FOR WHEN BUYING A SLING OR BABY CARRIER
• The sling should be comfortable for you to wear; it should hold the baby close to your body but not too low as that would strain your back.
• A sling should support your baby's head and back.
• Slings that are easy to put on and get off when you are by yourself are by far the most convenient.
• Slings that allow the baby to be carried in a number of different ways can be used until toddlerhood.

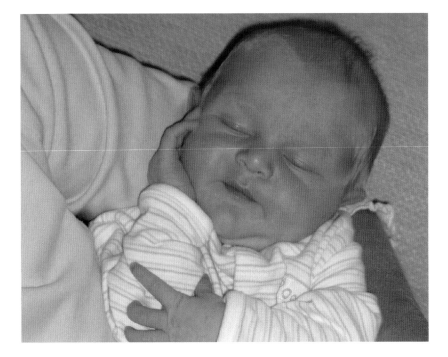

HOLD HIM CLOSE

Your baby got used to being close to you while he was in the womb, and so will crave a lot of close cuddles. These help him to feel safe and secure.

TO SWADDLE A BABY:

• First place the blanket/sheet on a flat, safe surface, such as a changing mat, carpet, or your bed.

• Lay your baby onto the cloth with the back of his neck in line with the long edge.

• Bring one side of the cloth over your baby's body, crossing diagonally across his shoulder and tucking under his body on the other side. You can either tuck his arm down or bend it at the elbow so that his hand is near his face.

• Make sure that the cloth is wrapped securely and firmly but not too tight – you want to contain your baby, not squeeze him!

• Tuck the other side of the cloth over your baby's body in the same way, crossing his other shoulder and tucking under the other side of his body.

• You can tuck the bottom of the cloth up under him or leave it loose at the bottom.

than babies in Western families. Further research has given support to this observation, indicating that babies who spend nearly all of their time being carried and held close cry and fuss less, are calm, and sleep well. Many parents in the USA and Europe have adopted these ideas, sharing their experiences and advice on dedicated websites and via books, such as those written by William Sears and Jean Liedloff (*see* Further Reading on p.248).

If this approach is attractive to you, it will certainly benefit your baby. However, it can be a very demanding parenting approach for some parents and it doesn't always fit easily with the lifestyle and experiences of families. Social conditions are very different for parents in the West. In traditional societies mothers carry their babies all day in slings, but they carry on with their everyday lives. Babies and mothers are held in the centre of communities, rather than being segregated in private homes, so mothers are not isolated and unsupported in a way that they can be here in the Western world.

Swaddling

Swaddling can help to soothe your baby to sleep or help him to sleep better. Swaddling mimics the close confinement of the womb and it also stops him from waking himself up with sudden jerky movements. Many young babies find swaddling very comforting. However, do be aware of the potential for over-heating with a swaddled baby; it is a good idea to use a cotton blanket or a

THE COMFORT OF BEING WRAPPED UP

Swaddling your baby is a good way of mimicking the close confinement he knew in the womb. As a result he will probably find it very soothing.

sheet in warmer weather. Swaddling is a great way to soothe some younger babies; however, as babies get older and want to move around it is too confining.

Rocking

If swaddling mimics the confinement of the womb, rocking is thought to work because it recreates the movement of the baby in the womb as the mother walked around. Many babies love to be rocked, especially when held vertically and rocked back and forwards. Babies often like to be rocked fairly quickly, at about the same rate as your heartbeat.

Sitting in a rocking chair with your baby lying against your shoulder can be soothing for both babies and parents. Other parents find mechanical rocking chairs and cradles useful for when they need to put their baby down. However, most babies would prefer to be rocked by a person and these devices can be expensive, so have a trial if possible before you spend any money.

Background noise

The womb environment is surprisingly noisy and some babies may miss the background noise. It may be worth experimenting with "white noise", such as the sound of a vacuum cleaner, untuned radio, or washing machine. You can also buy special "womb noise" tapes, which some parents find useful in the earliest weeks. You may discover that music is very comforting to your baby, especially music that he heard while in the womb.

Nursing and feeding

Babies love to suck, and they quickly learn to associate sucking with the good feeling of a stomach full of warm milk. Offering a feed can be the quickest, most effective way of soothing a restless baby. Frequent breastfeeds will of course stimulate your breasts to make plenty of milk, which is important while you are establishing feeding or when your baby is going through a period of fast growth (see the feeding chapter, from p.80). However, always offering a feed when your baby is unsettled may not be the best policy if in fact he needs soothing rather than feeding. It is true that a breastfed baby cannot overfeed, but he may get into a pattern of sucking frequently for a very short time, which means he will only get the foremilk rather than the more satisfying hindmilk. If you suspect that your baby is not feeding effectively carefully observe him to see if he is always hungry when he cries. It may be that sometimes he can be soothed in another way.

Bottle-fed babies can overfeed by too frequent sucking on the bottle; however, as you can see how much he is getting you can regulate his intake and it is likely to be reasonably clear when your baby is hungry and when he needs soothing in other ways. If your baby is very "sucky", sucking on your finger or his own hand or fingers may soothe him.

see also

self-soothing   120–21

Self-soothing: helping him to help himself

As your baby matures over the first few weeks he will be learning many things about the world. He will learn skills such as how to feed effectively from the breast or bottle, how to focus his eyes on faces and objects, as well as how to communicate with the people in his world. He can also learn how to calm and soothe himself, with the help of those around him.

Babies are born with a number of different abilities, most of these being to do with keeping adults close by and getting their needs met. As they begin to master their environment, some babies can also be helped to extend the things they do to calm and soothe themselves. Helping your baby to develop the skills to soothe himself is a useful step towards establishing a sleep routine.

Babies differ in their ability to soothe themselves, and parents differ in the importance they put on self-soothing. Some parents believe that it is much more important that they comfort their baby personally. Others feel that encouraging their baby to be independent by learning to soothe himself is helping him to develop skills that he will need later, for example getting himself to sleep alone. Only you and your partner can decide where you stand on this issue.

What is self-calming?

If you observe your baby closely when he is distressed rather than jumping in straightaway with a cuddle or a feed you can discover what your baby can do for himself and what he likes. One day you might like to try leaving him alone for a couple of minutes when he is crying or fussing (and you believe he isn't hungry) to see whether he can quiet himself. Next you could see if he can be calmed by simply seeing your face and/or hearing your voice. If he is still unsettled you could try putting your hand on his tummy and then holding his arms still. If he is still upset you can try picking him up, rocking, etc. What you are looking for is an idea of how much you need to do before your baby calms down, and what he responds to best. You may discover that, when your baby is not hungry, talking to him is enough. A baby who likes to listen may also be calmed by music. You may discover that your baby can calm himself by looking at the sides of his Moses basket or a mobile.

Sucking

Most babies are born with an instinctive ability to bring their hands to their mouths and to suck on their fingers – this is known as the Babkin reflex. Ultrasound scans

A SOOTHING ENVIRONMENT

If your baby is very unsettled and you have difficulty soothing him or helping him to soothe himself, it may help to take a wider look at how you live. Think about the levels of background noise and the general level of hustle and bustle in your home or while out and about. For example, you may be used to having the radio on all day and barely notice it, but a sensitive baby may be listening to it all day and becoming far too stimulated.

Too much play and too many visitors can also be over-stimulating for babies. Babies like to be played with and talked to but they are quickly tired by this intense activity and so need quiet times to calm down. By carefully watching your baby's reactions you will be able to see when your baby has had enough and needs some peace and quiet to unwind.

have shown that many babies suck their thumbs in the womb. Sucking even when not hungry is a useful self-calming skill for many babies in the first few months. If parents discourage thumb or finger sucking in the early weeks the instinct will not persist, so you can decide what approach you want to take. Some parents introduce a dummy (which can be disposed of after the first few weeks), *see* box, right.

It has been shown that thumb sucking in older babies and children can cause the teeth to become misaligned; however, there is no proof that thumb sucking during infancy causes this problem. Very few babies allowed to suck their thumbs and fingers go on to do so much beyond the early school years, and the vast majority of thumb-sucking older toddlers and children only use this comfort from time to time.

Calm parent, calm baby?

Your baby will react to all that is going on around him and his main environment is you. You will find it much easer to soothe your baby if you are feeling calm and relaxed yourself. This may be difficult in practice, especially if your baby is difficult to soothe and you are feeling anxious or unsure, but here are some tips you can try:

• When using strategies to soothe your baby try not to jump quickly from one method to another. When you are feeling tired and stressed it is understandable to want a quick response, but your baby will feel confused and will also have no time to settle down and relax. This is why some parents try for ages to calm an unsettled baby, hand him to a new person only to watch the baby promptly stop crying and fall asleep. What seems to be happening is that the "new" person is less agitated, the baby picks up on this, and falls asleep with relief.

• Calming yourself by detaching yourself from your baby's agitation is a difficult thing for many parents to do. When you hear your baby cry it is normal and natural to feel upset and agitated – you may even feel like joining in at times. However, an upset parent may not be able to respond to what their baby really needs as effectively as one who can stay calm. Being able to be "with" your baby in a sympathetic way when he is crying is important, as he isn't crying to upset you or manipulate you. In fact he has no awareness of how he is making you feel at all.

• Some parents frequently misinterpret their baby's cries. For example, they may always hear their baby's crying as meaning that he is feeling lonely and abandoned, so feel compelled to rush to pick him up when he makes the smallest protest. Other parents may feel that their baby is always angry and also has unreasonable demands, so underreact to his protests. Babies can sound desperate, angry, and lonely when in fact they may be simply hungry, tired, or bored.⊙

If you find you are frequently upset by your baby's crying, reflecting on this (with the support of an understanding health professional or friend) can help you to make sensible choices in managing your baby's behaviour.

DUMMIES

Research evidence about the use of dummies in the early weeks is inconclusive, as long as babies are being offered enough time at the breast to stimulate milk production. There is some concern among breastfeeding specialists that until breast-feeding is well-established the use of dummies may cause "nipple confusion", where the baby fails to develop a good "latch" because the mouth sucks differently on a dummy than on a human nipple. However, it is clear that babies using a dummy are more at risk of middle ear infection, abnormal jaw development, misalignment of the milk teeth, and possibly delayed speech development.⊙

For these reasons, and the fact that high use of dummies is associated with lower breastfeeding rates, you may choose to avoid dummies altogether, or to restrict their use to when your baby is very young (less than six months old) – and then only for short periods each day. It is very important that dummies are sterilized as they can carry infection such as oral thrush and the bacteria that cause stomach upsets. Do not clean a dummy in your own mouth as you can transfer bacteria responsible for tooth decay to your baby. If your baby likes to suck, you may find that swaddling him with his hands free means that he can get himself off to sleep and soothe himself back to sleep if he wakes, without the need for a dummy.

Sleep routines

Books by experts claiming that you can teach your baby to sleep all night are frequently bestsellers, and it is easy to see why. Exhausted parents buy them by the shelf load. Unfortunately these books often promise more than they deliver. There will, of course, always be a group of babies who happily fall into a routine devised by their parents and sleep for long periods at an early age; however, the majority of babies are not nearly so accommodating. As with so many other areas of baby care, negotiation, flexibility, and understanding the needs and behaviour of your own baby are usually the keys to long-term satisfaction.

Research into sleep and babies shows that the most effective strategy for improving your young baby's ability to sleep at night is to find a way of establishing the difference between night and day, and to help him to sleep more "effectively".[⊙] This involves joining his naps together into longer periods of sleep so he is able to move between deep and light sleep without fully waking up.

Encouraging good sleep habits

With young babies it is more useful to think of encouraging good sleep habits rather than enforcing sleep training. As adults we have sleep habits without realizing it. Think about what you do in the half an hour before you go to sleep (watch TV, put on night clothes, brush teeth, etc). Most people have some sort of ritual at bedtime and they also have a favourite position that they adopt before going to sleep; this why it can be so difficult to get to sleep in the "wrong" bed, or without your partner.

If you need your routine to help your brain and body to prepare for sleep, it isn't difficult to see that your baby needs the same (see box, left). Encouraging a ritual, whatever it is, will help your baby to learn to tip himself over into sleep when he is tired. As he gets older you can add more ingredients to the routine and he may add his own ideas, perhaps adopting a favourite teddy or blanket to hold.

Sleep windows

You will have more success getting your baby off to sleep if you pay attention to when your baby is ready for sleep. Beginning the routine when your baby is in an active phase but timing it to end when you think he will be tired is a good idea as over-tired babies are harder to settle. If you are busy with your baby and he shows signals that he has had enough (see p.151), then begin his settling routine.

EFFECTIVE BEDTIME ROUTINES

It doesn't really matter what you introduce into your routine as long as it is calming, unstimulating, and you do the same thing each time. An evening routine for a three-month-old may go something like this:
- A bath or wash, nappy change, and change into nightclothes.
- A feed.
- Go to a quiet room where the baby will be sleeping.
- A cuddle with a gentle song.
- Tuck baby into bed and kiss him goodnight.

Sometimes a baby who is showing signs of tiredness will suddenly perk up again and appear not to be tired after all. Don't be misled. Your baby was tired but you weren't able to help him to sleep and therefore missed a "sleep window". Chances are that when this new wind wears off he will be even more tired than before and harder to settle. This is why being as responsive as you can to your baby's signals will help to make life easier.

Going to sleep alone

Some babies will happily drift off to sleep on their own after a bedtime routine as long as they are drowsy, while others will find this more difficult. Many babies will cry for a minute or two before going to sleep. It will help if you can distinguish your baby's "tired" cry (which means that he is about to go to sleep), from crying that means he is hungry or uncomfortable. Whether you feel alright about your baby crying before going to sleep alone is something that you need to decide about for you and your baby. Bear in mind, though, that if your baby needs you to hold him, rock him, or feed him to sleep he will need you to do this every time he wakes.

Babies who are put into their cots while already asleep are more likely to cry out for you in the night when they wake up, as they are confused about where they are. How would you feel if you went to sleep in one place and woke up somewhere else? Babies naturally "surface" a few times at night and those who "know" where they are and are comfortable are more likely to go back to sleep without disturbing their parents.

Minimize night-time activity

As well as using bedtime routines to "cue" sleep, emphasizing the difference between night and day will help your baby to sleep when you want him to – at night. You will of course need to feed your baby at night-time but it is a good idea to make these feeds as low key and relaxed as possible. Keep the lights dim and avoid playing or chatting with your baby. Only change his nappy if it is dirty or you think that it is really necessary.

Be confident

Babies who sleep well may be responding to the confidence and certainty of their parents. Whatever choices and arrangements you make for getting your baby off to sleep they will only work well if you are confident that you are doing what is best for your baby and your family. Parents who are anxious and uncertain about bedtimes can communicate this to their babies and young children. Having confidence that your baby can sleep will give him a strong message. If you are feeling fearful or uncertain for whatever reason and you think this may be affecting your or your baby's sleep, get help and support with this as soon as possible.

GOOD SLEEP HABITS

In the early months, focusing on encouraging good sleep habits is a more positive and effective approach than trying to enforce rigid sleep training methods.

see also

baby language   150–51

Where to sleep

Many expectant parents have clear ideas about where their baby will sleep, and they rearrange their homes and buy new equipment accordingly. However, it is not unusual for those parents to find that things turn out quite differently once the baby arrives. Babies, of course, have their own ideas about where and when they will happily settle, and parents also discover that the opinions they held so strongly before the baby arrived are changed by experience. As long as you observe current safety advice, the choice about where your baby should sleep is entirely yours. Different solutions suit different families and their babies, so work with what feels right to you.

Nursery or parents' bedroom?

Although you may have planned (and decorated) a nursery, most parents choose to have the cot or Moses basket in their own bedroom in the early months. Evidence suggests that babies that sleep in the same room as their parents are less likely to suffer sudden infant death syndrome (SIDS), although why this should be is unclear. It may be something to do with the baby being stimulated to breathe by his parents' breathing. Having the baby in your room also means that you won't have far to go for night-time feeds. With a cot or Moses

FEELING COSY AND SAFE

Many young babies appreciate the cosy containment of a Moses basket, placed near to where their parents are sleeping.

USING A MOSES BASKET SAFELY

• Baskets should only be used with stands specifically purchased for that purpose. Perching a basket on other furniture may be risky – it is better to put it on the floor.

• Moses baskets are not designed for transporting your baby. It is much safer to move a basket only when your baby is not sleeping in it.

basket next to your bed you may not even have to get out of bed. There are some cots that can be attached to your bed frame on one side (three sides of the cot stay up and one is taken off), so that your baby is close and can be touched and patted during the night without actually sharing your bed.

Cots and Moses baskets

In our culture cots are seen as mandatory baby equipment, and chances are that you will have already bought or acquired one. All new cots are subject to safety guidelines so you can be sure that they are appropriate and safe.

Moses baskets are popular for new babies, because, even though they only last for a few months (until the baby gets too big), they are a more contained space for a new baby, so he feels safer. Moses baskets are also convenient as you can find space for one in most rooms and you can use them on holiday (*see* box, left).

COT SAFETY
• If you are using a secondhand cot you will need to check such things as the width the cot bars are from each other (they should be no more than 45–65mm/ 1¾–2½in apart), that there is no lead paint, and that a new mattress will fit exactly, with no gaps at all between it and the frame.
• It is recommended that a new mattress is bought for any secondhand cot.
• Pillows and duvets should not be used in a baby's cot. Well-fitted sheets and cellular blankets are best as they can be added or removed easily, depending on the room temperature.
• Always put your baby to sleep on his back with his feet near to the bottom of the cot, "feet to foot". His covers should come up to his chest. This is to stop him from slipping down under the covers in the night.
• Cots that have mattresses that can be raised are very useful for new babies and will save your back; however, as soon as your baby can sit you must lower the mattress in case he learns to climb up.
• Cot bumpers must be removed once a baby is mobile as the baby can use them as steps.

SIDS (Sudden Infant Death Syndrome)

This used to be known as "cot death", and is defined as the sudden, unexplained death of an apparently healthy baby in the first year of life. Most sudden infant deaths occur in babies under six months old. SID is the cause of much anxiety for new parents; however, it is extremely rare. Research over the last 20 years has helped to identify risk factors, and advice to parents since the 1980s has made cot death even rarer. (The Foundation for the Study of Infant Deaths, www.sids.org.uk, was founded in 1971 for the purpose of researching the causes of cot death.) *See* box, right, for further information.

TO REDUCE THE RISK OF SID:
• Always put your baby down to sleep on his back and in a "feet to foot" position in his cot, Moses basket, or cradle.
• Make sure that your baby's head is always uncovered when he is asleep. Use sheets and blankets; no pillows or duvets.
• Don't let your baby get too hot. A room temperature of about 18°C (64°F) is fine at night. Test your baby's temperature by touching his tummy or neck (hands and feet often feel more chilly).
• Have your baby sleep in a cot in your room for the first six months.
• Cut out smoking in pregnancy and encourage your partner to stop smoking too, as this can have an effect on lung growth in your baby at a critical stage of development and affect how he controls his breathing once born.
• Never smoke in the same room as the baby.
• If your baby seems at all unwell take him to see the doctor.

Some parents find the noises that a baby makes in the night disturbing and choose to have the baby sleep in a separate room. The advantage with this is that you won't hear all the little noises a baby makes when he rouses and so you won't disturb him by responding to every whimper. However, this can mean that your baby has to be at shrieking point before you hear him, at which point he might be more difficult to settle again (and he may well have disturbed the rest of the household).

Bedsharing and the family bed

Some parents decide from the outset that they want their baby to sleep in their own bed. In fact in many cultures this is not a choice at all but an assumption. If this is what you decide to do you will need to consider safety issues (just as parents using cots and baskets need to), and you may certainly want to consider buying the largest bed that you can afford; babies, especially older ones, can take up a remarkable amount of space.

Bedsharing is associated with higher rates of breastfeeding, and many mothers find it especially convenient to be able to feed their babies without even needing to sit up, let alone get out of bed. In fact research has shown that in the early weeks breastfeeding mothers who share a bed with their newborns are able to obtain more sleep than those whose babies sleep separately from them.

The intimacy of bedsharing and the high levels of skin-to-skin contact are very supportive of breastfeeding, and many parents enjoy the increased closeness as much as their babies do. Mothers who return to work, and fathers who are out of the house for long hours, may particularly relish the intimacy of nights together with their baby.

"I had planned to have my baby in bed or in a Moses basket by my side, but found his snuffling noises kept me awake. By the third night he was in his own room in a cot."

- Bedsharing babies must not sleep with their heads near to pillows or in a position where they can be covered by a duvet. A separate blanket for your baby, or you all changing to sheets and blankets for a while, is safest.
- Babies should not sleep near to the edge of a bed unless the bed is pushed up against a wall or a safety rail or guard is in place, and there is no space at all between the mattress and the guard/furniture/wall.
- You should never fall asleep with your baby on a sofa, armchair, or waterbed. The surfaces of these are not flat or firm enough.
- You should not bedshare with your baby if you are under the influence of drugs (including prescription medicines that make your drowsy) or alcohol, or are in any way likely to be less responsive to your baby's movements.
- Parents who smoke may be putting their babies at higher risk if they bedshare.
- To avoid overheating, babies who are bedsharing will not need to wear as many clothes – a vest and nappy may be sufficient.
- Babies shouldn't be left to sleep alone in an adult bed.
- Once your baby is mobile you should consider putting your mattress on the floor and childproofing the room (consider a stair gate across the bedroom door).

Uncertain methods, or "mix and match"

While some parents choose bedsharing as a positive choice, many parents end up bedsharing in the early weeks through necessity. You may find that your baby will sleep happily in his cot or Moses basket until the early hours of the morning but then after that the only way you can get any sleep is to bring him into your bed. Even though your baby starts out in his own bed you are still bedsharing, so you do need to observe all the relevant safety advice.

Some parents feel that using such changeable arrangements is in some way conceding a defeat and there will certainly be those around who will talk of "making a rod for your back" or utter other dire warnings about "bad habits". Babies and children do get used to certain arrangements and will protest if these change suddenly, but they also develop and need different things at different times so you can make changes as they get older. Denying your baby the intimacy of sleeping with you because you are worried that he will continue to insist on sleeping with you when he is 15 is clearly unrealistic. It may be reassuring to know that in most families with young babies, parents do whatever it takes in pursuit of the sleep that they all need. Taking a pragmatic attitude, considering the needs of everyone involved, and reassessing over time is a sensible way forward.

As time passes if anyone in the family is not happy about the sleeping arrangements, whether it is the baby or parent, negotiations will need to take place. Family life really is a whole lot easier if everyone is well rested.

"I had my second child sleeping in bed with me since he was born. I found breastfeeding and sleeping to be much easier for both of us that way, and I wasn't constantly checking that he was OK as I could hear him breathing right next to me."

Coping with broken nights

During pregnancy new parents often worry about how they will cope with broken nights and lack of sleep. Losing sleep can, of course, have a huge effect on one's health and wellbeing, and some parents certainly do suffer in the early weeks especially. However, having some coping strategies up your sleeve can make a real difference.

LOOK AFTER YOUR GENERAL WELLBEING

• Coping with lack of sleep can leave you vulnerable to illness, so make sure that you look after yourself as much as possible.

• Eat and drink well. Avoid the peaks and troughs from eating high-sugar foods and opt instead for nutritious meals and regular snacks incorporating whole grains and fresh fruit and vegetables.

• Eat and drink regularly. Plan to have a drink and a snack at least every time you sit down to feed your baby. It doesn't need to be much: a piece of fruit or slice of toast and a drink will keep your energy levels constant.

• Avoid restricting your diet – this is not the time to try to lose extra weight.

• Take exercise. Paradoxically, regular exercise can help you to feel much less tired. Walking in the fresh air will help you to relax later in the day and will raise your mood if you are feeling down.

• Do at least one thing each day that makes you feel good, such as soaking in a bath, listening to music, or reading. Reward yourself for all your hard work.

Why does broken sleep have such an effect?

As discussed on page 114, sleep is not a single state but is made up of a number of states that occur in a cyclical pattern. We need both deep sleep and REM sleep to make us feel fully rested. When adults are very tired their brains tend to move quickly to deep sleep as this is most refreshing, especially early in the night. This is why it feels so awful to be woken about one hour after having gone to bed, as at this point sleep is at its deepest and waking up is difficult.

Towards the morning, when our bodies have had a good deal of deep sleep, we spend more time in REM sleep. However, REM only occurs towards the end of one sleep cycle and so if you are woken often you may miss out on REM sleep. Getting insufficient REM sleep can make you feel emotional, anxious, and stressed.

For these reasons getting a period of unbroken sleep, say about five hours, is more important in terms of making you feel rested than getting ten hours in bed but being woken every two hours. Also, when you are woken from deep sleep your metabolic rate rises, so if you are getting out of bed every few hours to look after a baby, even if you end up with roughly eight hours sleep in total, you will use up more energy and can therefore expect to feel physically more tired during the day.

Useful strategies

Here are some strategies that may help you cope more readily with disturbed nights (*see* the boxes for further ideas too).

GET A PERIOD OF UNBROKEN SLEEP WHEN YOU CAN

• If your baby is unsettled in the early hours of the morning, maybe you can take turns to deal with the baby at this time. A baby who is unsettled after an early morning feed can be looked after by one parent while the other gets back to sleep. Fathers may be able to help in this way even if the baby is breastfed.

• You could go to bed really early to get a stretch of unbroken sleep in before the more restless pre-dawn hours.

• You and your partner could take it in turns to have a long lie-in at weekends to catch up on much needed REM sleep.

• If you are breastfeeding, once your milk supply is established you may be able to express some milk so that you can occasionally sleep through one of the night-time feeds while someone else feeds the baby.

SPEND MORE TIME IN BED

• As a child-free adult you were probably used to spending nearly all of your time in bed asleep and so have a bedtime and getting-up time that reflects this. Now that you are sleeping more lightly and waking more often it is sensible to spend more time in bed even if you are dozing, sleeping lightly, or simply resting. Make your bedroom a nice place to be. Have food and drink to hand. Make yourself as comfortable as possible.

• If your baby is particularly restless or you are especially tired, consider spending the day in bed with your baby. Staying tucked up together with lots of skin-to-skin contact will soothe you both and you can simply rest or drift in and out of sleep as you need to. This strategy is especially helpful if there are any breastfeeding concerns; a day spent cuddling and offering frequent breastfeeds will have a good effect on your milk supply.

• When your baby is napping in the day go to bed; even if you don't actually sleep, resting is very useful.

• Use your answering machine or a telephone answering service to take calls when you are resting. Also consider a "mother resting, please come back later" notice on the door so that you are guaranteed some undisturbed time while you sleep or rest.

I'm exhausted but I can't sleep

Some women become extremely exhausted because they have trouble going back to sleep when they are disturbed. While the oxytocin that your body releases when you breastfeed may be enough to make you drowsy again after a night feed, some women have difficulty sleeping when their baby is sleeping.

It may be that you come to dread being woken at night and almost don't want to go to sleep as you know what will happen later. Remember that, even if you are not sleeping, resting in your bed is better than being up and about in terms of combating tiredness.

You may be unable to rest because of anxious feelings or intrusive thoughts. If this is the case it is important that you speak to someone who will listen and support you. Exhaustion, sleep problems, and postnatal depression are very closely linked and help is available. Do not be put off by the idea that "all new mothers are tired"; if you aren't sleeping but your baby is then you need and deserve some extra support.

POWER-NAPPING FOR PARENTS!

• We know that even 20 minutes spent completely relaxing can be enormously useful. You don't have to sleep – simply relaxing your body and thinking soothing thoughts will help you to keep going.

• If you plan to have a daytime sleep, try to sleep at a time when you can get at least 90 minutes. This will give you one complete sleep cycle and leave you feeling more refreshed. Many parents find a nap after lunch works well.

Daytime naps

As your baby grows, his ability to settle quickly at night and to sleep for longer periods is affected by how many naps he has during the day. Ironically, too little sleep during the day can leave a baby fractious and unable to settle in the evenings. What you are aiming for is to keep your baby calm, alert, and busy during the day with regular naps so that he doesn't get over-tired and unhappy.

Newborn babies, as we have seen, tend to drift between a number of states, from alert to deep sleep, fairly chaotically and unpredictably. While most will sleep for a while just after a feed, then wake ready to interact before becoming grumpy and irritable before the next feed, this pattern can change from day to day. Some babies are more restless than others and some are sleepier. Parents in the early weeks should be prepared to go with the flow as much as possible. Remember to look out for signs that your baby has had enough (see p.151) so that you can anticipate when he needs to sleep before he becomes over-stimulated and cross.

Some very sensitive babies may have difficulty going to sleep during the day as they are disturbed by too much noise and activity. If you think your young baby is tired and ready for sleep but he seems unable to "let go", try taking him to a quiet undisturbed place away from the noise of the household. Try soothing strategies, such as swaddling and sucking, too (see pp.118–19).

Once your baby is between six weeks and four months, some predictable patterns will probably start to emerge and you can begin to count on periods of the day when your baby will have a nap. Babies differ in the amount of sleep that they need as well as how their sleep is clustered. Some take long naps in the daytime while others have very short naps and sleep longer at night. In general, at four months many babies take up to three daytime naps totalling about four hours. By six months most babies are down to two naps, one morning nap of about an hour and one after lunch of about two hours.

If you are hoping to encourage less night-time waking it may be tempting to try to cut down on daytime sleeps. Certainly too much sleep later in the day will affect how readily a baby will go to sleep at bedtime; however, reducing daytime naps too drastically can have the reverse effect. If your baby becomes over-tired he will be difficult to get off to sleep and he may sleep more restlessly. Regular naps keep babies calm and rested, which helps them to be calm at night-time.

Beware of catnaps, when your baby sleeps for less than an hour. Initially he may seem well rested but this will not last long and he will get grumpy and fussy

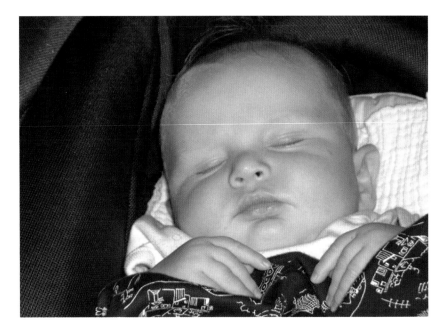

TAKING NAPS

Babies all need different amounts of sleep, and the length and frequency of your baby's daytime naps will also change as he gets older.

again quickly. Babies who adopt this pattern seem to be waking as they move from one sleep state to another. Observing his sleep behaviour, helping him to be calmer while awake, and using soothing strategies may help him to have better naps.

Should I have a special routine for daytime naps?

How you arrange your baby's naps depends on how you want to organize your day; it's up to you. Older babies are easier to keep awake until the time you want them to nap (although not always, of course!), and with consistency you should be able to adjust sleeping patterns with a baby of this age. Interestingly the rather outdated routine of putting a baby in the garden for his afternoon nap may have had some validity, as new evidence suggests that if babies have more daylight in the early afternoon they are more likely to sleep well at night. If you prefer to be flexible, and let your baby take his naps when he has a chance to (such as when he is in the car, being pushed in his pram, or sitting having a cuddle), then that's fine, too. Bear in mind, though, that some babies can become very grumpy if they don't get the chance to drop off when they need to.

Many parents find that a late afternoon nap can mean a later time for settling in the evening. This might be your preference – if you or your partner like to spend time in the evening with your baby, then a late afternoon sleep, which keeps your baby lively and happy in the evening, might be just right.

If your baby is over six months old and you have decided to use one of the sleep training methods discussed on pages 134–5 you will probably have more success at bedtime if you use the same strategy at nap time.

see also

soothing and comforting your new baby   116–19
baby language   150–51

Sleep and older babies

By the time your baby is four months old you will probably have been asked many times whether your baby is "sleeping through". Having a "good" baby who doesn't disturb you at night can become a badge of parental success, and some parents feel judged by others and lose confidence if they feel they aren't doing very well. It is important to remember that babies are individuals and every family is different – what is normal for one is not for another. When making choices in this area always be confident enough to do what feels right for you and your family.

It is important to remember that it is normal for babies to wake during the night. As mentioned on page 115, babies wake during the night as part of their natural sleep cycle. Just like adults, their sleep begins with drowsiness and then alternates between deep sleep, very deep sleep, REM (dream sleep), and light sleep. It is during the light sleep periods that babies will wake or stir, and this is quite normal.

Once your baby has woken, it is an ideal opportunity for even an older baby to feed. The idea that babies should be able to last all night without food is relatively new. It is only since the middle of the last century, with the vast increase in bottle-feeding rates, that we have come to expect babies not to need feeding during the night. Early formula milk was very difficult to digest, and so a baby would sleep for a large portion of the night because he was full. Modern formula is digested much quicker, so now formula feeding is rarely the answer to broken nights – formula-fed babies regularly wake during the night too. However, our parents, grandparents, and many health professionals believe that formula-fed babies need feeding less frequently than breastfed babies, and parents are left feeling that their baby's night-time waking is unacceptable.

Most parents are not delighted by the idea of broken sleep, but many accept that their baby is simply not ready to sleep through the night. If you feel like this, you can still try to get as much sleep as you can, when you can, until your baby sleeps all night of his own accord. For some parents a few moments alone with their baby during the night can be a special time for them. This can be especially important for parents who have to share their daytime attention with other children, or for parents who work.

The amount of sleep a baby needs will vary quite a lot from child to child, and from day to day. If your baby has been busy, or is ill, he will probably want to sleep more than usual.

Who's disturbing who?

Sometimes it can be helpful, when you hear your older baby at night, to decide if he really is awake and needing a feed. It is common for babies to make quite a lot of noise when they stir in their sleep, some even cry for a bit when they "surface" but aren't truly awake. If you dash to pick up your baby every time he makes a noise you may be waking him up when he would have gone back into deeper sleep if you had left him for a minute or two. If you wait until your older baby cries definitely and "hungrily", you can still respond to his needs without accidentally waking him.

Some parents inadvertently disturb their babies by frequently checking them in the night. If you feel very anxious about your baby then a cot close to your bed, or attached to the side of your bed, can help. However, do consider getting extra support for yourself; there are probably reasons behind why you are feeling so anxious, and the opportunity to discuss and understand what is happening can be extremely helpful.

Stepping up the bedtime routine

If you would like to adjust your baby's sleeping patterns to fit in with your family, the first strategy you could consider is using the bedtime routine to make bedtime a more regular, predictable fixture in the day. Older babies tend to respond much better to routines than younger ones as they learn quickly what to expect and they like to predict events.

As with bedtimes for younger babies it doesn't really matter what you do as long as you do the same thing every day. Consistency is important and can be

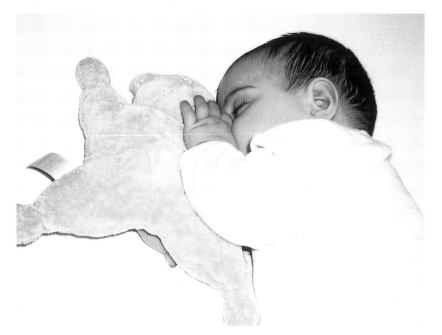

HAVING A BEDTIME COMPANION

Snuggling up to a "familiar friend", with its own special smell and feel, is very comforting for many older babies at bedtime.

ENCOURAGING NEW SLEEP ASSOCIATIONS – INTRODUCING A "LOVEY"

Anecdotal evidence ⊙ suggests that babies and toddlers who sleep well independently have often adopted a lovey – a soft blanket, cloth, or toy that they hold as they go to sleep. This item comes to represent the security of the mother's presence. Your baby may choose one for himself or you can choose it for him, but the important thing is that it is always there when your baby is happily dropping off to sleep.

If you are choosing a lovey, remember it is a good idea to have replacements available, so something that is "everyday" such as a piece of flannelette sheet or muslin cloth is ideal. You may like to make sure it smells of you by carrying it inside your clothes from time to time.

EARLY MORNING WAKING

Some babies sleep well at night but wake persistently before 5am. This is a very common problem but it does resolve itself in time. It may help to think of ways you can prolong the "night" by bringing your baby into bed with you or putting toys in the cot so he can play on his own for a bit. Some babies are helped by blackout blinds, or moving them to a quieter room in the house.

In a few cases a slightly later bedtime may help to "re-set" the routine; however, many parents find that their early waker simply wakes at the same time, only in a grumpier mood. In this case your baby will probably always be a bit of a "lark" and so it is wiser to simply find ways of coping with this, either by going to bed earlier yourself or taking turns with your partner to look after him in the early morning.

very useful, if, for example, you need to settle your baby while away from home. Keeping the same elements in the same order will be soothing and satisfying to an otherwise disrupted baby.

By using an established bedtime routine you can change the time your baby goes to bed, moving his bedtime forward or back. Some couples like to spend an evening together after the baby is in bed while others like to have more family time with their baby in the evening. It is worth knowing, though, that bedtimes aren't infinitely flexible. Many babies will actually sleep much better if they have an early bedtime. In hectic family homes it can be difficult to notice that your baby is actually ready for sleep at 6.30pm so by the time you are trying to put him down at 8pm he is already over-tired and far more difficult to settle.

Feeding the older baby to sleep

If you are still feeding your baby to sleep, remember, if it's okay with you then it's okay. If it isn't working for you, though, and you suspect that your baby is waking you in the night because he needs to suck rather than have a feed every time he surfaces, you might like to think about developing new sleep associations for him. Some babies get very used to going to sleep while sucking on your nipple or a bottle. You can break this association gradually if you wish by encouraging your baby to let go of the bottle teat or your nipple just before he goes to sleep.

Should I start sleep training?

If you find that implementing a bedtime routine doesn't seem to be helping your baby to go to sleep in the evening, or if you find yourself dealing with constant waking in the night, you may want to consider sleep training. Most sleep training schemes are variations on letting your baby cry once you have established that he doesn't "need" anything like a feed or nappy change. Because they require your baby to learn from experience, these methods have little success in babies under six months of age and shouldn't be used for younger babies in any case as your baby may well be waking because he needs a feed.

If you decide that you need to teach your child to sleep through the night before he does so by himself, there are several ways this can be achieved. These methods teach your child to go to sleep alone, and to go back to sleep if they wake during the night. If your baby hasn't found a way to do this, however hard you have tried to introduce more gentle sleep cues and habits, then sleep training may help.

CONTROLLED CRYING

This works by establishing a consistent, relaxing bedtime routine, as described on page 122, and then putting your baby to bed drowsy but awake. You then say goodnight and leave the room. If your baby cries when you leave, go back into his room to reassure him that everything is okay, say goodnight again, and leave. When you reassure your baby don't pick him up or cuddle him; be gentle but firm. If your baby is still crying after two minutes return, reassure your baby then leave. Keep repeating this, extending the time between each visit, until he falls asleep.

If your baby wakes during the night, and you're sure he's fed, dry, and healthy, wait five minutes before going to him in case he goes back to sleep by himself. When you go in, stay calm and be brief, reassure him that you are there by talking to him but don't pick him up, turn on the lights, or touch him. If he keeps crying, wait a little longer each time before you go in, then repeat the above sequence until he goes back to sleep.

For this method to work you must be consistent and very determined. If you break the routine and pick him up, or return to old comforting methods, you will have to go right back to the beginning again as your baby has learned that if he cries for long enough you will eventually "give in".

This method can be very stressful for parents, and while some babies settle down after about four nights others are extremely persistent and may take much longer. If you find listening to your baby crying unbearable then this method is probably not for you. You may find the gradual withdrawal method is more acceptable.

CALM INSISTENCE/GRADUAL WITHDRAWAL

Again an established bedtime ritual is the starting point. When your baby is drowsy, comfort him to sleep. Rocking or lying down together are the most common ways. Once you see that his face is motionless and he's in deep sleep you can leave. Over many evenings you gradually reduce your contact during the comforting phase. So, for example, if your baby is used to going to sleep in your arms you may start by not cuddling him but lying next to him as he drops off. When he is used to that you can try staying next to him but not touching him. Once he is used to that you may try sitting by the cot while he goes to sleep, then sitting in the room, then sitting outside the open doorway, etc, until you can at last put him down and go downstairs while he drifts off. This method is undoubtedly gentler than controlled crying but it takes a great deal of patience and may mean many evenings upstairs away from the family.

Sleep training can be the answer when you are feeling desperate, and certainly encouraging your baby to soothe himself to sleep at bedtime will mean that he will need you less during the night. However, in the short term it is more demanding for parents than a baby who is left to establish his own sleep pattern.

WHAT SHOULD MY OLDER BABY WEAR IN BED?
Once babies become more mobile you may find that they kick off their covers in the night and wake up feeling cold and needing you to tuck them in again. A useful solution is to use a baby sleeping bag. It is important that you use a specially designed sleeping bag for babies, which has shoulder straps so that your baby can't slip down and cover his face. However, these baby sleeping bags should only be introduced before he is able to stand in his cot. Introducing one later, once he is more mobile, may be dangerous as he may fall over in his cot. At this stage a fleecy all-in-one suit (a sort of baby dressing gown) may come in handy in the winter to keep him warm all night, no matter how much he moves around.

5 SIX WEEKS TO THREE MONTHS – YOUR SOCIAL BABY

- Your feelings at six weeks
- Understanding your baby
- Knowing your baby's temperament
- Baby language
- *Feature:* Crying out for help! Does my baby have colic?
- Why parents need friends
- Fathers' experiences
- Postnatal fitness

Your feelings at six weeks

After six weeks the initial post-birth excitement is wearing off and you will be getting used to the reality of daily life with your baby. Whether this feels like an anticlimax or a relief will depend on how things have gone for you, your personal circumstances, and your feelings about your new role. At this early stage everyone's experience is very different – but most people will have had good and bad days. Even though you may feel that you should be "back to normal" by six weeks, remember you are still in the early days. Be kind to yourself, take your time, and make space to get to know your baby even better.

A CLOSE BOND

Many mothers find that they have intense feelings about their baby at this time. This may mean that, for now, other relationships seem less important.

Life with a new baby is commonly referred to as a "roller coaster" of emotions.⊙ This is especially true in the first few weeks, but also remains a feature of the first year (and some would say the duration of life as a parent!). You may feel overwhelmed at times with feelings of love and extreme protectiveness towards your baby. Some new mothers, and fathers, describe themselves as feeling "skinless" and unusually sensitive to all that is happening around them. They may be upset by images in the news, especially where children are in danger, feeling that they share the pain of parents across the world. Although it may be uncomfortable, this heightened sensitivity is important and special as it helps parents to tune in to the needs of their babies.

You will probably also find that your thoughts are focused almost entirely on the wellbeing of your baby, and that you have difficulty concentrating on other things. This is so common that in academic circles it even has a name: "primary maternal preoccupation", a term first used by D.W. Winnicott (a paediatrician working in 1950s London who published many books about the importance of the emotional experiences of young babies and their parents, and whose work underpins an enormous amount of current knowledge). It describes the almost total absorption a mother experiences regarding the needs of her new baby.⊙ Winnicott believed that this preoccupation is both natural and important for the mother and child as it allows them both to make the firm loving attachment that will keep their relationship strong in the future.

Some women find these strong feelings confusing. They may be unprepared for the sheer strength of the feelings that they have for their baby, and perhaps feel guilty that all other relationships seem much less important in comparison. It can be helpful to know that this intense phase doesn't last forever. In time you will find yourself more able to keep your feelings for your baby "in perspective", and return to being more open to giving and receiving love from others. In the meantime it is useful for your partner to be aware that this preoccupation is temporary and that you will "come back" again after a while. Partners who can tolerate and support mothers during this phase are a real asset. They can take responsibility for dealing with all the practical "outside" pressures that can get in the way of the mother being able to focus wholeheartedly on her baby.

Women living in circumstances where it is not possible to ignore pressing issues in order to focus totally on the baby will need extra support from others. If you are in this situation, get all the support and help you can. Perhaps the extended family or a network of friends can help. Alternatively, perhaps there is somewhere you can stay where you will be taken care of while you adjust to your new life as a parent.

Being so focused on your baby, you will probably find that you have a strong need to talk about her and also perhaps about your birth experience. You may find that you do not want to talk about much else. Many of us have heard about what bad company "baby bores" can be, you may even have sworn not to become one, but that was before you had a baby yourself. It is important to be able to talk over what is happening at this time so don't feel that you must stop yourself.⊙ Find people who will listen – maybe your family or friends, or perhaps some new friends who also have babies the same age as yours. Joining an NCT postnatal course or postnatal drop-in will give you the opportunity to talk about your experiences with people in the same situation, and to make new friends.

Your need to talk things over may be particularly strong if you had a very difficult time at the birth or immediately afterwards. We know that people often need to talk over a difficult event in order to make sense of what has happened, to give a meaning to it, and then to integrate the experience into their own beliefs about themselves and their lives.⊙

Parents who have had traumatic birth experiences sometimes feel that they have "lost trust" in both themselves and others. They feel so shaken that they are unable to believe that they will be able to cope with events in the future. They may believe that they were let down by the professionals who they trusted to look after them, or other people who were present at the birth or in the early days afterwards.⊙ They may feel that they can't trust themselves to cope. If you are feeling this way you must get some support. Speak to your midwife or health visitor, as there may be a local "birth debrief" service. Alternatively, you can contact the Birth Crisis group for support (see p.239).

Feelings about the birth

Often women find that it takes a while for the reality of having a baby to set in before they really start to think about the birth. Most women minimize the worst of their labour, and feel that having another baby wouldn't be so bad after all. If

GROUPS FOR PARENTS AND BABIES
Once you begin to look around you will find a variety of groups available. Many are mainly an opportunity for you to meet and share experiences with other parents:
• NCT postnatal courses or drop-ins run by trained Postnatal Leaders (see box on p.157 for more information on postnatal courses).
• NCT postnatal support groups or "Open Houses" run by local parent volunteers.
• Parent, baby, and toddler groups in community venues.
• New parents groups run by a health visitor.

"I found with our first baby that every day seemed like a milestone. There is so much to learn and adjust to when you become a parent. Surviving to six weeks was a triumph, and getting to 12 weeks is really fantastic."

your birth was a positive experience it is likely that you will continue to feel good about it. It is also helpful for other mothers-to-be to hear about fulfilling birth experiences, so talking about it can help to reassure them.

However, for some women the birth experience may not have been so positive. Usually this is because either things didn't go as planned, or they felt out of control. Often the two go together, and a woman can be left feeling distressed or unhappy about the way her baby was born. Straight after the birth many women are able to cope with their feelings, but reality often sets in later. At this point, women may begin to have a wide range of emotional reactions. These usually take the form of grief, anger, or depression, but nightmares, flashbacks, and other trauma responses can happen too. While these reactions are not common, they are real and disturbing for the women who do experience such feelings, and for those close to them. Often partners feel as powerless to help as they did during the birth, so finding the right support is essential.

Some maternity services offer you the chance to talk through your labour and birth with a midwife, who will listen to your concerns and explain what happened and why. Some women find that talking to the midwife who was at the birth is best, others may find meeting that person, or people, again very upsetting. Often having the opportunity to ask questions and get answers is enough, but for some women the experience can raise further questions. If you are not happy with the support or information offered, do ask for what you want. There are also national support networks for women who have suffered traumatic births (*see* the list of useful organizations at the back of the book, pp.238–45) and you may find a support network locally. Sometimes home birth support groups can be a good place to get support; because most of the women who go will appreciate the importance of a positive birth experience, they will understand why you feel as you do.

If you are having to care for a baby who was premature, sick, or has special needs, you may also still be experiencing a great deal of anxiety and even shock about what has happened. Some parents find that it is difficult for them to feel confident about caring for their baby, especially if much of the early care was provided by medical staff. If you feel like this it is important to remember that you are special to your baby; she can single out your voice and smell from those of other people. Do all you can to build up the connection between you and your baby. Even if you felt you missed out on that early time together, it is never too late to build your relationship.

Day-to-day life

Despite your turbulent emotions at this time the emergence of some predictable patterns by now should help the days start to feel a little less chaotic. It is nice to have an idea of when you are likely to be able to take a shower or even have a long soak in the bath without interruption. Make use of these quieter times in the

---

ACTIVITIES TO SHARE WITH YOUR BABY

- Mother and baby yoga.
- Baby swimming.
- Baby massage.
- Toy libraries.

Why not also look out for postnatal exercise groups with a crèche, where you can enjoy adult activity and make friends while trained carers look after your baby.

Most parents find that getting out to a group regularly makes them feel refreshed and better able to cope with the demands of 24-hour baby care. It may seem like a hassle while you are getting everything ready, but the adult company and change of scenery is well worth it.

day to look after yourself and regain some energy for the more difficult times, such as disrupted evenings or being woken at night. Try to fit in at least one enjoyable activity for yourself each day. Choose something that you enjoyed before the baby came along, and which makes you feel good. It doesn't have to be anything big, you might just want to read a magazine or write some emails to friends. Avoid the temptation to catch up with housework unless you are absolutely sure that it will make you feel better. If having a clean house and pressed clothes is important perhaps you can delegate this job to someone else for the time being.

In these early weeks it is still important to try to go with the flow. Many parents feel disappointed or anxious because they expect too much of themselves and their babies. Don't expect to get everything right straightaway and don't feel you should "do everything". Focus your energies on yourself and your baby. If you feel like lazing on the sofa all afternoon cuddling your baby, go ahead and do that. If you feel like kissing her all over, do it. If you do nothing all day but lie in bed stroking her warm little body, then you are doing just fine.

RELAX AND ENJOY YOURSELF

Don't pressurize yourself to do too much at this early stage. Enjoy spending one-on-one time with your baby – and forget the chores!

Understanding your baby

You will have already noticed in the earliest days and weeks how your baby reacts and responds to the world. Your great sensitivity at this time will help you to tune in and be open to your baby's individuality. Every baby has her own strengths, vulnerabilities, temperament, and coping style. Understanding your baby by "reading" her behaviour will help you to feel confident about your ability to meet her needs. You will become an expert in your baby. This will enable you to make informed, confident decisions about how you want to parent her, and you will also be in a better position to take or leave advice by deciding if it suits your baby, yourself, and your family situation.

Babies are individuals. They each have very particular likes and dislikes. Parents with more than one child will generally tell you how very different each of their children is, and if you have spent time with other new parents and their babies you will have noticed that there are real differences in the behaviour of each baby. For example, some babies are more active and sociable, while others seem to prefer quieter surroundings and less activity.

We now know that babies are born with a variety of ways of reacting to the world.[⊙] Their reactions are influenced by the physical development of their brains, the reactivity of their nervous systems, and other physiological differences that are complex and that change over time. They also come with a number of skills that help them to interact with other people.[⊙] So your baby is not a "blank slate" but comes with her own temperament, preferences, and abilities. This is why parents who plan to "train" their babies to behave in a certain way often have difficulty. Babies are sensitive, communicative individuals who are ready at birth to make relationships with those closest to them. They are not passive recipients of our care and love but active partners in a growing relationship. As with all relationships, the way to success is good communication and negotiation.

Babies are strong communicators but their signals are not always easily understood. Even crying, the strongest baby signal of all, can be difficult to interpret: is she hungry, uncomfortable, lonely, or overtired? However, by learning more about baby communication, the non-verbal behaviour and body language, you can increase your confidence as a parent and enjoy your baby more. (*See* the baby language spread on pp.150–51 for more on this.)

Your baby arrives with many abilities. We already know that at birth she can identify her mother's voice and smell compared to that of a stranger.[⊙] In the first

few days you will also notice that your baby recognizes the voices of those who had daily contact with you when you were pregnant, such as your partner and any other children that you have.

Baby states

Like all people, babies have a range of states that describe how physically "aroused", wound-up, or relaxed they are. Young babies can move quickly from one to another, so some knowledge of these states will help you to understand and care for your baby sensitively. In many ways discussing states is just a more organized way of describing what sensitive parents already notice and act on; for example, they soothe a baby who is crying and stimulate a baby who is drowsy before a feed.

Knowledge of your baby's mood states will help you to make the most of your time with your baby.☉ When she is at her most alert yet relaxed, she will be in the best frame of mind to engage in activities such as bathing, dressing, and so on,

and you will be able to use this time to talk and communicate with her. Babies like to be in a calm, alert state, and helping your baby to feel this way means she will respond well and learn from what is going on around her. The six main states are:

- *DEEP SLEEP*

Your baby's eyes are firmly closed and her breathing is deep and regular. She may twitch and move occasionally but not wake up. Deep sleep is necessary for your baby to recover from the demands of the day. It is likely that you would like your baby to be in this state on a regular basis and most young babies will, in fact, sleep deeply about once every four hours. As she matures she will be able to postpone deep sleep for longer periods between naps. Adults, of course, learn to sleep deeply in blocks during the night-time only.

- *ACTIVE SLEEP*

You may have heard this described in adults as REM, or rapid eye movement, sleep. This is associated with dreaming in adults, which is believed to be the brain's way of making sense of the world. For adults, losing REM sleep increases stress and can affect learning. A baby in this state is more physically active than in deep sleep. You may see her eyes rolling under her lids. She may twitch, writhe, and stretch. Her breathing will be more irregular, often shallower and faster. You will notice facial expressions, grimacing, and often mouth movements and sucking. Babies in this state are more easily disturbed and woken by noise or touch.

• *DROWSY, IN-BETWEEN STATE*

In this state your baby's eyes may open and close but appear unfocused and dazed in appearance. Her breathing will be regular but faster and shallower than in deep sleep, and she will make smooth movements with her arms and legs. Babies in this state are easy to rouse for activities and playing.

• *AWAKE ALERT STATE*

Your baby is awake, calm, and alert. Her body will be relatively inactive but her eyes will be bright and shining. This is the time when she will be open to playing and communicating with you. If you talk to her she will respond, maybe imitating your facial expression and certainly fixing you with her gaze. This is when you can really connect with her. Making the most of her company at this time will be enjoyable for both of you.

• *ALERT BUT FUSSY*

This is when the baby is moving towards crying. You may be able to soothe her and bring her back to being alert and playful, or you may find that trying to play just makes her fussier. Her body movements will be jerky and uncoordinated and she may make herself more cross and upset with sudden, startling movements. Some babies seem to get in this state more than others, and all babies in this state need sensitive, careful handling. (*See* pp.116–21 and 152 for how to understand and respond to fussing and crying.)

• *CRYING*

All parents know what this sounds like and what it feels like to hear. Crying is designed to have a strong physical effect on caregivers, making them aroused enough to attend to the needs of the baby. Babies may cry for many reasons, including being hungry, uncomfortable, lonely, bored, over-stimulated, or in pain. The job of the parents is to find out which it is. Crying may also occur for no apparent reason and simply be a sort of discharging of accumulated stress built up through the day. Regular crying bouts are common in some babies, particularly at 4–12 weeks of age.

All babies move between the six states, but each one does so differently. Some babies move very quickly from deep sleep to crying, and seem to spend less time in the calm, alert state, while others are more drowsy and sleepy. Helping your baby to control her emotional state is a key task of parenting. It can also be emotionally tiring, which is one reason why looking after a young baby is so exhausting. You are probably losing sleep yet are also being challenged to be sensitive and responsive to another human being 24 hours a day. However, the rewards for parents who are sensitive to their baby's states and readiness to communicate are high.

RESPONDING TO THE WORLD

As well as a basic ability to move between the six states described, your baby will also have her own way of responding to what is happening around her. For example, you have probably already noticed how your baby reacts to sudden loud noises while deeply asleep or even in a drowsy state. Some babies will tolerate quite a noisy environment. They may stir slightly from a deep sleep but will soon go back to deep, even breathing. In an alert state they may jump if there is a sudden loud noise but after looking to you for some reassurance will be able to remain alert and calm. Others have more intense reactions and are much more difficult to console.⊙

Babies also differ in their ability to get used to what is going on, and to block it out if they need to sleep. Some babies will happily drift off to sleep in the middle of a family party, while others will have to be taken to a quiet room before they can relax into sleep.

Taking notice of the particular way that your baby responds to the world will help you to understand her particular temperament. This understanding can then be used to organize your daily activities and even your "parenting style".

Knowing your baby's temperament

Getting to know the individual characteristics of your baby can be enormously rewarding. Being able to predict what your baby will like to do, what she won't like to do, and what she may need encouragement to do, will help you to feel more confident. It will also help you avoid being drawn into debates about what parents and babies should and shouldn't be doing at each stage of life. You will have the confidence to know what is right for your baby and what is right for you.

As you will discover, most babies occupy the "middle ground". For example, on weight charts most baby's weights come somewhere in the middle. This is where the idea of "normal" arises. However, there will always be individuals who are at the ends of the range – for example, in terms of weight, either very small or very heavy for their ages. This is just as true for temperament. While most babies are somewhere in the middle range, some have characteristics that make them more unusual.

Having a baby in the middle range on almost any scale is usually a more comfortable, less anxious place to be. Parents with these babies often find that information aimed at babies in general is helpful and reassuring. However, having a baby who doesn't seem to conform to general expectations can be more difficult. This is where having an understanding of the characteristics and needs of your particular baby is especially important.⊙

Extra-sensitive "jumpy" babies

While all babies can be described as sensitive, as they are so responsive to the outside world, a small number of babies have a tendency to be extremely sensitive. These babies will often startle from a deep sleep if something in their environment changes. In an alert state they react very strongly to any sudden noises or movements. They usually respond better to soft voices and gentle touch than animated, exaggerated speech.⊙ They may also react strongly to having wet or dirty nappies and appreciate soft, comfortable clothing. Contrary to popular belief, you cannot make a very sensitive baby less sensitive by deliberately exposing her to the rough and tumble of daily life so that she can "get used" to it. What you can do, though, is to treat your sensitive baby with great gentleness in the early weeks until she has found her own ways of coping with the outside world.

THE UNIQUENESS OF YOUR BABY

Every baby is different, and getting to know yours will help you to look after her. For instance, she may be a sensitive baby, who likes lots of quiet interaction with you.

IDEAS FOR COPING WITH YOUR SENSITIVE BABY

• Always approach her slowly and gently, making sure that you do not make any sudden moves or noises.

• Avoid picking her up or putting her down suddenly.

• Avoid switching the light on suddenly when she is drowsy; consider dimmer switches and low lighting.

• Try to keep her environment as calm and gentle as possible, especially in the early weeks, and limit visitors.

• If she doesn't like to be undressed (and many sensitive babies don't), stick to "topping and tailing" in the early weeks – baths are not strictly necessary.

Restless, irritable babies

You may notice that your baby appears more tense and restless than others. She may have more jerky, uncoordinated movements and be unpredictable generally, such as when she is hungry and when she sleeps. Such restless babies often seem to spend more time in the alert but fussy state, and may have trouble staying asleep because they move between sleep states in an unpredictable way. They usually take longer to establish a pattern and may change their habits from day to day. Often intense in their reactions, these babies can be very demanding to care for. Evening crying can be a particular difficulty (*see* p.152).

IDEAS FOR COPING WITH YOUR RESTLESS, IRRITABLE BABY

• Acknowledge that your baby is a challenge but also be aware that, with sensitive handling, things will improve.

• Take good care of yourself so that you can meet your baby's needs without feeling exhausted.

• Swaddling can help to calm your baby as it reduces the times when she may startle herself with jerky movements (*see* p.116).

• Try massage, stroking, and various soothing techniques (*see* pp.116–19) to discover what works for your baby. Building up your stock of strategies will help you to feel more confident.

• Encourage regularity by being predictable and doing things at regular times, but always be prepared to be flexible. Trying to stick to strict routines will simply upset you both.

• Make the most of the times when your baby is alert and calm to play and talk with her. This will help you to feel more positive about her and should tide you over the difficult times.

Drowsy and/or less responsive babies

Other babies can appear to be much less responsive. Some parents describe their babies as appearing very "self-contained", and even that their babies don't seem to "need" them. They report that when being held, their baby feels rigid and doesn't seem to mould into them; these babies seem to prefer being left on their own.

IDEAS FOR COPING WITH YOUR DROWSY AND/OR LESS RESPONSIVE BABY
• If you think that your baby may have withdrawn due to being overwhelmed by the environment, you may find that she is more responsive in a quieter place with lower lighting.
• Holding your baby in skin-to-skin contact with you can be both reassuring and stimulating for her.
• If she seems to hold herself stiff in your arms she may enjoy eye contact and communication when propped up safely on cushions or in a baby chair, rather than when held.
• Your baby may simply take longer to be ready to interact with you. When you communicate with her, go slowly and try to mirror her pace.
• Make the most of the times when she is alert and relaxed. Don't be tempted to use her docility to get on with all the household jobs. Make sure you give plenty of time over to interacting with her.

"Goodness of fit"

Temperament is not just a matter of your baby's behaviour. How her behaviour impacts on your relationship will depend on your temperament as well. Some people call this "goodness of fit". This is how well the baby's temperament fits with that of the parents.[⊙] For example, one mother may have a very sensitive baby but she does not find this an issue. She may not even notice it if she has a tendency to sensitivity herself and likes a quiet and calm environment. She will instinctively pick up her baby slowly and gently, knowing how it feels when someone approaches her too enthusiastically. However, another mother with a sensitive baby might find the situation more difficult. She may be much more outgoing and active, and find the quiet pace the baby prefers a real challenge.

Fathers will also be affected by "goodness of fit". One may delight in the active intensity of his baby and happily play and chat with her, enjoying their growing relationship, while another may find his sensitive child's reactions rather confusing and off-putting.

No one size fits all in infant/parent relationships. This is both the joy and the challenge of bringing up babies and children, and the more you learn about your own particular baby, and the more flexible you can be, the easier it will become for you over time.

see also

soothing and comforting your new baby   116–19
crying out for help!   152–5

Baby language

Babies are social beings with a good range of communication skills. Unfortunately, in our society, where babies are not a big part of everyday life, many adults have had little contact with babies before they have their own. Sometimes new parents find reading baby signals difficult as a result. Having some basic information is useful, but so is taking the time to tune in to your baby, being as sensitive as you can, and going with the flow.

LEARNING TO COMMUNICATE

Babies love to spend time looking at their parents, and will respond to them. This helps to form a strong emotional bond between parent and child.

Babies like to look at faces in preference to anything else. They especially like to look at the faces of those with whom they have a close relationship, usually their parents and siblings. Making eye contact is one of the first ways that babies engage their parents. Parents also tend to find gazing into the faces of their babies extremely moving and enjoyable. Just as people falling in love tend to gaze at the object of their affection, so it is with babies and their parents. It is via eye contact and the use of facial expression, as well as touch, that emotional connection is strengthened and maintained.

It used to be thought that babies didn't see very well and that the world was a booming, buzzing confusion to them until they were at least a few weeks old. We now know that babies can see very well, albeit at a preferred distance. With their dilated pupils and initial difficulties with focusing their eyes together, babies tend to see best at a distance of about 25cm (10in). Interestingly, this is the distance that a baby's face tends to be from her mother's when she is held in her arms. In fact, adults seem to instinctively hold babies at the optimal distance for focusing. ⊙

When your baby is in a calm, alert state you will find that holding her so that her face is about 23cm (9in) from yours and her body is in a semi-upright position, with her head supported, can help her to focus on you, ready for a "conversation". ⊙ Even in the very earliest hours and days you may notice that she will copy your facial expressions. Try sticking out your tongue for a few seconds and see if she does it too. Her reaction may be slow but you will find her copying of your actions becomes more marked over time, especially if she has lots of practice. In the early weeks you may also see a fleeting smile pass over her face.

While your baby is looking at you, perhaps copying your expressions, you can talk to her and notice how she stills and listens to what you say. Babies often seem to prefer voices that are more highly pitched and "sing-song" in tone. Rather than understanding the meaning of each word, they are listening to the emotional tone and rhythm of the speech. Many people find that they talk to babies in this way without even thinking. Even fathers with their naturally deeper voices often find themselves adopting special squeaky baby voices during this phase, a cause of much enjoyment for babies and embarrassment for some fathers when caught in the act! This playful language is the building block of later speech development, when babies first learn to listen, then respond and take turns.

You may notice that during your conversation your baby's body movements reflect the rhythm of your speech, speeding up with excitement as your pitch and rate of speech goes up, and slowing in relation to your tone and pace. Babies certainly communicate their emotions through their whole bodies. Babies whose movements are jerky and uncoordinated may be able to focus better if they are contained, for example if you gently hold their hands or wrap them up.

I've had enough!

Although babies really enjoy conversation, it uses up a great deal of their energy and concentration. They are using many new skills, and the intensity of their concentration means that most babies cannot keep it up for very long. During a conversation they may take short "breaks" where they turn away before turning back and carrying on. Noticing when your baby is beginning to tire of an activity and is in need of a feed or sleep means that you will not overwhelm her. ⊙ Responding quickly to withdrawal signs also means that you may be able to avoid some instances of distress and crying (*see* box, above right).

WITHDRAWAL SIGNS

Here are the most common signs: looking away; shutting eyes; spitting up or "posseting"; hiccupping; yawning; sneezing; holding her hands in front of her face; finger splaying; clenching fists; arching back; squirming; staring with no expression; frowning; grimacing; skin colour changes; sucking; changing position; becoming fussy or crying.

SELF-SOOTHING

As well as showing withdrawal signals when they need a change of pace (*see* box, above), babies can also comfort themselves when they feel agitated. A baby who can soothe herself gains some control over her physical state. This does not mean that she stops needing you, but it does mean that she gains some mastery over the world. You can help your baby to find her own way of soothing herself by trying different things to see if she likes them:
• Swaddling and wrapping.
• Sucking her fist/fingers.
• Listening to your voice.
• Looking at a mobile.
There is more information and advice on soothing and self-soothing in the sleep chapter (*see* pp.116–21).

Crying out for help!
Does my baby have colic?

Persistent crying is the number one cause of stress for many parents in the first few months after their baby's birth. Common misconceptions about what causes infant crying can leave parents feeling anxious, guilty, sometimes angry, and often unsupported. However, recent research can help you to understand what is happening, even if it can't stop the noise!

The crying peak for almost all babies occurs between five and twelve weeks. As many as one in five babies cry or fuss for at least a total of three hours a day, for at least three days per week. This crying is commonly concentrated in the evenings, although this group of babies tend to cry more than average during the day too. Because babies appear to be in pain, and because this pattern almost always stops at three months, doctors often call this syndrome "three-month colic". In the past there have been many theories and myths about what causes this pattern of crying; none of these explanations has led to a cure. Here they are looked at in turn.

"PARENTS STRUGGLING WITH "COLIC" OR PERSISTENT CRYING ARE ANXIOUS FIRST-TIME PARENTS WHO OVERESTIMATE THE PROBLEM"
This has been proved to be untrue. What is true is that parents of first babies are more likely to seek help and advice from health professionals about infant crying. In a study of infant crying, a wide range of parents were asked to keep records of crying and fussing.[○] No difference was found between first, second, or subsequent babies in the amount of crying and fussing recorded. So parental inexperience is unlikely to be the cause. Asking a wide cross-section of parents to keep diaries of crying and fussing also showed that there were large variations between babies in the amount of time they spent crying and fussing.[○] However, a baby's gender, birth order, or feeding method has no effect.

"PARENTS WHOSE BABIES CRY A GREAT DEAL ARE LESS SKILLED, SENSITIVE, AND RESPONSIVE THAN OTHER PARENTS"
In the 1960s and 1970s child psychologists examined the best ways of caring for infants to ensure that they grew up to be secure, independent, and healthy as

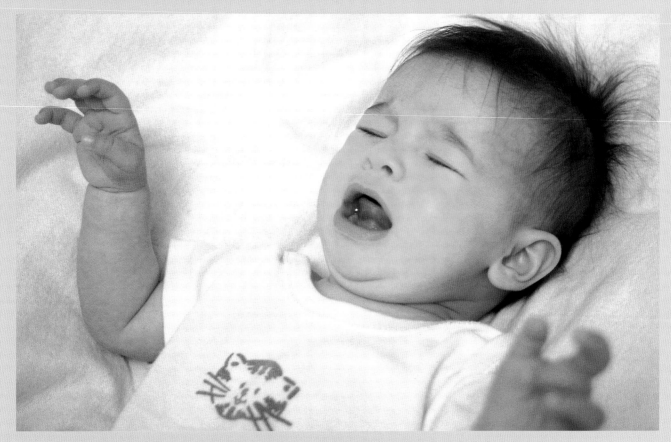

children and adults. Contrary to the old ideas of delaying responding to crying babies so as not to "spoil" them, they found that parents who always responded to their infant's cries quickly and sensitively had babies who cried less later.⊙ Somewhere along the line this important idea became distorted so that parents of babies who cried excessively started to feel as though they were to blame for their baby's behaviour. If you have a baby who cries a great deal in the early weeks don't feel guilty. Try to remain as responsive as you can to your baby's needs without damaging your own health and wellbeing and, crucially, without blaming yourself or undermining your own hard work. Remember that research has shown that babies of responsive parents "get better" over time more than those of less responsive parents. Looking after a baby who cries a lot is a very demanding task and you should be proud of your ability to stick with it. Interestingly, when simply looking at infants who cried a lot in the early weeks, Lynne Murray (a professor of psychology and director of the Winnicott Research Unit at Reading University) measured maternal responsiveness and sensitivity and found that mothers of persistently crying babies were no less skilled than other mothers. In fact mothers of persistent criers were the most sensitive and responsive of all – yet their babies fussed and cried for an average of 3½ hours per day.

COPING WITH A CRYING BABY
While you may feel desperate about the situation, do remember that it is not your fault, and you are not alone. Also realize that this is a passing phase.

"BABIES WHO CRY PERSISTENTLY HAVE SOMETHING WRONG WITH THEM, PROBABLY A DIGESTIVE PROBLEM"

This idea reflects the fact that "colicky" babies cry with great intensity. They appear to be in pain and their tummies are rigid. They also often pass wind and have gurgling guts. Breastfeeding counsellors are happy to discuss colic and may suggest things to try. Digestive problems may be the cause in a small proportion, but it may be worth investigating if your baby has other symptoms (*see* Common illnesses, pp.232–5); however, casual observation of sick infants demonstrates that, if anything, babies who are sick tend to cry less. Crying babies are usually thriving babies who feed well and put on weight.[⊙] The rigid tummies, wind, and so on could be a result of the intensity of the crying.

As we know already, babies communicate with the whole of their bodies, not just their faces. Observations of "colicky" babies show that the crying tends not to start suddenly but gradually builds from long periods of fussing, eventually towards bouts of crying – which, although intense, are not abnormal or different from other bouts of intense crying.[⊙]

So what is going on?

Research has found that babies who have "colicky" crying have crying that is unexplained and, most importantly, is unsoothable, not just by mothers but by trained experts as well – trained midwives and researchers who have years of experience also find these babies hard to soothe. So what is happening?

The most recent research suggests that it could be babies' brain development that causes persistent crying.[⊙] In the very early days a newborn baby's crying is under the control of the mid-brain function, which means that it is completely instinctive. However, as the baby grows and develops over the first few weeks, control of crying is taken over by the cortex (the "thinking" part of the brain). There are two aspects to this control:
• Reactivity, which is the strength of the baby's response to what is happening around her (whether she jumps out of her skin or stirs gently).
• Regulation, which is how long it takes her to recover from her response (whether she calms down immediately or jumps and jitters for a period of time).

Babies with colic may be experiencing disruption during the change from one area of brain control to the other, particularly in their recovery response. These babies are extremely sensitive to their environment, have intense emotions and reactions, and then have difficulty calming down. The evenings are a particularly difficult time because babies (and parents) are tired and therefore more sensitive and have less "self-control". This may also be a time when the household gets busier: family members return home and talk about their day, the evening meal is prepared and cleared away, and television, radio, and music may be on.

Coping with "colic" or persistent crying

• Remember that this is an intense phase that will pass as your baby matures.

• Do not blame yourself or feel guilty for being unable to stop the crying. Look after yourself and stay as calm and relaxed as you can.

• If you suspect that your baby may have a food intolerance ask your doctor to investigate this.

• If you are breastfeeding, contact a breastfeeding counsellor to talk about other things to try.

• Keep your home as calm as possible in the early evening, look for withdrawal signals (*see* box, p.151) before your baby starts fussing, and reduce the stimulation accordingly. You may be able to stop the crying before it really gets going. See if you can discover ways your baby can soothe herself (*see* pp.116–21 for some ideas).

• Look after yourself so that you can cope with this stressful time: get out for a walk in the early afternoon or take a nap; prepare the evening meal earlier in the day.

• Enlist any willing helpers. Maybe those friends and relatives who are so full of ideas about how you might stop the baby crying would like to try them out? Could someone take the baby for a walk in the pram while you have a soak in the bath or catch up on sleep?

• You may like to investigate alternative therapies such as cranial osteopathy (*see* box, p.27), although research is undecided about whether it "works" in this case.

WHEN THE BABY IS ACTUALLY CRYING

• Try changing positions and walking up and down; however, don't switch from one thing to another too often, as your baby is probably overstimulated already. Repetitive rhythmic movements can help and they can be soothing for you too. Alternatively, your baby might be happier on her own for a bit.

• Remember to breathe deeply and relax your shoulders. If your baby is very agitated it can be easy to catch that stress from her. Do all you can to stay calm.

• Giving your baby a warm bath may help, particularly if you have a baby who enjoys being bathed. She could either come in the bath with you or you could bathe her on her own.

• You could try taking your baby for a purposeful walk. You could either carry her in your arms or place her in a sling or backpack.

• Playing calming music and slowly rocking your baby to the music may help.

• Playing music on a Walkman or using earplugs is worth considering when you are coping with prolonged crying bouts, but check your baby frequently.

• If you start to feel desperate and out of control, it is important that you get some space between you and your baby. Either give her to someone else or, if you are alone, put her carefully in a cot and go into the next room until you feel calm.

• For on-the-spot telephone support Cry-sis helpline is a lifeline in this situation. *See* its details under Useful Organizations on page 243.

TRY GIVING HER A BATH

If your baby usually likes being bathed, then a warm bath may do wonders at calming her down when she is agitated. Try it and see if it works.

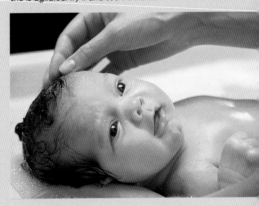

Why parents need friends

Friends are important throughout our lives, but new parents often find that their relationships with friends change in unexpected ways once the baby has arrived. Many new parents find that they are drawn towards those friends who already have children, and feel more distant from those who don't – even if they were close before. Parents who are the first in their group to have children may feel suddenly isolated and alone. Making a special effort to meet other new parents may seem like a huge effort when you are already tired and busy; however, having a local support network is invaluable during the early years of parenthood.

Old friends, new friends

Finding yourself suddenly out of step with your closest friends can be very disconcerting, especially at this sensitive time. This is often discussed in practical terms; for example, that child-free friends are difficult to see, as they want to go out in the evenings and stay out late. Practical arrangements can certainly be an issue; however, this difficulty is often a smoke screen hiding a more sensitive matter. The difficulty often is that new parents, and their child-free friends, suddenly become aware that they now have different priorities, experiences, and identities.

SUPPORT FROM FRIENDS

Spending time with friends, both old and new, sharing experiences, and supporting one another will protect you from the isolation that some new mothers experience.

Not only have new parents been through a radical, life-changing experience, but they are also completely wrapped up in their relationship with their newborn. From the friends' point of view new parents may seem unavailable, preoccupied, and boring. On the other hand, from the parents' point of view friends may also appear unavailable, preoccupied (with work issues, for example), and boring. No wonder there are difficulties!

It is true that many friendships flounder for a while after a new baby arrives; however, most do survive the experience. Over time the intensity of the parent/child relationship mellows and parents are more available both practically, for evenings out, and emotionally. There may be guilt on both sides about letting the friendship slide, but with goodwill things usually resolve themselves after the first few months have passed. It is often a very positive experience for parents to meet up with old friends later, as it helps them to regain a sense of their old selves before they became parents.

In the meantime, new parents can gain a great deal from making friends with other new parents that have babies about the same age, as well as with parents whose children are older. Becoming a parent gives you a new social identity, as well as plunging you into a world where you need to acquire a great deal of new knowledge and information. Other parents can help you to negotiate this new territory more easily.⊙

Real parents, real lives

In our society everyone has an opinion about parenting, and most people are not afraid to share it. The media is full of examples of good parents and, more often, bad ones. You may worry that you will never live up to all the expectations and responsibilities of parenthood. Suddenly you and your new family feel like public property and your instinct may be to withdraw to the safety of your own four walls. However, social isolation and parenting are a bad combination, and an effort put in now to find friends that are in the same situation can protect you from difficulties later on.

If you only read books, magazines, and childcare manuals you only find out part of what it means to care for a baby. Having a network of friends who are parents are your "reality check". Not only do you hear about how life is for them, but you see their babies and children in action. Babies in magazines are rarely spotty and covered in dribble, and toddlers in books may have tantrums but they stop when their parents do the "right thing". Babies and children in real life are quite different; they make a lot of noise, are awkward, and have smelly nappies. Real parents also do not look like the parents in magazines; they are likely to look pale, tired, and have circles under their eyes from lack of sleep. You may think you know this already, but seeing real parents regularly and on an informal basis, with real babies, is something else – seeing really is believing.

NCT POSTNATAL COURSES AND DROP-INS
Many parents' groups are organized by volunteers and are run on a very informal basis. They can be great places to meet new people and make friends. However, if you find groups daunting or are feeling vulnerable, it is well worth looking for a group that is facilitated and run by a trained organizer.

The NCT has a whole network of trained postnatal leaders who run regular courses and drop-ins for new parents. The atmosphere is informal and welcoming, and because the group leader is trained you can expect well-run sessions where you are treated as an individual. Postnatal leaders are trained to make sure that sessions are interesting, informative, and give everyone the opportunity to speak and be listened to. The sessions may cover topics such as sleeping and crying, coping with advice, changing relationships, and issues around returning to work (or not). The atmosphere is non-judgemental, impartial, and confidential. Postnatal leaders are committed to the idea that parents should be supported, encouraged, and given the confidence to do what is right for their babies, themselves, and their families.

To find your nearest course or drop-in run by a trained NCT postnatal leader you can ring the enquiries line at the UK office or use the NCT website (*see* p.246 for details).

Becoming part of a parent network is also useful as you can see for yourself that what is "normal" changes from day to day. If your baby is crying more than others one day, she may be quieter the next. However, if you do find that you or your baby are often out of step with other parents you can decide if you need to talk to a health professional for extra help and advice.

Being part of a supportive group of other parents

New parents often comment that during maternity leave and while at home with a new baby they become aware of a whole new community that operates during the daytime. This is a community of mostly mothers and older people. Many new mothers are surprised to find that they suddenly feel a part of a larger group of women also caring for babies.[⊙]

Simply exchanging smiles, sympathetic glances, and possibly chats in the street can be very reassuring. Many mothers say that they suddenly feel part of some special club or sisterhood, and you may discover this too. However, for real emotional and social support many women (and some men) find that joining a parents group is very helpful. In parents' groups you will find others who are prepared to listen to your experiences and also sympathize with your everyday dilemmas. You will have the opportunity to meet people who may go on to become good friends.

Some parents resist going to parents' groups, believing that the only thing they will have in common with the others there is that they are parents. This may be true; however, looked at differently this needn't be a problem. At work you may develop a positive relationship with someone who shares your office. You may pass the time of day, joke together, and make cups of coffee for one another. You may not be firm friends but you are good company for each other. If you look on other parents in a parents' group this way, it is not a necessarily a bad thing if you don't find someone who will be a close friend. On the other hand you just might. Many parents who attend such groups are also looking for friends in the same situation as themselves.

Friends who are new parents are invaluable as not only will they willingly talk about problems with sleep, feeding, and relationships, they are also likely to be available when you are, for coffee in the morning or for lunch. They will also get to know your baby well over time and you may be able to help each other out with babysitting, especially if you don't have family locally who can help.

FINDING THE "RIGHT" PARENTS' GROUP FOR YOU

Finding a parents' group where you feel at home is simply a case of trying groups out. Different groups have different atmospheres, and you can only get a feel for a group by visiting. It is worth visiting a group more than once to give yourself a chance of meeting everyone and settling in. However, if you go to a group where

"Sharing experiences with friends as we went along helped us realise I wasn't going mad after all and Emma was completely normal!"

you don't feel welcomed you are under no obligation to go again (*see* box, right). As with many services, personal recommendations are useful, but do remember that groups change over time. To find out about the local groups that are available, ask your health visitor or look at noticeboards in places such as libraries and community centres. If there is a phone number with the information it is worth ringing before you set out. The group may have stopped or changed its meeting place, for example. Also, if you have spoken to the organizer beforehand she will be looking out for you and can be ready to make you feel welcome when you arrive.

Most areas have a number of parent and toddler groups that are open to all. You will not be turned away if your baby is not a toddler; however, parent and toddler groups can be noisy and busy places. On the plus side, many of these groups have areas put aside specifically for parents with smaller babies where you can sit and talk.

As with all activities and groups it may take you a while to really settle in. You may find that some sessions are more enjoyable than others for a variety of reasons. If you are feeling very tired or sensitive you may find that one session is awful while the next week is much more enjoyable. It may also take a while to get to know people, which can be frustrating. Perseverance usually pays off. Try not to be upset if people at the group seem preoccupied and don't talk or listen to you as you would like; remember they are probably also tired and coping with looking after babies – and perhaps toddlers and older children too.

IF A GROUP DOESN'T FEEL RIGHT

If you regularly leave a group feeling worse rather than better it is time to start looking for another group. Some parents' groups are not well run and can drain your confidence rather than supporting you. Be on your guard for groups where discussion is competitive, where only one opinion is expressed, and where you feel overlooked and excluded. Sometimes groups are dominated by people who are happier doling out advice than listening to parents. If you find the advice helpful then fine – if not, have the confidence to say "no thank you" and find somewhere where you will be properly supported.

A NEW NETWORK OF FRIENDS

By joining a parents' group you may well find a number of new friends that live nearby. You will be able to meet up during the day and support one another.

Fathers' experiences

Having a new baby is the most unbelievable experience in life – one that most fathers will never forget. The creation of a new life and the responsibility for it is both overwhelming and elating. It's like discovering your own life has a whole new dimension that you were unaware of. Anxieties about being a good parent or worries about the new baby are more than worth the rewards of watching your child grow. It is emotional, and perhaps a bit clichéd, but many of the best things in life are.

YOUR ROLE AS A FATHER

In the early days make time to bond with your baby. You can also help soothe her, bathe her, and do plenty of nappy changing too!

The early days

Once the baby is born many fathers will bond with their child just as quickly as mothers do; if you don't try not to worry, as over the next few hours and days you will start to feel quite overwhelmed by how much you care for this new person. The early weeks are an ideal time to really get to know your baby (for information about baby communication, *see* p.150), as your partner will be tired from the birth and from frequent feeding. This also means that fathers can actually do a great deal at this stage, such as nappy changing and helping comfort the baby. In the busy early days when you are dealing with visitors and health professionals, make a special effort to carve out time for yourself to hold and enjoy your baby. Don't be sidelined into only making the drinks and doing the housework.

Mothers often know other mothers who they can talk to about their babies and how they are feeling themselves, but men have less of an opportunity for this unless close friends are also parents. You might find it helpful to speak to relatives or other fathers that you met at antenatal classes. Because you and your partner are both tired, you might find that you end up dazed in front of the television once your baby has finally fallen to sleep, and it is easy to forget in the early days that you can talk to your partner about any fears or concerns you have.

Most fathers really appreciate the chance to feed their child with expressed breastmilk, but some breastfed babies will refuse the bottle; this can be quite disheartening and it's easy to feel rejected. Don't forget that babies do want to see both parents and spend time with them, but they aren't yet able to express this clearly! So try to make sure you get quality time with your baby, even if feeding isn't part of this. Babies recognize their father's voice from when they were in the womb and will turn to them more than a stranger; therefore your baby will be comforted by your voice and by spending time with you.

The role of the father can seem very overwhelming in the early days, with responsibilities for the baby, home, and partner; even more so if the mother has had a caesarean or is suffering from postnatal depression. It can feel that your life has changed unequivocally and there is only nappies, crying, and lack of sleep – whereas before there were romantic evenings, lie-ins, and time to relax (things always seem better looking back!). If you do become aggravated with constant crying take a step back and take a few minutes to clear your head; it happens to everyone and is a normal reaction (*see* p.155).

It is worth considering what can be done to make your and your partner's life easier. A basic routine for bedtime tends to help, however unlikely you think it is to work, but in the early days bedsharing could help take off the pressure. Fathers should never worry if they're told they're "making a rod for their own backs", as what feels right usually is right for your child. Parents should trust their instincts, let the baby take the lead, and respond to what she needs. For example, if she cries and you want to pick her up and comfort her – do so.

One of the biggest pressures for parents is being told by others how they should be looking after their baby: when she should be sleeping, feeding, what stage she should be at – there is no end to the useful advice. Men are less likely to put much store in such information, whereas groups of new mothers in the context of only discussing babies can easily lose the faith they had in themselves. Fathers who can actively support their partners and give them confidence when they feel undermined will be invaluable in the early months.

Juggling work and home

Work can rather get in the way of being a parent, especially for men. Despite a great deal of rhetoric about supporting parents, men often find that this support is aimed at mothers. Although paternity leave is now a legal right the payments are at statutory level in most companies, so financial pressure can be an added strain at just the wrong time.

If there are any universal lessons for new dads about to return to work, they are probably these. Try to negotiate at work for what you want; work-life balance is a trendy term with not much to back it up, but if you can find a personal arrangement that suits your family then that is great, if not then a new job may be needed. Try not to worry too much, and enjoy each day as the clichés are true: young children do change fast so try to relax into being a parent, get involved and your baby will reward you a thousand times over. It will be tough for both you and your partner at times, especially if postnatal depression, sickness, money issues, or anything else adds to the stress of being a new parent. The important lesson here is to keep talking – as with all successful relationships, communication is the key.

GETTING CLOSE TO YOUR BABY
• New babies often need a great deal of reassurance. If your baby wants to sleep on you, why not? It's a great feeling to be able to provide such comfort to your child.
• If your baby doesn't like having a bath on her own why not bath with her?
• Try to go out alone with your baby. It's a little like passing your driving test and driving alone for the first time – when you've been out once it'll seem like the hurdle never existed.

"Just keep your head down for the first few months and accept that you may not be the cause but you will be the focus of your partner's frustrations."

Postnatal fitness

Your body went through some amazing changes during the nine months of pregnancy to enable it to grow and protect your baby. In the short space of six week since her birth, you will have noticed equally dramatic changes as your body returns to "normal".

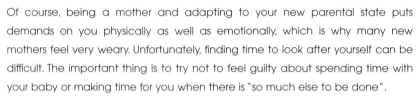

BACK CARE

TOO MUCH STRAIN

When carrying a baby's car seat do not hold it in one hand as this can pull your muscles out of alignment.

IN BALANCE

Carry the seat in both hands, centred in front of you. One hand should be under the seat and the other supporting the back. Hold the seat close to you.

BEND YOUR KNEES

When lifting any heavy object, always bend your knees rather than your back. Make sure the object is as close as possible to your body.

Of course, being a mother and adapting to your new parental state puts demands on you physically as well as emotionally, which is why many new mothers feel very weary. Unfortunately, finding time to look after yourself can be difficult. The important thing is to try not to feel guilty about spending time with your baby or making time for you when there is "so much else to be done".

During pregnancy the stretching and lack of use of certain muscles, such as the abdominal and pelvic floor muscles, will have weakened them considerably. Even though they may look as though they have returned to normal, they are likely still to be weak, and you will now need to work at getting them back to normal if you want to avoid problems such as backache and incontinence.

The abdominal muscles are particularly important in protecting your spine, especially when lifting and carrying things. Of course, your baby will need to be carried for many months and you will want to keep her close to you. As she grows and gains weight, you will find you are less tired if the muscles you use for lifting and carrying are as strong as possible. This may be a great opportunity to get these muscles in better shape, and perhaps even firmer and stronger than they were before you became pregnant.

Back care

There are right ways and wrong ways to lift and carry heavy objects, such as car seats. Taking care always to bend your knees and keep your back straight when you lift or carry anything will protect your back and spine. Ensure that whatever you are carrying is held in both hands to distribute the weight evenly, and that it is held close to your body to avoid unnecessary strain on your back.

Triceps dips

This exercise works the muscles at the back of the upper arms. These muscles have a tendency to get flabby as you get older, so if you want to keep them looking toned and firm try "dipping" on a regular basis.

Sit on a comfortable surface with your knees bent and your feet about hip width apart. Place your hands resting flat behind you with fingers facing towards your bottom. Gently bend your elbows and lower your body towards the floor, then straighten them again in a smooth, gentle movement. Keep your tummy muscles pulled in to protect your back and work your abdominal muscles.

Abdominal exercise

Lie on the floor with your knees bent and feet flat on the floor. Make sure your back is in the neutral spine position (*see* illustration, below right). Keep breathing normally and draw your belly button towards your spine as you tighten your abdominal muscles. You should feel the muscles at your sides tightening but your back should not move. Slide one leg at a time along the floor until it is straight, keeping your spine in neutral by working those abdominal muscles. Return the leg to the starting position and repeat on the other side. Do eight repeats per leg, then rest the abdominal muscles.

This exercise will work your abdominals safely and effectively. You can also do a similar exercise lifting one arm at a time above your head instead of leg sliding, providing your keep your abs tightened as described.

The benefits of walking

A brisk 15–30 minute walk out in the park with friends, or back from the shops, is an excellent way to keep fit and burn off those extra calories. Stepping out with a slightly longer stride and a little faster than usual will give you maximum benefit. The early days after birth, especially if you are breastfeeding, is not really the time to start dieting, but by keeping active most days of the week and avoiding high-fat foods you should find yourself shedding the extra weight that you gained during pregnancy.

Pelvic floor exercise

Try to do these exercises little and often throughout the day. Imagine you really need to go to the loo. Pull in around the front passage as if to stop yourself, or imagine you are pulling in your vagina as if to hold onto a tampon that is slipping. Hold for four seconds and keep breathing normally. When you release you should feel the muscles let go. Repeat this process ten times at least three times a day. As you get stronger you can hold for longer; up to about ten seconds. Try also tightening the muscles quickly – squeeze, release, squeeze, release – only holding each one for about one second. Research has shown that alternating between these fast and slow tightenings is the most effective way of strengthening your pelvic floor muscles.

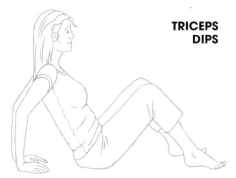

TRICEPS DIPS

Sit with your knees bent and feet hip-width apart. Place your hands behind you with your fingers facing towards your bottom.

Gently bend your elbows and lower your body, keeping your tummy muscles pulled in as you do so. Gradually straighten your elbows again.

ABDOMINAL EXERCISE

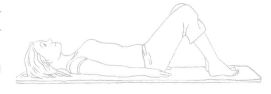

Press your back flat to the floor then arch it up. Halfway between these two is the neutral spine position.

Slide one leg at a time along the floor until straight, keeping your spine in the neutral position.

6 | THREE TO SIX MONTHS – YOUR SETTLED BABY

- Becoming a family
- Living with your "settled baby"
- To work or not to work
- Deciding to return to work
- Your childcare options
- Making childcare work
- Learning to learn together
- What your baby can do when
- The best toys for three to six months
- Premature babies
- Teething
- Immunizations

Becoming a family

As you emerge from the fog of the early weeks, the impact of becoming a parent on your identity will become increasingly noticeable. Your life has changed irrevocably and you will probably feel quite differently about almost everything. Family relationships may come under a new spotlight as your position in the family changes from "child" to "parent". However, many new parents find that the relationship that changes the most is the one between themselves and their partner.

WORKING TOGETHER

In these early months, as your family unit is getting established, try to work together and enjoy being new parents.

Changing partnerships

When a baby is born parents must begin the adjustment from living as a couple to establishing a new family unit. Although you may have given this some thought during pregnancy, the reality can still be a considerable challenge. You will need to accommodate each other's needs as well as coping with a vulnerable new baby. Issues about shared and individual responsibilities and task sharing may become particularly heated as each partner grapples with what is reasonable to expect from the other. At a time when you are both tired and stressed it is easy to take each other's contribution for granted, and either one of you can feel unappreciated and misunderstood. An effort to communicate honestly but kindly and with patience at this difficult time will pay off in the months to come.

At this stage of early parenthood the difference in the daily experiences of each partner may be extremely marked. Most new fathers work full time, while most mothers are based at home, either for the foreseeable future or for the duration of maternity leave. Many fathers feel the need to work extra hard, as they are aware of their new responsibility to support their family, but many also feel sad that they are missing out on time with their new babies. Conversely, mothers may feel jealous of their partner's greater physical freedom and time spent out of the home. There is a changed relationship over money too. Often the earning partner may feel that they have most say in how money is spent, while the non-earning partner may find it hard to have to ask for money for things they would not have talked to their partner about before.

Some new mothers feel that their lives have changed beyond recognition but that their partners live very much as they had before. What used to be a relationship built on equality and similarity can start to look like the traditional role-differentiated marriage of past times. While some women relish their new role, feeling that they are doing what they are "meant" to do as wives and mothers, others feel anxious and frustrated, as their hard-won independence seems to be disappearing. Issues of dependence and independence – emotional, financial, and physical – can be difficult for both partners to deal with. It can be helpful for you both to remember that this stress affects nearly all partnerships at this stage, and that with patience and time the situation will change. Discussing the small annoyances as you go along is probably better than bottling it all up for a huge showdown later. Talking to friends and family can help too.

Sex and your relationship

Many new parents find that their sexual relationship changes significantly in the first year after birth. The sheer tiredness of early parenthood means that bedtime is more about grabbing sleep than anything more active. If you are bedsharing, or the baby is sleeping in your bedroom in his cot, that may act as another deterrent, although of course a sleeping baby will not be disturbed by quiet love-making and you could always have sex in another room.

For some parents it is not so much that they don't have the physical energy for sex but that they don't feel like it. Some men find that they go off sex for a while when the baby is young, and in fact it has been shown that testosterone levels do fall in new dads (although why that should be is unclear). Some fathers are also affected by witnessing the birth and find that they see their partner in a different way for a time. Some may be frightened that they will hurt their partner during intercourse. Going slowly and finding non-penetrative ways of having sex for a while can help to re-establish intimacy.

New mothers may not feel like sex for a variety of reasons. The physical changes that occur in a woman's body in pregnancy, birth, and breastfeeding may make her feel less attractive, although by contrast some women feel more sexy as they experience the power and fertility of their bodies. Physical sensation may be altered, and some women find that it takes a while to get in touch with this. You may also find that the ongoing physical intimacy that you have with your baby makes the drive for sex much less strong. Some women report that having held a baby in their arms for most of the day, what they really crave is time alone. Their partner's desire for sex can seem like just another need to be met. If this is the case it may be that you need to take more time for yourself, or to ask your partner to do something nurturing for you, such as give you a massage.

If either partner is not happy with the way the sex life is going it is important to talk this over without resorting to anger and blame. Most couples find that their sex lives change permanently after they have children. Typically sex happens less often, but when it does it is more intimate and satisfying. Also keep a realistic view of your sex lives before you had the baby. If you were already having less sex before you got pregnant it is unlikely that sex will suddenly become more frequent afterwards. However, many couples find that their interest and desire for sex increases again once their baby reaches toddlerhood.

WHAT IS A NORMAL SEX LIFE FOR NEW PARENTS?

Two thirds of parents find that their sexual relationship changes during pregnancy – typically they have sex about half as often as they did before, and nearly all find that this continues to be altered after the arrival of the baby. However, statistics suggest that the range of "normal" in terms of sex after birth is wide. For example, the majority of couples will have had sex by three months after birth (65 percent), some new parents have sex quite soon (20 percent by one month), but there is a small group (4 percent) who still haven't had intercourse after the first year. (Figures taken from an NCT survey.)

Living with your "settled baby"

Babies at this stage are sometimes referred to as "settled" because this is the period when their behaviour generally becomes more predictable and manageable. Feeding is usually well-established and, barring minor colds and upsets, most babies put on weight in this period relatively quickly and constantly.

Your baby will probably still be sleeping for longish periods each day, and will wake refreshed and ready to play. Three-to-six-month-old babies tend to be sociable and communicative and will love being talked to, stroked, tickled, and sung to. They will readily mimic noises and expressions and can be great fun.

Persistent crying and fussing, especially in the evenings, should be lessening by now, and crying in general will be decreasing. This is partly because parents now have a greater understanding of their own particular baby and what he needs, so that they respond more effectively. However, research also shows that at this age restlessness and fussing tends to diminish in every baby.[⊙]

Some babies who were very fussy and miserable in the first few weeks will continue to be difficult to manage in this phase. Coming from a different starting point the decrease in crying, although apparent, is less noticeable in such babies. It may be at about this time that parents of these more sensitive, reactive babies really start to notice a difference between their experience of parenting and that of their friends. It can be demoralizing caring for a baby who isn't often happy. Parents may mistakenly feel that they are getting it all wrong if their baby is still unsettled. It is important to remember that, while parents of more placid babies can get away with alright, average parenting, parents of sensitive, reactive babies need to acquire and use top-level parenting skills. Let go of the image of perfect parents and placid babies and learn to value and reward yourself for what you are doing.

"Stop trying to get everything 'done' and just get out of the house with the baby was the best thing I learnt in this early stage."

Getting out and about

This is the time when many parents become especially motivated to get out and about with their babies. Outings with a baby are very different from the sort of casual popping out you may have been used to. Getting used to negotiating outings with a pram or pushchair is a skill that everyone has to learn, and many parents feel self-conscious early on.

You will also need to decide how much to carry in your baby-changing bag – for example, how many nappies, wipes, and changes of clothes are necessary.

A CHANGE OF PACE

At this stage most parents are keen to get out and about with their babies. However, do remember that you will need to take things slower than you used to – most activities take longer with a baby.

Checking and restocking the bag each day when you have a quiet ten minutes, and keeping a ready-packed bag near to the door, can make getting ready to go out much less stressful. It is a good idea to spend some time finding out the best places in your area to go with a young baby. Other parents and your local NCT branch can be useful sources of information about where are the nicest baby-changing rooms, and where are the best places to breastfeed or get bottles warmed.

When you are planning outings remember to pace yourself. You need to assume that at some point during any outing your baby may need a feed or nappy change. Trying to do too much while out (as it has taken so long to get ready in the first place) will leave you and your baby tired and frazzled. In general, shorter, more local outings, doing one thing each day, seem to work best for most new parents. This may be a real departure from your usual routine before you had children, when you may have spent all day at the shops or have done a full week's grocery shopping in one hour. With a baby most things take longer. If you find this change of pace difficult, remember that this stage won't last forever and both you and your baby will enjoy outings more if you don't try to fit in too much.

To work or not to work?

Before you began your maternity leave, returning to work or education probably seemed a long way off; after all, you didn't even know how you would feel about being a parent until you had your baby. However, with the excitement of the birth and the bustle of the early weeks, time rushes by, and by the time your baby is three months old it is likely that you will be beginning to think about what will happen when your maternity leave ends.

SHARE THE CARE
Depending on finances, one possibility for parents who both want to work may be for each partner to work part time or work shifts, in order to split the childcare. You may then require less paid childcare, although if one partner starts and finishes work early, and the other works late, it may mean a decrease in time you can have together as a family.

If you worked for your employer before you became pregnant (or for 26 weeks by the 15th week before your baby was due) you will be entitled to a further 26 weeks unpaid maternity leave on top of your 26 weeks paid maternity leave. As additional maternity leave is unpaid you may not be able to afford to take this extra time off. You should find out about additional tax credits or other benefits you may be entitled to during the additional maternity leave period. Depending on the terms of your employment contract, it may be possible to postpone making the final decision until your baby is a few months old, but you may still want to start thinking about how your new role as a parent affects your choices.

Trying to decide what to do at the end of your maternity leave can be a difficult decision. You will probably find that everyone you talk to will have an opinion, and that society has plenty to say on the costs and benefits of being a working mother or not. Some parents feel pressured by this volume of well-meant advice, but it is important that you do what is best for you and your family.

Your reasons for returning to work will depend on your circumstances and your feelings about your job. You may feel that time away from home will help you to be a better parent, as you will return home feeling stimulated, refreshed, and ready to be with your baby. On the other hand, you may want to stay at home, but need the income in order to have a standard of living that is acceptable to you. Before you make your decision, take time to consider everybody's needs: yours, your partner's, your other children's (if applicable), and your new baby's. Many decisions around work and home are compromises based on finding a balance between what you would ideally like to do and what is possible. Don't be too hard on yourself if you can't find the "perfect" solution; you will find a compromise, and you can probably change your decision if you find that things are not working out as you had hoped.

If you have a network of friends and colleagues who have gone back to work with small children you may be able to gain support and practical tips from their shared experiences. It is possible that the experience of caring for your baby will have beneficial effects for your working life, as you may have improved your time-management skills or your ability to cope with pressure or solve problems. Parenting may also have helped you become more adaptable, or more resilient, than you were before you had your baby.

For most parents, the costs of raising a child are likely to mean a drop in their material standard of living. In addition, living on one income, one partner opting for part-time working, or the cost of childcare can increase pressure on your budget. To make your finances work you will need to discuss your priorities and agree a solution that is acceptable to you both. Talking about these issues can help to prevent conflict later. If you are having difficulties making these decisions as a partnership, you may find it helpful to talk it through with someone impartial.

Staying at home

Many mothers relish the idea of taking a few years to care for their children, and feel enormously fulfilled. However, it can take a lot of courage for some women to say that they want to stay at home, and if you want to bring up your children full time you may need a lot of support – both practical and emotional. Caring for children is hard work and emotionally draining, even when it is rewarding. Sometimes mothers who decide to stay at home find that they feel isolated and marginalized, or feel that they are not contributing anything – especially if they have given up a job and have few non-working friends. Getting out and meeting other mums and celebrating all the things you are doing for your child can really help to boost your self-esteem.

If your time at home is only going to last for a couple of years you could continue to use your skills in some way, so that you don't feel so alienated from the workforce. Volunteering for the NCT or another organization that you are interested in can provide you with an outlet for your talents in an environment where you can use your skills.

Full-time dads

For some families it may be the man who gives up work rather than the woman. However, as this is still a less common arrangement, fathers in this position may experience more isolation than women. Some men are comfortable attending coffee mornings and toddler groups where they may be the only man, while others may find this difficult and may have to look hard for support. There are now groups especially for fathers, and it is worth contacting fathers' organizations, such as Fathers Direct, for support and information (*see* p.240 for details).

"I never thought I was the full-time mother type, but hey, never say never! Working evenings from home when possible, I wouldn't have swapped this for the world."

SHARING THE LOAD

Nowadays more and more couples are sharing their childcare responsibilities. Occasionally the man gives up work completely, or you could consider both working part time.

Deciding to return to work

Returning to work after your maternity leave can feel like a big hurdle. Many working mothers find the separation from their babies difficult at first – even those who really enjoy their jobs and want to return to work. The early days of juggling work and baby will probably feel stressful, but gradually some sense of order will descend as you learn to manage your old and new responsibilities.

Your employment rights

Since 6 April 2003 parents of children aged under six, or of disabled children aged under 18, have the right to apply to work flexibly. You are not automatically entitled to reduce your hours or to job-share, but your employer has a duty to consider such a request seriously and can only refuse for business reasons. Subject to certain conditions, a father may have the right to up to two weeks paid time off around the time of the birth to care for the new baby and support the mother.

When you return to work you are entitled to breaks to breastfeed your baby, or to express milk, and you should be provided with somewhere private and hygienically acceptable to do this. The Maternity Alliance is able to advise on the most up-to-date legislation for working parents. The toilets are not a hygienic place to feed a baby, or express milk, so your employer should not ask you to use them. If you are expressing during your working hours, you will need a fridge or a cold cool box in which to store the milk – and a means of transporting it home still cold.

Paid leave for adoptive parents

Since not all new parents are birth parents, there are also rights to adoption leave and pay. Adoption leave is available to individuals who adopt, or to one partner if you adopt jointly as a couple. The other member of the couple, or an adopter's partner, has the right to paternity leave and pay.

Rights to parental leave and time off for dependents

If you have completed one year's service with your employer you are entitled to an additional 13 weeks' unpaid parental leave to care for your child. Parental leave can usually be taken in blocks of weeks at a time, up to four weeks a year, and up to five years from the date of birth or date of placement in an adoptive home. It is also available to both parents. Unfortunately, parental leave is unpaid so in reality few parents can afford to take this amount of unpaid time off. If your child is disabled, you are entitled to 18 weeks' parental leave up to the child's

18th birthday. Parents are also entitled to a reasonable amount of unpaid time off work to deal with emergencies or unexpected situations involving their children.

When it seems too soon to go back

If your baby was born early you may feel that you have not had the opportunity to enjoy your baby at home before your maternity leave is over, especially if your baby spent a long time in hospital. If you feel that this is an issue for you, contact with a support group for the parents of premature babies can help, both with practical issues and with an understanding ear for the emotional difficulties of parenting a baby that was born very early (*see* pp.190–91).

If your baby was born with a disability or illness, or if you have been ill, you may feel that your maternity leave was not long enough for you to get used to being a parent. Discuss with your employer whether you have the option to take unpaid leave, or to rearrange your working hours. Remember: if you worked for your employer for 26 weeks by the 15th week before your baby was due, you are entitled to take a further 26 weeks unpaid additional maternity leave.

Delaying your return for longer

If you decide to stay at home and concentrate on your family full time for a while, you may worry that a long period away from the workplace might be disruptive. If you intend to return to work after a few months, or even a few years, you may find it helpful to think about how you could use your career break to add something positive to your skills, rather than viewing it as time off the career ladder. You may find it helpful to discuss the issues with your personnel department, or your boss. For suggestions of the issues you should consider *see* the box, right.

Returning to education

Many of the issues you will need to deal with if you want to go back into education are the same as they are for women who return to paid employment. However, few of your fellow students may be parents and you may feel isolated, especially if you miss out on the social side of education. The erratic pressures of exams and coursework deadlines can be difficult if you have a small baby, and it is worth asking what allowances can be made and what support you can get. Find out whether your educational establishment has a student counsellor you can talk to, or there may be a member of staff who is responsible for your personal needs.

If you want more information about your employment rights, the Maternity Alliance can provide you with your current rights under law (*see* p.242 for its details). The ACAS website (www.acas.org.uk) also has further details on family-friendly policies. If you want advice on current benefits, tax issues, or other entitlements contact your local Tax Office, Citizen's Advice Bureau, or Social Security Office.

DELAYING YOUR RETURN: ISSUES TO CONSIDER
• How will you cope with the loss of income?
• Does your company have a career-break scheme?
• Could you do your job on a part-time, job-share, or more flexible basis?
• How will a break affect your company benefits, particularly your pension?
• How will you keep in touch with what's going on in your field, and how will you keep your knowledge and skills updated?
• How long do you intend your break to be?
• Do you intend returning to the same job, or changing career? Women sometimes find that they refocus after having a baby and they decide to re-train, either for a job that suits their new view on life or for one that offers more child-friendly working hours and conditions.

Your childcare options

Choosing childcare is important, as you will want the best for your baby. It is helpful to think about the type of care that you are seeking. For example, do you want one-to-one care or do you want your baby to be part of a social group? You will also need to consider the practicalities – do you want care that is close to your home, or care that is close to your work so that you and your baby spend travelling time together and you have the option to see him during your breaks?

Choosing childcare is not restricted to those who are returning to work, as you may feel that you would just like some time for yourself. Many women find that taking a break from their children helps them to recharge their batteries and feel better about themselves. Enjoying some time alone or engaging in an adult, perhaps pre-child, activity can help to prevent you from feeling as though your life revolves totally around your children. Whether this is a regular arrangement, or an occasional one-off, the same principles apply.

It is important that you feel confident about the care that your child will be receiving. Just because a setting comes highly recommended doesn't necessarily mean that it will be right for you. You and your baby are individuals, and what suits your family, friends, and neighbours may not suit you. Trust your instincts.

Most parents have concerns about the effects of childcare on their babies and children. This is an area where there has been a lot of research. Recent studies have shown that good-quality childcare, which is sensitive and responsive to the needs of each individual child, does not put children at an emotional or educational disadvantage, especially if their relationship with their parents is strong, supportive, and nurturing.

You may worry that your child will learn to depend on his carer, or you may be concerned that you will feel threatened by the closeness between your child and his carer. However, it is important that you support your child in forming a relationship with a carer that will meet his emotional needs. His ability to make an attachment to his carer is an extension of what he has learned in his relationship with you.

Research has shown that children who have many changes of carer, or where the childcare provision is poor, seem to fare worst both in terms of school readiness and in forming early social relationships. There is evidence to suggest that children who have good-quality childcare score higher in some areas. When children are stimulated to use language and join in activities with

CHILDCARE OPTIONS

You have a number of options for part-time or full-time childcare. The majority of parents use one of the following:

- Childminder.
- Day nursery or crèche.
- Nanny.
- Au pair, mother's help, or babysitter.
- Grandparents and other family.

their peers, they tend to develop language skills more quickly and score more highly in tests used to measure school readiness.[⊙] However, researchers have noticed that children who are in full-time childcare (over 45 hours a week) before their first birthday show slightly more difficult and aggressive behaviour than their peers at age four and a half.[⊙] These findings may be because children have to compete for attention sooner and are asked to share toys and play cooperatively with other children before they are ready. It is not clear if this is a temporary phase or if it continues into school, as the studies only measure the effects up to five years old.

If you have concerns about childcare, talking to other parents is a useful starting point to getting help. Many NCT branches have working mums' or working parents' groups, where you can talk about the ups and downs of being a working parent with others who are experiencing the same things.

Whatever you decide, for most families childcare is the biggest cost of returning to work, although it is currently subsidized for low-income families. Prices for childcare vary enormously from area to area, so it is worth asking friends and colleagues what the current rates are where you live. Generally, childminders and au pairs are the cheapest form of paid childcare and nannies the most expensive, with day nursery and crèche costs falling somewhere between the two.

In some areas childcare costs are subsidized by the local authority or by employers. Details of registered childcare providers in your area are held by your local Children's Information Service – contact your local authority for more

"I have returned to work part-time after maternity leave with each of my three children. I am a calmer, happier, less frustrated mum for having some time away from them, but good childcare is the key."

REGISTERED CHILDMINDERS

ADVANTAGES

• Childminders are registered and annually inspected.
• Childminders provide an environment very close to what your child would experience at home. They may go to toddler groups and for regular outings to the shops, park, and so on.
• Your childminder may be able to accommodate "out of hours" care.
• Your child will usually have other children to play with of various ages, rather like in a family.
• Your child will have continuity of care, especially if your childminder is prepared to take your child to and from nursery or care for them after school.
• Because children are not segregated by age, siblings can be cared for together – as they would be at home.

DISADVANTAGES

• Childminders are likely to be dealing with a wide range of ages and your child may have no same-age peers.
• Your first-choice childminder may not be flexible about hours or may need to organize their daily routine around other families and their own commitments.
• Childminders may not be able to look after your child if he is ill.
• You will need to make alternative arrangements if your childminder is ill or on holiday.
• As they are self-employed, childminders have the right to set their own fees.

information. You could also look in your local telephone directory for nurseries or childcare agencies, or advertise locally for nannies or babysitters.

Registered childminder

A childminder must register annually with the government's regulating bodies. They will be checked by the police, and their references, training, health, and home will be inspected every year to make sure that they provide a safe and suitable environment for children. All childminders in England and Wales are required to have completed a training course, which includes first aid. Rules governing childminders in Ireland and Scotland can be obtained from their professional associations – the Northern Ireland Childminding Association and Scottish Childminding Association. It is good practice for a childminder to agree a contract with you to cover hours, holidays, and fees.

A childminder may look after children of any age – registration regulations only apply to children under the age of eight. A childminder is registered to look after six children under the age of eight, including their own children. Of those six no more than three should be under the age of five, and only one should be under the age of one, although exceptions can be made for twins and multiple births.

DAY NURSERIES AND CRÈCHES	
ADVANTAGES	**DISADVANTAGES**
• A day nursery will be registered and inspected and has purpose-built accommodation.	• Your child may not have continuity of carer; however, most nurseries operate a "key worker" system, where each child is assigned to a particular member of staff.
• The hours that care is available are usually long and nurseries are open all year.	• The hours may not be flexible.
• Your child will be cared for by experienced, qualified carers.	• Nurseries can be expensive.
• Your child will have a structured learning programme and will be among children of his own age.	• Popular nurseries have long waiting lists.

Day nurseries and crèches

Both terms cover the same type of setting, although "crèche" is commonly used to describe employer-provided care or short-stay placements – for example at a shopping centre or gym. Day nurseries normally care for children up to five years of age, either full time or part time, and occasionally nurseries will provide holiday or after-school care for older children. They provide both care and education in purpose-designed or adapted premises, and most follow a government-approved early years curriculum with children grouped together according to age. Nurseries have to be registered with the government regulatory bodies and are inspected by OFSTED every year. The maximum child-to-staff ratio is strictly regulated:

- Children under two – ratio of 3:1. If there are many young babies on the premises, it might be necessary to have a ratio of 2:1.
- Two-year-olds – ratio of 4:1.
- Three- to seven-year-olds – ratio of 8:1.

Nannies

A nanny is someone who cares for your child within your own home. Nannies usually either come to your house each day, or live in your house and you provide them with a private bedroom and food. Sometimes it is possible to share your nanny with another family. For example, the nanny may be able to look after your child on certain days and other people's children on other days, or look after both sets of children together. If the other family's children are to come to your house for their childcare you may need to check your insurance arrangements before this happens.

If there are more than two families nanny-sharing the nanny is regarded as a childminder, and will need to be registered as such. To give all parties security, you should agree a contract with your nanny, and nanny-share partner if necessary, to cover aspects such as hours, salary, and holidays.

CHILDMINDERS

Childminders look after children in their own homes, so your child will experience a safe but relaxed domestic environment, with the possible added benefit of ready-made playmates.

NANNIES	
ADVANTAGES	**DISADVANTAGES**
• Hours can be arranged to suit your needs. • All the children in your family can have the same carer. • A nanny usually has a childcare qualification. • Your existing childcare routines and lifestyle can be followed easily. • Your child remains in his own home. • Nannies may be prepared to babysit in the evenings, especially if they live in.	• Nannies are not currently regulated, so you are responsible for ensuring that any nanny you employ is going to provide safe and appropriate childcare – it is essential that you check all references thoroughly and speak to previous employers. • Nannies need not be trained. • Some nannies are very young and may not have much experience with children. • Tax and National Insurance must be included in the costs of hiring a nanny.

Au pairs, mother's helps, and babysitters

Au pairs, mother's helps, and babysitters can be a real help to busy parents, but most are not suitable for full-time, sole-charge care as they are usually young and inexperienced with children. They are not registered with the government regulatory bodies and will rarely have any childcare qualifications. If you use any of these carers you will need to be on-call if necessary, or arrange for another person you trust to be so.

An au pair is an overseas visitor who comes to learn another language and culture, and helps out in a family home in return for board and pocket money. An au pair lives in your house as part of your family and is entitled to a private

AU PAIRS, MOTHER'S HELPS, AND BABYSITTERS	
ADVANTAGES	**DISADVANTAGES**
• An au pair or mother's help can help with light housework, taking and collecting children from school, or looking after children for short periods after school. • A live-in au pair or mother's help is a "'built-in" babysitter, though you must agree terms and conditions for this beforehand and you shouldn't expect them to babysit for more than two or three nights a week. You may be expected to pay extra for this. • An au pair can be a personal "ambassador" for another country to your child. • They are often young and enthusiastic, and great play companions.	• Au pairs, mother's helps, and babysitters are usually unqualified and won't be registered. • They aren't suitable for full-time, sole-charge childcare. • You may find it hard having someone else living in your home. • It's your responsibility to make sure they know the basics of childcare and first aid, and to have suitable back-up in case of an emergency. • With an au pair there may be a certain level of language or communication difficulties. • You may need to provide some emotional support for a young au pair. • Rates vary widely, so it helps to ask around to find out what is expected.

bedroom. Au pairs are normally expected to work approximately 25–30 hours per week, and must be allowed time off to attend language classes or other study programmes.

A mother's help is like an au pair but from your own culture; someone who lives in your house and helps you look after your children. They normally have English as a native language and can work up to 45 hours per week. A mother's help is entitled to a private bedroom and proper time off. This arrangement works best in families where one parent is at home because mother's helps are rarely qualified or experienced childcarers.

A babysitter is someone who comes to your house occasionally to look after your children while you go out for short periods. For your own piece of mind, they should be over 16 years of age.

Grandparents and other relatives

When your child is cared for by a blood relative, either in their home or yours, care is not registered or inspected in any way. This means that it is your responsibility to make sure that your relative is fit enough to be able to look after your child, has a basic knowledge of the essentials of childcare and first aid, and that the house is safe. Although you are dealing with a family member, you may still want to agree a contract about hours, holidays, or time off. You may also want to negotiate on financial matters, which can be hard to do with family. It may help you agree a fair fee if you consider linking it to the current rate for a childminder in your area.

CARED FOR BY GRANDPARENTS

Your parents may love the opportunity to spend more time with, and care for, your child, but make sure you discuss all the arrangements before they start doing so.

GRANDPARENTS AND OTHER RELATIVES	
ADVANTAGES	**DISADVANTAGES**
• A close family member, especially a grandparent, is likely to love your child almost as much as you do.	• Family may have pre-existing commitments.
• Your child will probably develop a close bond with this relative, which will enrich both their lives.	• They may have different views about issues such as discipline or potty training. The family relationship may make it difficult for you to ask for things to be done your way rather than theirs.
• A family member may live locally.	• If they are looking after a baby or toddler in their home you will probably have to buy an extra set of equipment for them to use.
• They will probably be flexible about the hours they look after your child.	
• They may be able to look after your child if he's sick.	• You may want your child to meet other young children, but relatives may not feel comfortable attending play or toddler groups.
• Your child may be able to have his friends round to play.	• If your employer or college is contributing to your childcare costs, they may insist that you use registered childcare.
• Your child will be cared for in a familiar environment.	• If things don't work out, it could cause long-term family rifts.
• Your child will have continuity of care.	• Educational opportunities may be limited.

Making childcare work

You have a date for returning to work and have carefully chosen childcare that is right for your baby and family, now all you have to do is to make it work. Many women experience mixed emotions at this time. Leaving the seclusion of life at home may feel like a considerable challenge, or it may be a huge relief – for many women it can feel like a bit of both.

INTRODUCING YOUR BABY TO HIS CARER

It is important that you make sure your baby is familiar with his new carer before your first day back at work. This will make the transition easier for all of you.

Planning ahead reduces stress

If you are enjoying life at home and not looking forward to returning to work it can be tempting to put the imminent changes out of your mind. Similarly, you may be finding life with your baby so busy that it is a challenge to find the time and energy to plan ahead more than a day or two. However, preparing in a practical way for your return to work will reduce the chance of last-minute panics and emotional stress.

It is possible that, when you first start planning for your return to work, your baby's sleeping and feeding times will be totally out of step with the pattern you will need to establish when you return to work. In the two or three weeks running up to your return to work you may want to alter your baby's routine to establish a more "work-friendly" pattern, or you may choose to go with the flow and simply wait and see how things work out. It very much depends on your own personality and your baby's temperament. Be aware of how you cope with change and think about how your baby responds to changes in his routine. This will help you to decide which approach will work best. If he dislikes change then gradually and systematically altering sleep and feeding times is a good plan for a smoother transition. If your baby is more unpredictable or easy-going you may not need to be quite so focused.

Getting your baby used to the carer/nursery

Taking time to get your child used to his new carer before your first day back at work is very useful, especially if you have anxieties about your imminent separation. Going from being with each other constantly to spending hours apart will be a big change for both of you and it is best not to have to face this on your first day back at work. Good carers will understand that both you and your baby need time to adjust and settle into the new arrangement. They should be happy to arrange a shortish first visit followed by a longer second one before the usual routine is established. You will of course have to pay for this, and you may feel some reluctance about paying for time away from your baby, especially in the last few precious days before you return to work. However, giving yourself and your baby the chance to feel comfortable before the first day is important.

When you first leave your baby with his new carer you may feel some strong emotions. Some parents feel very sad and anxious while others feel excited and elated. Either reaction is entirely normal but, whatever your reaction, remember you won't feel like this every day. It is likely that you will quickly settle into the new routine and your emotions will settle down too.

Is my baby happy with the new carer?

Most parents worry about this at some point. Some babies react to the change in routine by becoming more unsettled, sleeping less well, and appearing less relaxed. However, over time things should settle down. If you are wondering whether your baby is happy, look out for the body language between him and his carer. Does he look comfortable with her, cuddling in and making eye contact? Even though you may be surprised at your mixed feelings about this, it is important that your baby builds a loving relationship with his carer. Babies need this sort of bond with their carers to thrive and be happy.

Some older babies worry parents by crying bitterly at every parting. This can happen even in babies who, when younger, seemed to manage "goodbyes" quite happily. However, crying on separation is totally normal; he is making a bid to exert some control over the situation and demonstrating his growing ability to predict events. Giving your child the opportunity to make this protest, while remaining outwardly calm yourself, is important. If you crumble in the face of his tears he will assume that there really is something to cry about and will become more fearful. Tempting though it might be, don't avoid the tears by sneaking off without saying "goodbye". This can lead to an increase in your child's anxiety, because if you keep disappearing without warning he will have to keep on the look-out all day for this sort of surprise. The best way to manage this situation is to allow a little time after you arrive for him to settle with the carer and say "hello" to her. When he is relatively settled say goodbye and leave calmly. If the sound of the crying rings in your ears and makes you miserable you can either wait outside until you hear it stop, or you can call your carer a little later to see how things are. Nine times out of ten your baby will have calmed down almost as soon as you have left.

Another way to put your mind at ease is to pay an unexpected call on your carer and child. It can be hugely comforting to be able to observe your baby happily playing before he knows you are there. Don't do this too often though or you run the risk of alienating your carer. Good carers will understand your anxieties and concerns and will do all they can to reassure you. If you do have concerns it is best to discuss them honestly and straightaway rather than letting situations get too entrenched. Remember, if at any time you are unhappy with your child's care you have a right to change carers.

PRACTICAL TIPS FOR MANAGING ON WORKDAY MORNINGS

• Get everything you need for the next day ready the night before, including your baby's clothes, baby's bag, and your own clothes and lunch.

• Get up early enough so that you won't need to run around in a mad panic.

• Get yourself ready before getting your baby ready so that if he takes longer than usual to feed, dress, or change, you are at least ready to make a quick exit afterwards.

• Have something nourishing but quick to eat. A bowl of cereal or even a sandwich made the night before can be enough to keep you going.

• Have contingency plans in case of lateness or illness. For example, what if your baby, the childminder, or you are unwell?

YOUR FIRST DAYS AT WORK

Whether you spend hours tearfully glancing at your baby's photograph or embrace with relief the adult world of work, the first few days back can feel quite odd. If you are breastfeeding it will take your body a while to adjust, and your breasts may feel very full by the end of the day. (For more information about expressing and storing milk see pp.98–9).

Be prepared to feel very different about your work. Office politics may seem far less important now, and you may turn into a much more efficient timekeeper with a new keenness to finish on time and get back to your baby. Enjoy your reunions with him and make the most of your family time.

Learning to learn together

By three months you will be getting to know your baby well. You will already know what he likes and dislikes, and what things soothe or excite him. You are the expert on your baby. Your constantly developing relationship provides him with the security that he needs to be able to deal with, and learn from, the outside world.

If you have shown your baby, through your care, that his world is a secure, happy place he will grow, learn, and develop at a natural pace. Research suggests that babies who have their needs met consistently grow up more confident in their relationships than those who are regularly left to cry. At this age your baby needs to learn how to learn and he does this through "the learning relationship". He learns how to predict what will happen and how people respond to each other. You are setting up the foundations for the social skills your baby will need for the rest of his life. Children who understand the world well are likely to be better communicators and form better relationships with their peers and partners.

From birth until around five years old your baby is learning more rapidly than he will at any other time. Talking to your baby about what is going on around him, or what you can see on television or in a book, helps to establish early patterns of communication. Some parents find this ongoing conversation with their babies instinctive, while others find it takes practice to keep the conversation flowing, and have to concentrate on responding at first. By six months most parents find that they are communicating with their babies freely and easily whenever the babies respond.

Great achievers

As a parent it can be interesting to compare your baby with others of a similar age but, while it is great to see your baby doing things first, comparisons can lead to anxiety if your baby seems to be slower than others. Individual achievement and success is highly valued in our society, and this can even extend to the development of babies. It is natural to want your baby to keep up with his peers, and information about what babies should be doing when can be reassuring, particularly if you have had little previous experience with babies. However, milestones are a marker, not a race. Almost all babies will pass through the same stages on the route to independence, and they will all learn and develop at different rates. Because babies are individuals they will find some skills easier to master than others; your baby's own personality will go a long way to determining whether he is a cautious walker or an early-talking chatterbox. Let him go at his own pace, and provide all the encouragement that you can for his achievements.

Although the chart on pages 184–5 gives approximate ages for each developmental stage, remember these are averages and there will be as many babies getting there "late" as there are getting there "early". Even if your baby reaches the milestones much earlier or later than indicated, he will rarely go on to the next step until he is confident with the one he is at. It will help his confidence if you encourage him, but try not to push him onto the next stage before he is ready, as moving too quickly could frighten him and make him reluctant to try again. Development is more of a "what and how" than a "when", and is largely dependent on his brain developing sufficiently to tell his body what to do, coupled with his personal motivation to do it. Often a reflex action is lost to make way for a deliberate and controlled version of the same movement, so it may seem at times that your baby has lost a skill that he had. For example, the newborn grasp reflex disappears and is replaced later by a conscious action to take or pick up an object. Sometimes, when a baby is concentrating very hard on learning a new skill, some of the ones already mastered may go unused until he has got the hang of the new one, but then he will be able to do both and will be ready to move on to something more challenging.

For some parents, every step their baby takes towards independence feels like they are losing a little bit of babyhood, or makes them feel unsure about coping with the next stage of being a parent. Talking to other parents can help enormously. You may find that most mothers find some aspects of parenting easier than others, so sharing ideas and tips gives you the benefit of other people's experiences. At any gathering where parents are together, it is inevitable that at some point the conversation will turn to whose baby is doing what. For some parents this type of talk can create pressure. If you find yourself in this situation and you don't enjoy it, you are rarely under any obligation to continue meeting with a particular group of parents. You may find that there are other groups where you will feel more relaxed. If you do have to meet up, for example if they are family or you enjoy other aspects of the group, then prepare yourself for these types of comments and perhaps have some answers up your sleeve.

If you are ever concerned about any aspect of your baby's development, seek support. Talking to someone else can help you to decide what the problems are and help you to find an explanation or solution if it is more than the variation in the rates children develop skills. Your health visitor or GP will generally be the first person to talk to, and you don't need to wait for the routine development check-ups. Usually you will be reassured that everything is okay, and be given an explanation as to what is happening with your baby, but occasionally it may mean that your child needs extra help and support. In many cases the earlier you get that support, the more progress you will help your child to make.

THE LEARNING RELATIONSHIP
Babies and children learn best through play and activities that are relaxed and fun, and with people whom they love and trust.

PERSISTING IN GETTING SUPPORT

If you feel that your concerns are not being listened to it can be helpful to remember that, although you may not be a medical expert, you know your child better than anyone else and you have a right to have your concerns listened to and taken seriously. If the first person you talk to does not offer you the support or explanations you need, then speak to somebody else. You will find someone who will help you to deal with your concerns, or tell you why things are at the extreme end of normal.

There are many support organizations that can provide practical help and a listening ear from someone who has been there; they are listed at the back of this book (*see* pp.238–45). The NCT's Special Experiences Register can put you in touch with another parent who has been through the same, or a similar, situation, so you know you're not alone.

What your baby can do when

AT BIRTH

Your baby has grown from a pair of single cells to a miniature person, capable of independent life. When you first meet him he is curled up, his spine curved with his legs tucked in. His movements are jerky and uncoordinated. He is soothed by close contact with your body, by your voice, and by the feel and smell of your skin – especially if he is skin-to-skin with you. His primary needs are for food and comfort, and a replication of the safety of the womb.

He can tell your voice from any others, as he has heard it for several months already, and he turns his eyes towards you when you speak. By 36 hours old he can recognize your face if it is closer than 30cm (1ft). If you move your face close to him, he will follow it with his eyes.

The only way he can communicate is by crying, but you will quickly get the hang of what his cries mean and what to do to help. He will be learning to make burbles of pleasure.

At this stage he loves eye contact and exaggerated expressions. He will begin his first conversations by looking towards your voice and smiling face. He will respond by smiling back as soon as he is able.

AT ONE MONTH

Your baby is beginning to uncurl his spine, but his legs are still bent. He is beginning to hold his head up and may lift it when you place him on his tummy. His neck is still floppy, so he needs constant support.

If you hold your baby under his arms and rest his feet on a firm surface he makes stepping movements. This is a reflex action, part of the natural instinct of a baby to seek out the breast and feed.

Your baby's grasp reflex is very strong; he holds his hand in a fist and holds on tight to anything placed in his palm. At this stage he can't let go.

Your baby sees best at a distance of about 25–30cm (10–12in), but he can see movement across the room. Black-and-white high-contrast images and human faces are most interesting for him at this stage.

When you talk to your baby he tries to mimic your expression, and opens his mouth when you talk.

He is still comforted by being carried or held close to your body.

AT TWO MONTHS

Your baby now spends less and less time curled up. He can support his head when you hold him, and when he lies on his tummy he is able to hold his head up for a few minutes. He is learning to smile, and shows his delight at your face.

When your baby makes noises and you repeat them, he makes them back. Taking turns like this helps to develop early conversation skills.

His hands are open much more of the time now, and his grasp is becoming voluntary.

Your baby enjoys watching his fingers when he moves them close to his face. Colourful rattles are good toys at this stage, as your baby holds onto anything you put in his hand. He enjoys both the movement and the sound.

He enjoys being able to see his world, so a bouncy chair or a pile of cushions to prop him up will buy you a few minutes to do something two-handed. For a baby who wants to be carried for most of the time, a sling helps you to do a few of the things you want to do while still carrying your baby.

AT THREE MONTHS

Your baby is past the newborn stage, he is uncurled with his legs stretched out. He is able now to hold his head up and look around.

Your baby keeps his hands open for most of the time – he can grab things, but can't hold onto them for long.

He will concentrate deeply on watching his hands, and may go cross-eyed with the effort. Once he has connected seeing with doing he will begin to reach out towards interesting things, even if they are well out of range! At this age colourful mobiles and baby gyms, which he can touch and make the pieces move, are fascinating.

He will make squeals and gurgles of pleasure when you speak, and will enjoy playing face-to-face games and singing. He will also start making ma-ma-ma, da-da-da, ba-ba-ba noises, and cooing sounds.

Your baby is now quite sociable, and may protest when he is left alone. He may also start to cry for you when he wakes during the night. This is all part of learning that he is separate from you. Although it may be tiring, especially if you are not getting enough rest during the day, it is normal and not usually a sign that he is hungry. Even so, you may find that a quick feed is the easiest way to get you both back to sleep, and helps you to feel more rested.

AT FOUR MONTHS

Your baby is able now to support himself on his forearms when he is on his tummy. He is able to rock from side to side, and may roll over by accident. He can lift his head and legs at the same time so he looks like a skydiver.

Your baby can put his hands in his mouth, and he will enjoy sucking his fists and watching his fingers.

About now, your baby will have enough coordination to put everything he touches into his mouth. The nerve endings on his lips and tongue are more sensitive than those on his fingers, so he will explore new textures and sensations through his mouth. This is a stage of nerve and brain development that is not to let you know that he is hungry, but rather that he is learning more and more about the world in which he lives.

Your baby will now be learning to judge distance. When he sees something interesting he will see if he can touch it, usually with a fist at this stage. Mobiles with string are better moved away now; he will enjoy toys secured to the cot sides, or held in your hand.

He may now lift his arms to be picked up when he sees or hears you, and will show delight when anyone pays him attention.

AT FIVE MONTHS

Your baby is now able to roll over at will, and can lift his head clear off the floor with his arms outstretched.

Your baby can now grab things with two hands and bring them to his mouth – he probably does this a lot with his feet and socks!

At this stage he can focus well, and can follow a moving object. He will be aware of strange situations, and can show fear and frustration as well as delight.

He will be developing an interest in mirrors, and will enjoy looking at himself in one.

Your baby may now begin to show fear of strangers, but familiar people will be greeted with a beaming smile.

From this age onwards, musical boxes can become a valuable part of any wind-down to bedtime routine that you and your baby may be establishing.

As your baby becomes better and better at handling objects, he will begin to enjoy bath toys that move, pour, and splash.

AT SIX MONTHS

Your baby may be sitting unsupported for a couple of seconds by now. He may enjoy sitting propped up with cushions for safety, and he can twist and reach out for his favourite things, which he can now pick up in one hand.

He will make jumping and bouncing movements when held upright, and he will enjoy bouncing games. He will also begin to explore faces with his hands by patting or pulling hair.

Your baby no longer has to look from an object to his hand and back before he knows where it is in relation to his body; he knows how far to reach, and can control his hand to curl his fingers round his chosen treasure. He enjoys touching things with different textures, and loves things that make a noise when he holds them.

At this stage he will be ready for the introduction of solid food. He can hold his head and spine straight so he can chew and swallow, and can put things in his mouth by himself. Waiting until your baby is ready makes weaning a quicker and easier process for both of you.

The best toys for three to six months

You are undoubtedly your child's best and favourite toy. This is because you move, you make noise, you react, you respond, you are also familiar, and yet always different. Your baby is busy learning about the world and about people. By playing with him you are not only having fun, you are teaching him the skills he will need to take him through life. You are also learning about him: his likes, his dislikes, and his emerging personality.

Conversing with your baby

The more you talk to your child, and the more "conversations" you have, the quicker he will learn to communicate, especially if you look at him when you are talking to him and look and listen when he responds. This stage of communication is known as "turn taking", and is considered to be an essential part of developing language. Babies who don't learn this dialogue often find speech difficult later.

Learning to converse requires sensitivity on the part of parents. It is not so much doing things "to" your baby but doing things "with" him that helps him to learn the social skills we take for granted. At this age he will enjoy singing and repetitive games such as peep-o, and, even though he can't join in yet, he will be listening and learning, and turn taking will become spontaneous. Your baby's responses will tell you if you are responding to him in a way that he enjoys, and he will be able to tell you if he has had enough and is tired more clearly than he could when he was younger.

Learning a new position

It is recommended that your baby spends some of his waking time on his front. Even though you should make sure that your baby always sleeps on his back, it is not necessary for him to spend all his waking time on his back too. By encouraging your baby to lie on his tummy you will be giving him a fresh view of his world and therefore will be increasing his learning opportunities. You are also encouraging him to make early moves towards crawling, as babies are more inclined to reach and wriggle forwards to get a toy from this position. Putting your baby on his front also increases his opportunity for exercising different muscles and developing new skills, which will help his posture later on.

If your baby doesn't like lying this way at first then it may help to do it for short bursts of no more than a minute or two until he gets used to it. Babies who are

regularly placed on their fronts from birth seem to show less resistance to seeing the world this way than those who spent their first months lying on their backs only.

Things for him to look at

Books are always great to share – even before your baby can understand the words he will enjoy the shared experience. Your baby enjoys listening to your voice whatever you read to him. The best books are those with simple colourful pictures that you can look at together and you talk about. Thick board books have pages that are easy to turn and don't tear as easily as paper ones. Cloth and plastic books are tougher, and can withstand chewing, so they are ideal for a baby who wants to hold and play with the book himself. This is a great age to introduce the idea of a bedtime story. Even though books are important at any time of the day, there is something very intimate about sharing a favourite book as part of a comforting bedtime routine.

Colourful mobiles give a baby something interesting to look at and can buy you a few extra minutes in the morning, or the chance to have a sit down and a drink. They don't have to be expensive – your baby will not know the difference between a few carefully chosen objects or pictures stuck on string and pinned to the ceiling and an expensive mobile or baby gym. If mobiles are easily portable,

PLAYING ALONE

Your baby will enjoy playing with a range of toys by this

age, and so will tolerate playing alone for short periods.

This will free you up to do other things.

you can use them wherever you and your baby are at the time. By the time your baby can reach out and grab them he will be wanting to play with toys, so at that point anything reachable on strings is unsafe; it is time to move on to toys on the side of the cot, or attached to a baby gym.

Pictures of faces, both familiar and unfamiliar, are interesting, so you might want to stick up photographs for your baby to look at. He will also be fascinated by his image in a mirror. If it is an unbreakable toy mirror he will have lots of fun touching and moving it about too.

Your baby will love anything that rattles or moves when he bashes or shakes it. As well as being fun, these toys are teaching your baby hand–eye coordination and cause and effect. Washable toys are a good idea, because your baby will want to test everything by putting it into his mouth. It is not necessary to sterilize toys at this age, although you may like to if the toys are secondhand or have been played with among different children.

Learning to amuse himself

Even though you are still your baby's favourite toy, it is probably not practical to spend all day carrying and playing with him. When you need to do something else, a bouncy chair or a firm pile of cushions to prop him up against is very useful. If your baby can watch you, and you are able to talk to him while you get on with other things, he will be able to tolerate sitting alone for much longer, and you may find that you are able to have a bath or cook a meal while your baby enjoys being part of what is going on. Keep communicating, telling him what you are doing and why; even though he can't yet understand the words he will know from the way you are speaking that you are interested in doing things together and in including him.

Your baby will also be happy and entertained by a huge variety of household items; a saucepan and a wooden spoon make a great noise, and, when you are fed up with the banging, he can spend ages filling up a pot with pasta, yoghurt pots, napkin rings, or cookie cutters. Be sure to check that your baby can't hurt himself or choke, and don't leave him unattended while he plays with such items.

Since your baby will only play with some toys for a month or two, you may not want to buy expensive items. You may have a toy library in your local area, or you can see if anyone will let you borrow toys for the short period your baby will want to play with them. NCT nearly new sales are also a source of bargain toys and equipment, especially as at this age toys are usually outgrown before they start to look well used.

Premature babies

When your baby is born prematurely, your attention will be focused on his development day by day. Milestones, such as breathing unaided, learning to suck, and moving out of an incubator, will be extremely important. Perhaps it will be days or weeks before your baby can be discharged. It may even be months. But as your baby becomes stronger and stronger the question you will really want answered is, "When can I take him home?".

Often babies are transferred from a regional to a local neonatal unit as they get stronger. This is because regional units have high-dependency and intensive-care cots, whereas local units might just have a special care baby unit for babies needing lower-level care. This move is tremendously exciting, as your baby is literally closer to home. Parents are not allowed to travel with their baby during the transfer by ambulance. For the first 24 hours your baby will be in isolation in the new neonatal unit to prevent any transfer of infection. The move may be your first experience of change with your baby, and you will need to give yourself time to adjust to new staff and practices.

Taking your baby home

The idea of taking your baby home can bring a sense of joy and high expectation. However the natural anxieties of parenthood, wondering whether you will be able to cope or if he will be alright, can be magnified for the parents of babies who have already struggled in life. Do remember, though, that your baby is only going home because the staff believe he is well enough, and that you will be capable of looking after him from this point onwards. Nevertheless, leaving the hospital environment with your baby is a big step. You may need time to adapt to not having the structure and medical support and advice provided by the unit, even though you will have become more involved in your baby's care. Perhaps you have never had the chance to shop for your baby and need to buy some essentials.

You should plan carefully for your baby's transfer home. The staff will help to ensure that you are able to provide all the care he needs, which may include giving you basic resuscitation training and guidance on safe sleeping, but you should also double check that you know how to give your baby medication and use any specialist equipment. Some units have facilities where you can "room in" overnight. This means you can practise caring for your baby independently while still being near the staff. The transition from hospital to home may take your baby time to

WEIGHT IS ONLY A GUIDE

You will probably weigh your baby regularly for some time, but try not to become fixated by growth charts. Your baby's prematurity will be taken into account when looking at his development. For example, if he was born four months ago and was three months early then his "corrected age" is one month. This does not mean that he will be at exactly the same stage of development as babies of the same "corrected age", it is simply a guide.

adapt to. After all, everything is new and different. Your baby will probably want to be held a lot because you and your partner are familiar and therefore reassuring. For more information see the BLISS leaflet, *Going Home: your questions answered.*

Premature babies tend to make an enormous amount of noise when they are sleeping (despite their size!). Between feeding and your need to respond to every wheeze and gurgle, you may find you do not get much rest. If your baby will take a bottle (of expressed milk or formula) then you may want to let your partner give some feeds where appropriate, not least because it is a great way for them to bond with the baby.

No doubt family and friends will want to visit you. However, if your baby is still under 37 weeks, it's a good idea to keep his environment quiet and stable, so do limit visitors and make sure he isn't passed around from person to person, as it may still be over-stimulating for him. Remember, too, that this is your time to adjust, so try not to make yourself too busy looking after visitors. Keep your own needs in mind. Make sure you are comfortable with who is visiting – for example you may want to ask someone who has a cold, or shares a home with someone who is poorly, to come when the baby is older. Dealing with questions from all and sundry about your baby is a challenge you would probably rather not have to face either. You may find it helps to have a stock answer, like, "He had a difficult start, but he's fine now," combined with a determined change of subject. However, if you find a sympathetic ear, do talk over your experiences if you feel it would help.

Although you may have longed to have your baby home, it can still be a tough time. With a baby that may have ongoing problems and may be a very demanding feeder, you are likely to be stretched simply coping with day-to-day activities. Just taking your baby out may be stressful to begin with, although it is perfectly safe to do so. Waiting a few days until your baby is used to his new surroundings is a good idea though. As your baby may be more at risk of picking up infections it is best to avoid places where there are large groups of young children, crowded public places, and large air-conditioned buildings, such as shopping malls.

The earlier your baby was born, the more likely it is that he will be considerably smaller than other babies of the same age. Not only this, but your own experiences of childbirth are likely to be very different from those of the other parents you meet, unless you have had previous full-term deliveries. If you did meet parents antenatally, then seeing those people again may be a good way to establish a friendship circle. However, you may find that this emphasises how different your baby is, especially if he was very premature and/or very small for his age, so do what is right for you.

There is so much to deal with as the parent of a premature baby that it can be hard to see a way through. Knowing you are not alone with your experiences is important. Learning to live with what you have been through may take a long time. Your baby's first birthday may prove particularly poignant; no doubt you will celebrate and remember what the year has brought you.

GETTING SUPPORT

As parents of a premature baby you and your partner may have a lot of ups and downs after the experience. Extremely difficult experiences of delivery can result in postnatal depression, which needs to be supported (*see* p.72). Some parents find they begin to struggle with their thoughts and feelings many months after their baby comes home. This can be really hard, as it may coincide with a time that other parents perceive as being much more settled and secure. It may be hard to feel that anyone else can understand what you and your baby have been through. Some parents talk of feeling isolated, because they find it difficult to find the energy to go out, or they feel so different from their peers.

The neonatal unit will encourage you to call them if you have any concerns once your baby is discharged. Some areas have neonatal community nurses who will visit you at home for the first four to six weeks of your baby's care, or longer if your baby is going home on oxygen support. Your health visitor will have been notified of your baby's discharge and will get in touch. Health visitors are responsible for the wellbeing of baby and parents, and are an important source of support. They will visit you in your home and later see you at clinic when you weigh your baby. However, some may not have had much experience dealing with prematurity. If you have any concerns, speak to your GP or get in touch with the neonatal unit that looked after your baby. Do not be afraid to ask to see someone new or call the BLISS helpline on 0500 618140.

Talking to other parents who have had a premature baby is a great idea. Local NCTs hold a Special Experiences Register, or visit www.nct-preterm@yahoogroups.com. Speak to your local hospital and see if there is a support group you can join, or get in touch with BLISS. Sharing your feelings with another person who has been through something similar can make a big difference.

Teething

The average age for the appearance of the first tooth is about six months but, as with everything baby-related, there is a wide range of normal development. Some babies are born with their first teeth already visible; others do not have any teeth until well into their second year.

The eruption of a tooth usually begins with grumpiness, a red cheek, and lots of dribbling – all of which disappear as soon as the tooth breaks the surface of the gum. If the tooth is about to appear, you will be able to see a reddish-purple patch on the gum, sometimes with a white centre. Many parents report that teething symptoms come and go for a while before the teeth finally emerge. This may be because the teeth are moving in the gums, even though you can't yet see them.

Some babies seem to get teeth without any warning at all, while others will be very miserable and may even get mild diarrhoea or nappy rash. You know your baby well by now, and you will be aware if he is finding teething painful, or if something else is making him ill and fretful. If you are concerned about your baby's health, seek medical assistance. You can try soothing him in his favourite way, or distracting him from the pain with a familiar game or song. Your baby may like to bite on hard or cold objects to help relieve the irritation, so make sure that he has something safe to chew. There are various preparations available over the counter to relieve the symptoms of teething; local anaesthetic gel, painkilling syrups, and homeopathic remedies are the most common. These usually need to be used regularly, according to the directions on the packaging, to be most effective. If you want further advice on their suitability for your baby you should talk to your GP or health visitor, your pharmacist, or other registered practitioner.

Looking after teeth

Sugar in our food is turned to acid by the bacteria in our mouths. This acid eats away at the hard enamel covering on our teeth, causing decay. If your baby has a lot of sweet foods and sugary drinks, his mouth will contain more acid and he will be at greater risk from tooth decay. Research by dentists has shown that if sugary drinks are given in a bottle then the risk is greatly increased, as the teat of the bottle bathes the teeth in sugar and acids that dramatically increase the chances of decay. Dentists now recommend that bottle-fed babies move onto drinking from a cup as early as possible, and certainly as soon as they are being weaned. It is also recommended that juice is not given in a bottle because even

GROWING TEETH

Your baby's teeth started developing in his gums when you were about 20 weeks pregnant, and they will have been fully developed within his gums for a while before they appear. His first teeth will gradually appear in pairs until, by the age of two and a half, he will have a full set of twenty milk teeth. By around the age of five or six, his jaw will have grown and he will have gaps around these first teeth. He will begin to lose his milk teeth in the same order they came, and these will be replaced by permanent adult teeth.

low-sugar juice contains fruit acids. Breastfed babies take milk in a different way as the nipple goes to the back of the mouth and doesn't really drip if the baby is not actively feeding so it is fine to continue giving your baby breastfeeds. However, if you are giving other drinks they should be from a cup.

KEEP THEM CLEAN

Although he will lose them, your baby's milk teeth are important and tooth decay is painful, so it makes sense to care for them properly. From the moment your baby's first teeth appear you should clean them regularly. It is recommended that you clean teeth before bedtime and at another convenient point during the day. At first you only need to wipe your baby's teeth with a clean, damp facecloth. Gradually you should move to a soft-bristled child's toothbrush and then add a pea-sized blob of toothpaste, so that by the time your child has a full set of teeth you are brushing them well. Brushing your baby's teeth away from the gum line and brushing the biting surfaces thoroughly will ensure that the teeth are clean and you don't damage his gums. There are many toothpastes on the market, but if your child does not like toothpaste, or eats it, then just brush with water at first. Be aware that some children's toothpastes also contain sugar, colourings, or flavourings.

Making teeth cleaning into a game helps most children see it as a fun activity rather than an unpleasant chore. Singing songs, counting teeth as you brush them, and spitting out the toothpaste can all help make teeth cleaning appealing.

VISITING THE DENTIST

Your baby will need to be registered with a dentist and should visit regularly from the time he has his full set of milk teeth. It can help your child to be relaxed about the dentist if you take him to visit when you go, and for the dentist to look in his mouth while your baby sits on your lap. If you are nervous about going to the dentist yourself, and you worry that you may pass that fear on to your child, it may help if someone who is happier at the dentist's takes your child on his first visits.

Weaning and breastfeeding

It is fine to start weaning your baby before he gets his teeth because his hard bony gums will be able to bite and chew well enough for soft finger foods. Also, it is not necessary to begin weaning just because your baby is getting teeth, as there are other signs that are better indicators of your baby's readiness for solid foods. Weaning, and how to tell if your baby is ready, is discussed on pages 206–7.

The arrival of a tooth need not signal the end of breastfeeding. Because of the way your breastfeeding baby covers his lower gum with his tongue when he feeds, his new teeth will not damage your nipples while he is feeding. If your baby does bite, then a firm "no" and the swift removal of the breast usually gets across the message that mummy does not like to be bitten.

ENCOURAGING TEETH CLEANING

Children learn best by copying, so if your baby watches you clean your teeth he will probably want to have a go, and then you can help him to finish off.

see also

weaning: when to start   206–7

Immunizations

During the first few weeks of your baby's life you will be asked to make some major choices for your child. One of the most concerning issues for many parents is immunization against serious diseases such as meningitis, measles, and diptheria.

The decision to immunize your child is influenced by your views on the risks posed by these diseases compared with the possible risks associated with the vaccines themselves. Some people regard childhood diseases as mild illnesses that children will not be harmed by, but all of the diseases for which we have vaccines can be very serious and lead to dangerous complications in a proportion of children. Many parents find decisions about immunizations a huge responsibility, and media scares can make you feel as though you are deliberately taking a risk with your child's health. Remember that scare stories make headlines. And don't forget that information on the Internet is very variable in its quality. It is important that you feel comfortable with the decisions that you make, and that you have plenty of time to discuss your thoughts and feelings. If you have any questions or concerns you can leave making the decision about vaccination until you feel that you have enough information to make the choice that is right for you and your family.

How immunizations work

If you catch an infection, antibodies are produced that fight the infection. If you are exposed to the same infection again a rapid response is triggered, which usually prevents you getting the illness. Immunization uses this mechanism to stop future infections. It stimulates your body to produce antibodies, so your immune system is ready to fight off an infection without you ever having caught the illness. This is called "active immunity". Immunizations are given in the form of vaccines, usually injected into the body or swallowed – this is also known as inoculation. Vaccines will either contain fragments of the disease-causing organism or contain the whole organism that has been killed or weakened.

For most dangerous diseases vaccination, combined with improvements in hygiene and nutrition, contributes to the safety of your child and makes the disease less likely to spread and cause an epidemic. When a group of people are immunized against an infectious disease, making it more difficult for the disease to find an unprotected person to infect, it is called "herd immunity". For a highly infectious virus, such as measles, it is estimated that about 95 percent of people need to be immunized to give herd immunity and stop the spread of the disease. Herd

CHOOSING TO IMMUNIZE YOUR BABY

In recent years there has been much public concern about the relative risks and benefits of immunization. If you are anxious about immunization, discuss the issue with health practitioners that you trust, to help you to make an informed decision.

immunity also helps to protect people who are very vulnerable to disease, such as those with damaged or weak immune systems and those unable to have vaccines.

Vaccination has completely eradicated smallpox, and polio has almost disappeared from most of the world, so eventually no one will need to be vaccinated against them again. However, some diseases will never disappear – tetanus, for example, can't be eradicated because the spores are present in soil.

The vast majority of UK parents choose vaccination. In 2000, nearly 95 percent of two-year-olds were fully immunized against diphtheria, tetanus, whooping cough, hib (a type of meningitis), and polio. In 1995 nearly 90 percent had the MMR vaccine, although by 2003 this had dropped to 80 percent (NHS data).

Protection against illness can also be given by "passive immunity"; this happens when your body is given antibodies rather than producing them itself. Your new-born baby has some passive immunity to infections from antibodies passed to him via your placenta and breastmilk. This obviously depends on what immunity you already have and will not give life-long immunity. Some diseases can be prevented by this kind of immunity through vaccines given as an immunoglobulin injection. The most common of these is the tetanus antitoxin injection, which is given if you have an injury that puts you at risk of a tetanus infection. Children are offered booster vaccinations to make sure that babies who were not fully immunized by the first vaccination are protected. The ages that are suggested for these are recommendations, and the gap between vaccines is a minimum. If you delay a vaccination in a course you may not necessarily have to start the course again.

Premature babies

It is thought that babies who are born early have less mature immune systems and have had fewer antibodies passed on to them from their mothers. Your neonatal team or your local support group will be able to help you find enough information to make decisions for your child. Generally, premature babies are given their vaccines at the same age after birth as other babies (i.e. from eight weeks old), unless they are too ill to receive them.

Making the decision

You have the right to decide what vaccinations your child has and when. In the UK vaccinations are not compulsory; however, your GP and healthcare team will recommend them for almost all children. You can discuss the issues around vaccination with your healthcare team, or with any alternative practitioners you choose. Your GP or health visitor will also be able to advise you if you think that there is a reason, such as an acute illness, which may make vaccination inadvisable. If you want to know more about the content or origin of vaccinations, perhaps because of dietary or religious beliefs, your GP, pharmacist, or health visitor should be able to find the information for you to be able to make your own informed decision.

THE GOVERNMENT-RECOMMENDED NATIONAL SCHEDULE

THE VACCINE AND DISEASE	HOW THE VACCINATION IS GIVEN	THE RECOMMENDED AGE
MenC Meningitis	Single injection	8, 12, and 16 weeks
5 in 1 Diptheria, whooping cough (acellular), tetanus, polio, and hib (a type of meningitis)	Single injection, does not use mercury-based preservatives	8, 12, and 16 weeks
MMR Measles, mumps, and rubella	Single injection	Around 13 months and 3–5 years (pre-school)
TDaPIPV Diptheria, tetanus, polio, and acellular pertussis	Single injection	3–5 years (pre-school)
BCG Tuberculosis	Skin test Injection if skin test shows no immunity	10–14 years (sometimes given shortly after birth)
TdIPV Tetanus, polio, and low-dose diphtheria	Single injection	13–18 years

ESTIMATING RISK

When considering immunization it can help to think about how you view the risk of complications if your child catches a disease, in relation to the risk of the vaccination itself. Vaccination is not a definite guarantee of immunity, but it greatly reduces the risk and usually makes the disease much less severe if it does occur. The risk of your unimmunized child catching a disease will depend on the herd immunity in your area.

7 SIX TO NINE MONTHS – YOUR ACTIVE BABY

- Living with your older, active baby

- How your older baby is changing

- Weaning: when to start

- Weaning: what to start with

- Your baby is growing – and moving

- Learning to communicate verbally

- Having fun with your baby

- Your special needs baby

- Safety first, last, and always

Living with your older, active baby

In the six months since your baby was born you will have met many challenges. In the second half of the first year life will settle down to a more predictable pattern, compared to the chaos of the early weeks. You will probably feel more confident in your ability to anticipate and meet your baby's needs and have a clear idea of what your baby likes and dislikes. This clearer understanding of your baby's individuality and personality will help you to feel more confident as a parent, but the next few months will still provide many new challenges. Your baby will continue to grow, change, and develop, and you will need to keep adapting too.

Six months after your baby's birth, your identity as a parent will have become more deeply embedded. In the early weeks there may have been a feeling of unreality about your new role, as the changes in identity were almost too big to grasp. Feelings of overwhelming responsibility, coupled with your lack of confidence, may have made you feel that you weren't properly "in charge" but were only really "borrowing" this baby and would be asked to give her back by those more qualified! However six months down the line, you are clearly much more qualified and you are definitely in charge.

However, this newfound confidence may not be the whole story. When faced with any new challenge, you may have a sudden loss of conviction and worry about whether you are doing the "right" thing. Some parents are much more prone to this anxiety than others. If you have a baby who has special needs, or who is simply much more sensitive, active, or awkward than others, you may find that you need to do things differently with her, and you may receive less support for your choices than other parents. It takes some confidence and strength to swim against the tide; however, it is important that you do what feels right for you, your baby, and your family, rather than doing something just because others recommend it. Your baby needs you to be genuine and honest in your approach to her, and this is difficult if you are simply following the instructions of someone else. Remember that you know your baby better than anyone else and you have known her long enough to know how she will probably react to any changes you make. Other people's ideas and experiences can be useful, and tips and hints may help you to try new approaches, but if something doesn't feel right to you put it aside for the time being; you don't have to follow every piece of advice you are given.

YOUR INQUISITIVE BABY

As your baby gets older there is more opportunity for her to play. It's her way of learning about the world around her.

Finding your "new normal"

Some parents who have coped well with the early dramas and uncertainties of caring for a young baby may find these later months of babyhood more challenging than they had expected. You may have thought that you would be "back to normal" by now, and yet you still feel quite unlike your old self.

Mothers may feel especially sensitive about their body image at this time. Pregnancy and birth may have changed your body more than you anticipated. You may still be carrying extra weight, and although your stretch marks and the linea negra (line of pigmentation) on your tummy may have faded, the skin on your stomach may still be loose and baggy. In the early weeks you may have been far too busy and preoccupied with your baby to care very much, but now your attention might turn to yourself more and you could feel sad about the changes to your body. Our culture puts a high value on youthfulness, and fashion icons tend to be thin, narrow-hipped, with smooth tight skin; your post-baby body is likely to be none of these things.

Getting into your pre-pregnancy clothes may become a big issue and part of a symbolic attempt to get back to being the old you. If you find that your body shape has changed a good deal you may be disappointed to find that favourite items still don't fit. If you have the opportunity, it is a good idea to look for clothes that flatter your new shape. Find ways to accentuate the parts of your body that you like. Having at least one good outfit that makes you feel less "mumsy" can be a huge boost.

Adult company

As you "come up for air" after the demands of the early weeks you are more likely than ever to feel the need for some adult company. Your intense concentration on your baby will be diffusing a little and you will find it easier, and more necessary, to concentrate on "non-baby" activities. Many women speak of feeling the need for more mental stimulation at this time. Some feel more restless and bored than before, and the constraints of motherhood may feel very acute for a while. This may be especially true if you have not returned to work. While a number of new mothers enjoy the intensity and exclusivity of life at home with a very young baby, by the time she is six months old, awake more often, and demanding plenty of attention and entertainment, staying at home for a whole day with just the two of you can be quite a challenge. Babies can be great company, they are responsive and often funny, but they don't ask you how you are and they also don't share your interests (yet!). Adults differ in the degree to which they enjoy the company of babies, but it is a rare adult who can happily spend all day without the company of adults. If you find that you are frequently spending the day alone with your baby it would be a good idea to look into how you might get out more. Most parents find that just a couple of hours out of the house each day makes a huge difference to how they feel. The more stressed you are by the demands of parenthood the more crucial this time out is, and it should preferably be in the company of a person or group of people whom you find supportive, positive, and fun. Having coffee with a friend may feel like a luxury but it is actually a necessity for your mental wellbeing.

Parents who have adult company at work may also feel isolated, but in a different way. Some parents feel that their colleagues don't take their new role as a parent into account and that their change in outlook and perspective is out of kilter with people at work with whom they previously had much in common. Parents in this situation may find themselves drawn to a new set of colleagues who also have children and so understand the impact of becoming a parent and are happy to hear about baby issues. If your time outside work is simply a round of household chores, and is spent exclusively in the company of your baby, you may need to plan activities that are rewarding to you as an adult and parent.

Balancing everyone's needs

Whether you are working full or part time, or are a full-time mother, you will not escape the parental dilemma of how to meet your baby's needs while still finding the space to meet your own. Every parent finds her or his own balancing point, and this will change frequently over the early years of parenthood. Our society gives parents strong messages about what they "should" do for their children, whether it is to respond selflessly to their every need or to teach them independence from infancy. Rather than feeling guilty about the things that you are or are not doing, it may be helpful to remember that the most important thing for any baby is the relationship it has with its parents. Activities and arrangements that you feel damage this relationship should be avoided, while those that enhance the relationship should be sought. You know best what makes your baby happy, and you also know best what you and your family need to get along and be happy together.

A BALANCING ACT

All parents need to find their own way of fulfilling both their needs and their baby's. The most important thing for your baby is to know she is secure in her relationship with you.

How your older baby is changing

In the early weeks and months your baby grew faster than she will at any other time in her life. In this new phase she will be learning faster than ever. Her appetite for life will be voracious. Older babies like to be entertained; they like company and they like to practise new skills. This is an exciting time, as you see your baby changing before your eyes and her individual personality becomes more obvious.

"There are good bits and trying bits about each stage of development. I try to focus on the good bits to get me through the trying bits."

Help me! Help me!

As your baby develops new skills such as sitting, crawling, and walking she will want to practise them, over and over again, and she will probably need you to help her. You may spend your days repeatedly "rescuing" your baby, who has managed to stand up holding on to the furniture, and then can't sit down. Later you may be required to hold her hands while she practises walking – for what may seem like endless hours. While these periods don't last long they can be wearing on your patience (and hard on your back). How patiently you can accommodate this will depend on your personality and situation. Parents who have thoroughly enjoyed the snuggling, quiet "conversation" phase of an immobile baby may find that they enjoy this period in their baby's lives less than they thought they would. Others take delight in actually being able to "do something" in terms of play and games with their baby. For example, this can be a time when playful, enthusiastic fathers really come into their own.

Enjoying each others' company

As your baby spends more time awake and becomes increasingly aware of the outside world, you can begin to introduce her to activities that you like. If you love to walk in the country get a backpack and take her along. If you like to listen to music, listen with her. Many parents believe that they should always plan baby-focused activities and embark on a variety of "clap and sing" groups and baby swimming entertainments to fill their leisure time. If this suits you and you enjoy it then carry on. These groups are a great way to meet other parents and your baby will probably enjoy every minute. However, your baby will enjoy most activities if it is clear that you are enjoying them too. Although she is keen to acquire skills she is also very sensitive to your emotions, and baby swimming, if you don't enjoy it yourself, will only stress her. If you would sooner spend some time gardening, think of how you can garden with your baby.

If the activities that you enjoy cannot be adapted for a young baby to join in with then you will have to make other arrangements for the time being. While the basic principle of passing on your passions and interests remains, do look out for signs that your baby is not enjoying herself. Most babies are happy to watch you for a while but will probably get bored with this sooner than you will.

Space invaders

While newborn and young babies may take up a lot of space – in terms of equipment such as prams, changing mats, and cots – you will probably find that that your older baby takes up even more space. Toys, baby nests, mats, and later trolleys and sit-on toys will gradually invade your home, and you will have to get used to a pile of untidy-looking wooden, furry, or plastic toys even if this was not how you envisaged your home looking.

Once your baby can move around, you may also find her rearranging your possessions – pulling books off shelves and emptying cupboards. It is not difficult to baby-proof your house (*see* pp.222–3), but it is more difficult to keep control of the greasy hand marks and general mess. Babies of this age dribble a great deal, have sticky hands, and put things in their mouths. Some parents find this messy stage stressful, and wonder how they will keep up the levels of cleanliness and sterility that were important when the baby was young. It may seem strange to be sterilizing a bottle while your baby is crawling about on the floor and putting every available item into her mouth. Current research has shown that a reasonable level of everyday dirt does a baby no harm, and may even strengthen her immune system and protect against atopic diseases, such as asthma, eczema, and hayfever.[⊙] However, it is important to protect your children against infection from harmful bacteria, which can cause food poisoning and other infections, so bottles of formula milk should be sterilized for the first year. Other feeding equipment should also be cleaned thoroughly in hot, soapy water.

Clinginess and fear of "strangers"

Some time during the second half of your baby's first year you may notice that she becomes wary or anxious in the company of strangers. These "strangers" may even be grandparents, or friends and family who you don't see every day. This can be disappointing for people who were previously welcomed by your baby with loving smiles. This anxiety tends to be a passing phase and becomes less of a problem when the child gets older, has a greater memory for relatives and friends, and can overcome initial shyness during visits. Family and friends who can resist the urge to "force the pace" by approaching and touching the baby too fast will usually be rewarded with a cuddle and kiss later on in the visit.

This fear of strangers tends to happen alongside a new clinginess towards the parents, especially the mother. Some babies are particularly intense in their need to be close to mummy at all times, and may cry whenever she leaves the room. While this can be extremely wearing for the "chosen" parent, it is in fact a sign that your baby has made a good, loving attachment to you. Learning to love with enthusiasm and affection starts at home and is the basis for loving relationships later in your child's life.

Your baby's personality

Your baby's temperament and personality will become extremely obvious during this phase, so much so that when she is ill or very tired you will be able to tell that she is "not herself today". Parenting an active, adventurous child will be very different from looking after one who is sensitive and cautious. While your friend's child may be crawling around the house getting into messes and needing constant supervision to avoid an accident, your child may be happy to sit on a blanket looking at toys but may be unable to be left alone – crying fiercely whenever you leave the room. At this stage, as with the others before, it is important to know your own baby and to try not to compare her too critically with others. While it may be hard to cope with a baby who seems very different from those of your friends and family, do try to appreciate and support your child's emerging individuality. She needs you to be her number one fan and to be proud of her – whoever she is.

"I found that my daughter went through clingy phases every so often. Sometimes it was because she was feeling unwell, and sometimes because she was teething, but sometimes there seemed to be no reason to it. I tried to reassure her while remaining calm."

AN EMERGING PERSONALITY

At this stage your baby's individual personality and temperament will become much more obvious. Learn from, and embrace, this new knowledge of who your baby is.

"When Niamh started to walk I had mixed emotions. Pride that she had reached such a milestone and also a sadness that my baby was growing up so quickly."

see also

Weaning: when to start

In the UK, the guidelines on when to start weaning are based on current research that shows that babies benefit from six months of exclusive breastfeeding, which means breastfeeding without giving your baby any other foods or fluids.⊙

"I knew my little boy was ready for weaning when he was only happy sitting on my lap at mealtimes and used to watch every spoonful go overhead into my mouth as if he was watching aeroplanes."

This does not mean that your baby will wake up on the day of her six-month "birthday" desperate for solid food. In reality, some babies may show signs a little before that day, and some may be ready later. A "baby-led" approach to weaning sees moving to eating solid foods as a normal, natural stage of development, just like sitting up, crawling, walking, and talking. Some babies are cautious about the new tastes and textures of foods; others can't wait to begin trying whatever they can get their hands on. Supporting your baby, and following her lead, means there's no pressure to go at any pace other than hers.

At around six months most babies show they are ready for something as well as milk. This is about the right age for most babies to start eating solid food because:
• Most babies can sit up and hold their heads up, so they are less likely to choke on solid foods.⊙
• Babies can move food from the front of their mouths to the back.

TRYING SOLID FOODS

After approximately six months babies are ready to start on solids. Most are curious about the new tastes and textures, and like to explore by putting things into their mouths.

• At about this age they are starting to learn about hand–eye coordination, and can bring food to their mouths reasonably accurately.

• Babies begin to need a small amount of extra iron in the second half of the first year, which can come from a wide range of solid foods.

• Babies become curious about the texture and taste of new things at about this age, and like exploring things by putting them in their mouths.

• Babies are sociable and enjoy sharing experiences with the people they love, which makes it natural to let your baby join in with the food you are eating.

• Some babies start to have teeth from this age, which helps chewing.

Research shows that babies grow perfectly well and healthily if solids are introduced at around six months.[⊙] Three and four months have, at different times, been suggested as the lower end of the "right age" for weaning in the UK, but we now know that if babies are given just breastmilk for the first six months they are less likely to develop gastroenteritis or be prone to eczema. Starting your baby on solids at around six months is consistent with the World Health Organization's recommendation, and with those in many other countries too. However, you might still hear different advice. Babies used to be offered solids rather earlier. Parents and friends may be surprised that babies are, in general, better off with just milk for what seems to them a long time.

If you are bottle feeding, or mixed feeding, the research base is not so robust. Although the developmental reasons to continue on milk are the same, for instance waiting until your baby can sit up and move food from the front of her mouth to the back, there is no clear evidence that leaving solids to six months in formula-fed or mixed-fed babies is beneficial (in the way it is with breastfed babies). However, babies don't miss out on anything if they don't have solids until that age, and there is no advantage in giving solids earlier; it just creates more work for you. Babies' mouths, digestive systems, and kidneys are not ready for solid foods before 17 weeks at the earliest.

Another area where things may not be so clear is with babies whose growth is giving serious concern, or who were born pre-term. Speak to your health visitor, a dietician, or a paediatrician who understands nutrition when deciding on the right age for such a baby. However, generally speaking, if your baby is growing well on milk alone, whatever her history, you don't need to introduce her to other foods until she is about six months old.

If you are told that your baby needs more calories and she is still not aged six months, then introducing solids may not be the right answer. There are few first foods that you can give a baby that contain as much energy as milk. If you are worried about weight gain then offer more breastfeeds or milk feeds. Solids at an early age could actually reduce the overall calorie intake, as the evidence shows that they tend to replace breastfeeds.[⊙] It's not clear the same applies to formula feeding, so take your health visitor's advice on this.

EXPELLING MYTHS AND MISCONCEPTIONS ABOUT WHEN TO INTRODUCE SOLID FOOD

• Waking up at night is not a sign that your baby needs solids sooner than six months. The research shows that babies given solids earlier are no more likely to sleep through the night than babies who remain on milk only.[⊙]

• There is no evidence that milk feeding to six months will influence babies' acceptance of foods, speech development, or ability to chew. In fact it can make it easier as they are offered foods at a time when they are ready from a physical point of view.

• At six months babies don't need to start with spoonfuls of purees and then work up to lumps. Babies who lead their own weaning seem to prefer to start by picking up a lump of food and trying it themselves. They don't need a lot of sloppy food and can do much of the work themselves (such as picking it up and chewing it).[⊙]

Weaning: what to start with

If you have no special concerns about potential allergies or food intolerance, your baby can have most foods from the age of around six months. There are only a few "rules" to follow, which are detailed below.

• Serve your baby's food in a way that makes it easy for her to eat it. Small, bitesize chunks are not easily managed at first – your baby needs food she can hold in her fist and bring up to her mouth. Picking up smaller bits with finger and thumb will come later as her fine motor skills develop. Bread sticks, batons of fruit or vegetables, and strips of meat are easier shapes for her at this stage. (Babies that are too young to pick up foods themselves do need purees and this can be very time-consuming and messy for parents, especially as they often spit out as much as they eat.)

• You may need to spoonfeed foods such as yoghurts, fromage frais, and smooth or semi-liquid items – such as lentil dhal – but you don't need to make everything else into a puree. Instead, give your baby experience with different textures, including lumps, and help her get used to feeding herself.

• Don't add salt to your baby's food. Her system does not need it and too much salt can make her very thirsty. Large quantities of salt or salty food can even be dangerous for a young baby as her kidneys cannot cope with it. When cooking foods to which you would normally add salt, either remove your baby's portion and cook it separately, or add salt for yourself at the time of serving.

• Salty, sugary pre-packaged foods that are aimed at adults or older children are not suitable for your baby.

• Sweetened foods contain fewer useful nutrients and may encourage a sweet tooth as well as being bad for her emerging teeth, so don't add sugar.

Coping with likes and dislikes

All babies have preferences, and some babies seem to reject anything new at first. Be encouraging but relaxed – it doesn't necessarily mean your baby will not like the food, only that she is being cautious. You may need to offer a new food many times before your baby accepts it. Keep offering her the foods you would like her to eat, but do not make a fuss if she hardly touches them.

LEARNING NEW TASTES

There are lots of things you can offer your baby as her first taste. Try her with something off your plate when she's sitting on your knee, such as banana, apple, cooked carrot, or potato, that won't need a lot of chewing and which she can fairly easily hold in her hand – or which you can put into her mouth. Babies often prefer sweeter foods at first so you may like to try giving her foods such as cooked parsnip, carrot, or apple.

REACTING TO NEW TASTES
Your baby may be surprised by the taste of a new food
that is offered to her. Don't assume she doesn't like it –
she may well just be being cautious.

Food reactions

Babies can sometimes react to a new food and can seem to have problems with it – your baby might cry, seem to produce more wind, become constipated or have diarrhoea, or vomit after eating it. Don't assume this is an allergy – after all, your baby could be ill for a totally unrelated reason. It may be that your baby is reacting to the introduction of this food, but her response is not an allergic one. She is just having a harder time digesting the new food.

Offer the food again in a couple of weeks' time and then watch for a similar reaction. Obviously, if the apparent reaction first time round seems serious, you should take advice from your health visitor. Flare-ups of eczema, also known as atopic dermatitis, are common in babies who have had a new food, but, while this may be an allergic reaction, it may not last a lifetime.

Self-feeding

Self-feeding allows your baby to have some control over her intake and to respond to her appetite without you feeding her more, or less, than she needs or wants. In this way it continues the relationship with nourishment she has when she breastfeeds, where she is the one who largely directs the flow, the frequency, and the amount.

Self-feeding is a way of allowing your child to develop her repertoire at her own pace, and supports weaning as a stage in her development. You will need to be with your baby at all times when she is eating in case of choking or in case

"Anne-Sophie loved anything that was orange (carrots, squash, sweet potato, peaches, baked beans), but hated anything that was green."

she struggles with something she has bitten off. It's also easier (although messier) for you, and it makes mealtimes a sociable, enjoyable part of your daily routine with your baby.

Buying your baby's food

Manufactured baby foods can be useful, especially if you are away from home, if you are pressed for time, or if you are eating something that is not suitable for your baby. However, they will cost you more than if you share your own food with your baby.

Although artificial additives are banned from manufactured baby foods, the quality of ready-made baby foods on sale differs widely. Look for foods containing ingredients that you would use at home. Some manufactured foods contain a lot of water, and then starchy thickeners and gums have to be added to make it the "right" texture for slopping out of the jar. Alternatively, there might be a high proportion of sugars, even in savoury foods. Babies can get used to the taste of commercial foods and then need "weaning" on to family meals, so try to avoid only giving your baby such food.

Allergies and food intolerance

If you have any concerns, talk to your health visitor. She may think it appropriate for you to see a paediatric dietician, an allergy specialist, or a doctor with a particular knowledge in these matters.

Babies who may have a tendency to food allergy have additional benefits from exclusive breastfeeding to six months, and continuing to breastfeed while solid foods are introduced, as breastmilk protects the vulnerable baby's gut. The Food Standards Agency recommends that the introduction of highly allergenic foods, such as dairy products, eggs, sesame, citrus, wheat, fish, and shellfish should not occur before a baby is six months old. This is particularly true for families where an allergy such as asthma, eczema, or hayfever already exists. If this applies to you, you may want to avoid peanuts and any food containing peanuts until your child is at least three years old.

Cup feeding

Your baby can get all her needs for fluids from the breast or a bottle, but it can be a good idea to start using a cup for water about now. With help, your baby will manage to drink from a normal cup or a cup with a spout, which is known as a "trainer" cup.

Weaning progress after the early days

At first, solids (or complementary foods as they are sometimes referred to) are an add-on to the milk your baby continues to need in the first year. You don't need to time the solid foods to coincide with a milk feed, though it can be convenient for you and your baby if you do. If you want your baby to have a nap after lunch, for example, or if that's the time she seems to need one, then a breast- or bottle feed can sometimes help her relax and nod off with minimum effort.

At the start of weaning most babies need more or less the same amount of milk as they have been used to (in bottles, or in numbers of breastfeeds). You may find that this gradually changes. As your baby's intake of solids gets greater, she may not require as much milk because she will be less hungry for it. If you're happy to breastfeed your baby as often as you or she wants to, the number of times your baby feeds may not be different, but she will probably take less milk overall – older babies often have short feeds on the breast and come for quick snacks, with longer feeds getting fewer in number (though you can't assume that the time on the breast is always proportional to the amount of milk taken – some babies take quite a lot in a short burst).

You can help your baby to increase her self-feeding skills by beginning to offer chopped foods that she can learn to pick up with her fingers and thumbs. She will still grasp a handful of food but, with practice, she will become more adept at selecting individual morsels to pop into her mouth instead of shovelling in a large handful.

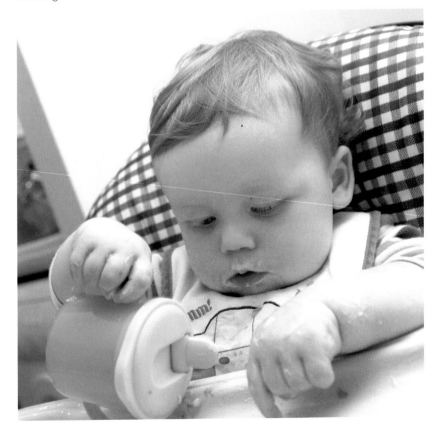

WATER
Once your baby starts eating solid foods it's a good idea to offer her water in a cup, as she may get thirsty.

Sometimes your baby will try to feed you, by holding a squashed sloppy bit of something-or-other out towards your mouth for you to nibble at. This is all part of the social experience of sharing a meal.

Continue the practice with a cup. If your baby has not had bottles then it makes sense to skip them altogether, as they are not good for babies' teeth and mouth development long term, and use a cup for her non-breastfeed drinks. Babies need to be nearly a year old before they can take large volumes of fluid from cups, so don't expect her to be able to satisfy all her fluid needs this way. She will still need to breastfeed or to have bottles.

What sort of milk?

Babies of six months and over can have ordinary pasteurized cows' milk as an ingredient in other foods, but their main milk drink should be breastmilk or, if you are not breastfeeding, formula (or a mixture of both). Breastfeeding is nutritious and still important as a way of protecting your baby's health. It does not lose its nutritional and immunological qualities over time. In fact some protective factors increase as babies start to explore the world.[☉]

If you use formula there is no reason to switch to follow-on formula, though this is marketed for babies over six months. Follow-on has more iron in it than cows' milk, but so has regular formula. It's a matter of personal preference if you change to follow-on or not, as very few babies need all the extra iron provided. Some babies can even become constipated; if this happens your baby will need to be switched back to what she was drinking before.

Current Department of Health guidance is to avoid cows' milk as a main drink until your baby is one year old. This is to give time for the majority of babies to have a wide range of solid foods, as cows' milk does not have a good balance of the minerals and vitamins babies need.

Milk intolerance

There are two forms of this in babies, and it's important to distinguish them:
• Lactose intolerance is very rare in babies. It is an inability, usually temporary, to digest the sugar part of milk. It often follows a bout of gastroenteritis, which leaves the mucosal lining of the gut damaged and unable to tolerate lactose. On a lactose-free diet the baby usually recovers and becomes able once more to drink milk.
• Cows' milk protein intolerance is an inability to handle the protein part of milk. Again, this may be temporary – children can grow out of it. Any reaction may be mild. However, in serious cases cows' milk, and anything containing it, has to be avoided at all times – forever. Breastfed babies who are miserable and colicky yet thriving and growing may be reacting to traces of cows' milk protein in the breast-milk (though you need to be fairly sure this is what's happening before you cut out dairy foods from your diet).

If your baby is unable to thrive on cows' milk, and is not breastfed, then your health visitor or doctor can advise you on other milks. There are several "predigested" cows' milk formulas available, some on prescription. The most commonly available alternative is soya formula, but there have been several concerns from experts about this. The Department of Health only recommends it when there has been a firm diagnosis of cows' milk intolerance or allergy. There have been concerns about the levels of phytoestrogens – hormone-like substances whose effect is unknown.⊙ The high sugar content may cause dental decay in baby teeth, especially if it's drunk from a bottle several times a day or night. In addition, there is a high amount of aluminium in soya formula, and this could be harmful to very young babies' kidneys.

If you need detailed advice about what to feed your baby because of an allergy, ask for a referral to a community dietician or a paediatric dietician.

Babies need more iron

Babies need more iron-rich foods than adults as they are growing so fast. Red meat is the best source. Vitamin C helps iron absorption from vegetarian sources of iron so include tomato, green vegetables, or citrus fruit at the same meal.

Sources of iron:
- Lean meat, liver, and kidney
- Dark chicken or turkey meat
- Fortified breakfast cereals
- Wholemeal bread
- Lentils, baked beans, and chick peas
- Green vegetables such as broccoli, peas, kale, and spring greens
- Dried apricots and prunes

More foods, more taste

Your baby will be enjoying a range of foods by about nine months, though there is no need for concern if she is still not on three regular meals a day. Some babies aren't ready for this yet, though all babies should be offered solid foods several times a day so that they can have them if they want them. At one end of the spectrum, your baby may be having breakfast, lunch, and tea with two or three snacks in between. At the other, she may be nibbling or licking on a few foods, without taking much in except occasionally. Most babies fall somewhere between these two extremes. As long as your baby is thriving, is being offered a variety of solid food she likes, and has as much milk as she seems to want, then it's unlikely there is anything to be concerned about.

VITAMIN D

Babies who are breastfed over the age of six months, with no formula or not very much formula, may be offered vitamin D supplements at the baby clinic. This is not because breastmilk is lacking. It's to compensate for the fact that modern-day lives are often spent indoors, away from sunlight, for much of the year. For the same reason the government recommends that pregnant women and breastfeeding mothers should take vitamin D supplements. Sunlight is used by the body to make vitamin D, and if a baby or child doesn't get enough of it, she could go short. (Formula-fed babies don't need the supplements because they are already added to the formula during the processing.) Some ethnic groups living in the north of the country may be especially at risk, as there is less sunshine available. Ask your doctor or your health visitor about this if you think you or your baby need supplements.

Your baby is growing – and moving

During the ages of six to nine months your baby will make great strides in her development. The majority of babies can roll over purposely during this time in order to see something, and can manage to get themselves towards an object in this way; many will start crawling or shuffling along on their bottoms. Babies will then start to pull themselves up to a standing position using the furniture.

DEVELOPMENT CHECK AT 7–9 MONTHS

This may take place at home or in a clinic, and is an opportunity for parents to discuss issues about health, growth, development, behaviour, or parenting in general.

The baby is observed, with particular attention given to her vision, hearing and early speech sounds, mobility and balance, hand–eye co-ordination, and social interaction. Play and reactions to stimulation may be looked at too.

So many ongoing changes occur at this stage, and the health visitor can give information about the ranges of normal milestones, feeding and diet, teething and dental health, immunizations, and home safety. Your baby will also be weighed naked, and both length and head circumference will be measured and plotted on her growth charts. Hips are re-checked by looking for full hip mobility, leg length, and equal skin creases. Boys will have their testes felt to ensure they have descended into the scrotum.

Do remember that babies develop at different rates. Some babies are content to sit for months longer than others, and make very little attempt to move on their tummies or in any other way, such as "cruising" round the furniture. (Babies are said to "cruise" when they use the furniture to move a few steps.) If your baby is like this, it doesn't mean her development is delayed. She may have more advanced communication skills, for example, or a less strongly developed sense of adventure.

Your baby's first efforts to crawl will almost certainly be towards something. You can encourage this by putting a favourite toy just out of reach, or by calling to her from a few paces away. Place her on a soft blanket or carpet and be prepared for her to fall, as she will still be too young to support her body weight on her arms.

During this time most babies learn to sit up. This learning period is a wobbly time. Your baby will need to be watched and placed somewhere safe, so that if she topples over she won't hurt herself. Gradually, she will be able to sit up for longer periods, and correct herself if she leans too far one way. She might at times get stuck, at which point she'll wail for you to rescue her.

STARTING TO CRAWL

At around this age your baby will start to get stronger and will probably want to explore her world more thoroughly by crawling all around it.

During these months your baby will be getting stronger and sturdier. At some stage she will show you how she likes to stand up, with her underarms supported by your hands, and enjoy bouncing up and down, stiffening and then relaxing her legs, and sometimes resisting being put down again.

Once your baby is crawling then it is likely she will soon be pulling herself to a standing position, although some babies crawl for months before actually walking. She may get up and not know how to get back down – resulting in a call for help. You can teach her to lower herself onto her bottom by pushing her down gently. This way she will soon get the hang of standing up and sitting down.

Fine motor skills

At first, your baby will be able to hold things in her fist but will not be able to manipulate them. As she gets older, she will learn how to hold something in one hand and then transfer it to the other, and how to pick something up with the other hand to hold on to two things. At this age, though, if she wants to hold something else that grabs her attention, she will let one of the objects fall.

Your baby can hold things in different ways according to their shape, finding by experimentation the best way to hold something securely. Watch how she holds her teddy by an arm or a leg, for example, because she can't manage to keep hold of it by its ear. She's learning by looking at, and feeling, different shapes and sizes, curves, and corners. Watch for when she manages to hold things between her finger and thumb, and examine them by turning them over. Her careful studies show her that things may look different from different angles, and yet remain the same. She will also bring them to her mouth so that she can try out the different tastes and textures. At about nine months babies can compare two toys or other objects by looking at them in their hands. Your baby may enjoy banging them together to see if they make a sound.

Babies of nine months are usually able to see that some things fit together. They may know that some things have lids, and that some shapes can fit into holes. At this age your baby won't understand that a square shape won't fit a tubular hole, but just seeing that sometimes things fit and sometimes they don't is important for her learning. Babies are interested in watching things being built up or screwed together, and then coming apart again. It's fascinating for your baby to see that different shapes can become, predictably, another different shape.

Babies can move a page by grabbing hold of it, understanding that this is something like turning a page, but picking up a single page and turning it is beyond their skills for a while as their fine motor skills are not sufficiently developed.

Your baby will be able to grab things, including her own feet, as they come into view. She'll play with her hands, and chew on them, too. This doesn't mean she's hungry. Deliberately putting hands and feet – or anything else – to her mouth shows she has developed an awareness of her body and how to manoeuvre it.

SIGNS OF INCREASED MOBILITY
Here are some signs that show your baby is becoming more mobile:
• She sits up and turns round without toppling over.
• She holds onto something for several minutes at a time.
• She reaches to pick something up that she's dropped.
• She holds something out to you with an expectation that you will take it from her.
• She reaches out to grasp something you are offering.
• She kneels at the bottom of the stairs and tries to move up.
• She can stand just holding your hands – first both, then just one.
• She shows she knows she can deliberately poke a finger into a hole.
• She knows small things are best picked up with finger and thumb while large things need a whole hand, or even two hands.

CLIMBING OUT OF THE COT
Some babies never actually realize it's possible to do this, even when they have the strength and the skills to do it; other babies discover they can do it as early as nine months or so. You can delay your baby's ability and desire to climb out of the cot by using a baby sleeping bag. It's important to do this before she realizes it's going to stop her from being more adventurous, so use one as soon as you see signs that she's more mobile in her cot (e.g., sitting up and grasping the bars), and beginning to try to stand during her daytime play.

Learning to communicate verbally

Babies learn to speak by hearing language around them and, in particular, hearing language that is directed at them. The early conversations you have with your newborn, when you make eye contact and tell her about what's happening, are essential to her language development. The age of six to nine months is when your baby's communications skills really advance.

MOTHER'S CHECK

Apart from your general health, at this point you may be monitored for postnatal depression again, using the same Edinburgh Postnatal Depression Score (EPDS) questionnaire that you would have been given 6–8 weeks after delivery (see p.73). Depression can affect some women up to a year after a birth, and therapeutic listening visits will be offered to you if you score above 12 out of 30 in the questionnaire.

Around the middle of the first year you will be aware that your baby is starting to babble. Babbling is actually a technical term and means using sounds individually and then later repeatedly, one after the other. Initially the sounds will be vowel sounds, later your baby will start to add in consonants. Most babies will be doing both by the age of nine months. Your baby will start by making sounds such as "aaaaaah" or "ohhhhhh" and then "da" or "ma" or "mi". She will then string these sounds together to make "dada" or "mama", and then, later still, "dadadada" or "mamamam", and perhaps "mmmmmmmm". Listen for her making a sound like "biddabiddabidda", which has two consonants in it. Early babbling can even sound a bit like speech, with intonation and expression.

By the end of nine months some babies have a sound that appears to attach itself to a person or an object. It may not necessarily be anything like the actual name – you might notice your baby says "babababababa" every time she sees the family dog, for instance.

It does appear that babies are programmed to respond to sounds and to the fact that sounds have a meaning. Babies understand this long before they show you by using words or sounds; they can look at a named person or object, for example. Say to your baby, "Where's daddy?" and she will turn and smile at daddy. See how many familiar people or objects your baby can show you she's aware of. See if she understands what to do when you announce a familiar game like "Round and round the garden". Does she give you her hand, ready to play?

It's important for your baby's language development that you avoid having background speech in your home all the time, such as the television or the radio.

There are various ways you can spot the signs that your baby is making real progress in talking, understanding, and communication in this period:
• She may be able to imitate the sounds you make to her.
• She is able to concentrate on your face, or a toy, for a longer period.
• She can begin to understand if people are cross or if they're happy by the tone

of voice they use and the expression on their face. You may notice your baby looks worried or anxious in response.

• She knows the difference between the people she loves and strangers.

• She knows how to predict things – for example, she knows it is time for food when she is lifted into her high chair and has her bib put on.

• She can communicate very effectively about things she wants to do and things she doesn't want to do, and can have strong opinions on both.

• She knows about jokes – sometimes, when what she expects in a game doesn't happen, she knows it's funny.

• She can attract attention, and knows if she cries loudly you'll see what it is that she wants.

• She can understand where a sound is coming from, and listen concentratedly. Making the link between the sound and its source is vital to language and learning.

• She can recognize some words, and can look in the right direction if you ask, "Where's mummy?" or "Where's the dog?".

• If she hears someone's name mentioned that she knows, she'll look round for that person, assuming they are there.

• She recognizes the ring of the doorbell, and knows what happens next.

• She can work out simple toys, such as shaking a bell to make it ring, or pressing a beeper, or putting a toy in a box. She will also try to do things she can't do yet, like placing a shape in a slot.

• She can wave "bye bye" when she hears the words. She's better at doing this when it's a familiar context – when you wave bye bye from the house – as she can't yet generalize that "bye bye" means the same when you leave anywhere.

MAKING CONVERSATION
Conversation with your baby is important for her learning. That means pausing when you talk to her, so she can make sounds back, before you start talking again. This helps your baby get used to the natural two-way "shape" of dialogue, and gives her practice at making new sounds.

HEARING TEST AT 7–9 MONTHS OF AGE
This screening test looks very simplistic, but it uses specific high- and low-pitched frequencies, at quiet levels, to distract a baby from looking at a toy shown. The toy is then hidden by the health visitor, who observes the baby's reaction to each sound made by another trained colleague; the baby should turn towards each and every sound, on both right and left sides.

In some areas of the UK, this distraction-hearing test has already been superseded by a neonatal hearing test known as the Oto-Acoustic Emissions (OAE) test. This test checks the sleeping baby's cochlear function with electronic clicks via an earpiece. Ultimately the distraction-hearing test will be withdrawn when the OAE equipment and training of health visitors is available nationwide.

Hearing tests via the audiology service will continue whenever a hearing concern is raised, as an acquired hearing loss can develop at any age.

COMMUNICATION SKILLS

Your baby's communication skills will advance during this period, for example she will begin to recognize the difference between the people she loves and strangers.

Having fun with your baby

When your baby gets to six months and older you'll notice that there is a lot more potential for play. Your baby's "work" is playing. It's what she does to learn new skills, to extend and practise existing ones, and to discover new things about her world and the people around her.

Sitting up
This means your baby has a new vantage point, and her increasing sense of balance and coordination means she can concentrate on things other than just not toppling over. Hold something just out of reach and watch her stretch for it.

Crawling/shuffling
This allows your baby to explore further. Notice how she often turns back to check you are still in view. You can turn this into a game by waving "Hello" every time she looks round. See if she learns to expect your greeting, and make her laugh by talking in a funny voice or making your wave different.

Cruising
Again this provides a different vantage point. See if she can reach something by leaning onto supportive furniture with just one hand – she may fall down at first.

Her growing understanding
Your baby will begin to understand that when she drops something and it falls out of sight, it still exists, and she can even deduce where it should be. That's why she loves dropping something out of her pushchair – many times. This is called "object permanence" and it is probably present from about six months on.

Manipulative skills
The pincer grasp, using finger and thumb, starts being practised any time from around eight months or so, but it takes a while for it to become perfected. It allows for precision – small objects can be held, moved, examined, and compared.

Language skills
Your baby's hearing and growing use of sounds (*see* pp.216–17) links in with her understanding that these sounds have meaning, and that you and she can exchange this understanding as part of your relationship.

Here are some games you can play at this stage:

- Gently blow on your baby's face.
- Blow raspberries and see if she responds by copying.
- Make clicking sounds with your tongue.
- Put a small ball on your baby's high-chair tray. Blow on the ball so it rolls towards her. See if she can try to blow it back to you.
- Touch different parts of your baby's body and name them. Touch the same parts of your own, or your partner's body, and do the same thing. "Mummy's eyes…daddy's eyes."
- Give your baby a nesting toy (one with shapes that fit into the next size up).
- Play "How big?" by asking your baby, "How big are you today?" Hold her arms up high and say "You're this big!" In time your baby will put her arms up herself when she hears the "cue" question.
- Play hide and seek – you can play this with objects or with people. Going and looking for someone behind the curtain, or the door, is hilarious for a baby who understands "object permanence" – and even funnier when she finds out that, sometimes, things are not in the expected place! At first your baby needs to see something peeping out of the hiding place in order to spot it – but not for long.

Books for your baby

Sharing books is important, and it helps if you point out pictures of objects your baby is familiar with. Show a picture of a teddy and give your baby her teddy as you do so. Babies of this age can't follow a story with a plot, but they do enjoy hearing the drama of a story in your voice, and they can recognize books they have come to see and hear often. You can make up your own story to go with the pictures if you prefer, or just talk about what you can see. (*See* box, top right.)

There are many different ways to stimulate your baby's senses

- Sight – show your baby bright colours, moving objects, and mirrors. Point things out to her on your walks.
- Hearing – play music, hang a wind chime up, and sing songs to your baby.
- Touch – collect different textures and put them in a basket for your baby to feel. Show her how different things feel against her skin.
- Taste – allow her to try different flavours, and look interested in her reactions.
- Smell – hold different things such as soap, perfumed cloths, or flowers near her nose so she can smell them.
- Share the experience. Talk about it. Respond when your baby shows that she's excited about something she's discovered. Put her feelings into words for her – "Yes – you smelt that lovely flower".

MAKE YOUR OWN BOOK:

- Cut sturdy fabric or cardboard into eight or ten square pieces.
- Stick a large, colourful picture onto each of the pieces and, if you want, write a single word or phrase in big letters on each page.
- Punch some holes in each square, place them on top of each other, and tie them together with ribbon.
- You can vary the pages by sticking down a small shatterproof mirror on one of them, or by adding some materials for your baby to touch – such as pieces of fabric or textured paper.

POINTING AT OBJECTS

Some children as young as nine months can point at something they want but can't actually reach (or know they can't have!). Watch for the time when this pointing changes to "declarative pointing" – it is a real milestone in learning. Your baby will point at something to draw attention to it, just to get you to look at it, too. Your baby doesn't necessarily need or want the item she's pointing at. She is showing you the object so you'll acknowledge it and talk to her by saying, for example, "Yes, that's a picture of a baby" or "Are you showing mummy the doggy?". This is a way for your baby to get you to share her experience.

Your special needs baby

Now that you have passed six months of life with your new baby you may be feeling that you are getting your lives and emotions back on a more even keel. There may be some issues still to be met, but, on the whole, things should have settled down. You may find that although you have found out more about her medical condition, there appears to be a seemingly endless list of things to fear in the future. You may find it helpful to ask yourself the question of whether it is worth losing sleep now over what may happen to your baby when she is older than you are. Yes, she may well have problems, but she is only a baby once, and you only get one chance to enjoy her today. Treasure the experience; these days will be gone all too soon. The future for her is just as much an open book as it is for anyone; the pages may be slightly different, but they are unwritten just the same.

GETTING TO KNOW HER

Enjoy your baby and the process of getting to know her. Like all babies, her individuality and personality will become more evident during this time.

It is only in the first few months of life that your baby really, truly belongs to you. In what seems like no time at all babies start to express their personal tastes, and this begins the long, slow separation from you until they belong wholly to themselves. Remember, this is as true for you as it is for all those other mothers with their "ordinary" babies.

It may be that your baby makes you look again at your reasons for having a child, and what your expectations were. Most parents never find themselves in the position of having to look too closely at their motivations and expectations, especially when their child is a tiny baby, but it is necessary to examine and talk about your feelings if you are to come to terms with your situation effectively. Counselling may be necessary for some couples. Remember your child is who she is, reaching her own potential and fulfilling her own desires, not yours.

By this time, provided there have not been too many medical difficulties, you should have been able to spend a good deal of time at home with your baby, and her disability will have become part of who she is. It is difficult sometimes to differentiate where the condition ends and where the baby begins, and it may be useful to consider only physical problems when putting things down to the condition. If your baby has low muscle tone, for instance, it is easy to understand why she finds it more difficult to master the skills of sitting or rolling. Understanding what your baby has to overcome can increase your pride in her achievements, while at the same time releasing you to enjoy her emerging personality for who she is, not what her condition says she ought to be.

Making decisions

You will have met most of the people who will be helping you to look after your baby in the early years by this time. It is at these appointments that a little knowledge can go a long way. Hospital protocols can make you feel as if your baby is public property, but decisions about sight tests, for instance, are yours, not theirs. It can be daunting when you first start making decisions independently of people such as the health visitor, but remember that you really do know your child best: you know her home situation and you know her capabilities better than anyone. Ask questions and do not be afraid to say no to some tests – ask if the information can be obtained in any other way if that is your preference. Will having the information from an invasive test change their treatment regime at all? After all, you will be the one living with the consequences.

Getting to know your baby

As your baby gets older and life settles into more of a routine, your knowledge of her and your confidence in yourself will increase. As time passes you will start to notice differences between your baby and her ordinary peers; remember, as babies grow their personalities become more evident, and this is just as true for your baby as it is for everyone else's. Your baby will have her favourite toys, and the games she likes to play with you. She may be a cuddler, or she may appreciate her own space. Together you are on an exciting journey of discovery.

Having fun with your baby

When your baby has special needs it can feel as if you have something to prove in getting her off to the best start possible. Various developmental checklists will be given to you, and there can be a subtle pressure to constantly stimulate her. There is a difference, though, in the therapeutic handling of a baby with special needs that builds physiotherapy and learning goals naturally, and overloading your baby.

Getting out with other mums and babies has immense value for you both. You can derive support from the experience of others, and she can enjoy social interaction with other babies. If you are nervous at the thought of being stared at or talked about, it may help to consider the fact that your baby brings as much to others as they do to her. Your baby is a living demonstration of the vast range of human difference, helping to break down barriers by her very existence, and the obvious pleasure you take in her mere presence is a lesson to everyone.

Most people who stop you do so because they recognize something that they have some level of experience of. Sometimes they say things that grate and it is helpful to remember that most people mean to be encouraging, even when they are making the most sweeping of statements. A few stock phrases such as, "She's a girl/he's a boy actually" can go a long way to diffuse your feelings and show that your baby is a baby first and foremost, not a label.

THINKING ABOUT HAVING ANOTHER BABY

The question of when, or whether, to have another baby is one that may preoccupy you from the early days of life with your baby with special needs. For your own peace of mind it is essential that you understand as far as you can the medical circumstances surrounding the birth of your baby, especially if they caused the condition your baby suffers from.

It can feel as if everyone has an opinion on how soon you should have another baby (or not). Some will believe that a brother or sister will bring on the child with special needs, while others will hold the view that another baby would take away the attention that your existing child needs. Another question worth considering is the number of children you want in your family. If your baby with special needs is your first baby you may well desire to have a "normal" brother or sister for her. Try to consider also the needs of the younger sibling. Whatever your decision, it is your family circumstances that count and you and your partner are the people who know them best, not anyone else.

Your needs as a mother also come into play. You may well feel that the circumstances surrounding the birth of your baby were traumatic and spoiled what was supposed to be a joyful experience. The desire to reclaim that feeling through having another baby can be very strong and is perfectly natural. You need to seek medical advice when considering becoming pregnant again, and you will need to think seriously about how much antenatal testing you are willing to undergo. These are issues that affect everybody differently, and are moral questions that you will have to satisfy within your own set of family circumstances and in your own time.

Safety first, last, and always

By this age you will have a baby who can reach for things and who is moving, rolling, and even crawling. This is the time, therefore, when you need to start thinking about safety issues, such as putting dangerous items out of reach and using the correct equipment.

Once your baby is mobile you won't be able to leave her on her own in a room, unless you are very sure she can come to no harm in a few seconds. So you will have to scoop her up when you go to answer the door or visit the bathroom. You may find a cordless phone comes in particularly useful from this stage.

A baby who can roll over quickly learns to roll over and over again. She can move across the floor like this, and into corners where she might hurt herself. You won't be able to stop her doing what comes naturally, so you will need to start thinking about your living areas and making them safe.

Once your baby can stand, pull herself up, and cruise round the furniture, these are some of the things you will need to be aware of:

• Watch for wobbly items of furniture that could tip over – bookcases in particular.

• If your baby's cot mattress is adjustable downwards, set it to the lowest level to make climbing out more difficult. Don't keep stuffed toys inside the cot – athletic babies use them as stepping stones to get over the bar.

• Be on the look-out for dangling electric cords, tablecloths, or curtains that your baby could pull down or get tangled in.

• Keep medicines, cleaners, pesticides, alcohol, and other poisons locked away out of your baby's reach. Be aware of the location of any pills or tablets in your house or in any house that your baby visits. Put child locks on all cupboard doors.

• Never leave your baby alone in or near water, even for a few seconds.

• Watch out for things that pinch fingers, such as door hinges or folding chairs.

• Move the house plants and ornaments up high, to where your baby can't reach them or see them.

• Protect the TV and video buttons and computer hardware with covers, or move the equipment out of her reach; also cover all electrical sockets.

• The safest place to change a nappy is on the floor, but if you use a changing unit or bed never leave your baby alone for a moment.

• Fit stairgates at the top and bottom of stairs as soon as your baby is able to start climbing even one step.

• Keep floors clutter free and watch out for small objects (such as tiny toys belonging to older children) that your baby could put into her mouth.

USING A PLAYPEN

A playpen can be a useful means of keeping your baby safe, for instance in the kitchen when you need to be by a hot cooker or kettle. But do not use it for long periods.

- Always strap your baby into her high chair or pushchair with a full waist and shoulder harness – if it becomes a habit then your baby is less likely to object, and if she does start to resist you will be less likely to skip it.
- Don't use babywalkers (walk-in chairs that raise your baby up and which allow her to speed across the floor propelled by her feet); they are a common cause of falls and other accidents.
- Don't use pillows, duvets, or bean bags for babies under one year.
- Keep plastic bags out of reach.
- Don't use ribbons or ties on clothing or dummies.
- Cut strings on toys to shorter than 20cm (8in), and remove any toys strung across the cot as soon as your baby starts to pull herself up.
- Don't leave your baby alone with food or a bottle.
- In the kitchen use short, curly flexes on kettles and irons and other equipment.
- Check your baby's dummy for wear, if she uses one.
- Don't drink hot drinks while holding your baby.
- Don't let your baby stand up in the supermarket trolley. Choose one with a safety strap to keep her seated. Don't let her stand up in her high chair, either.

Playpens

Playpens are a matter of preference – yours and your baby's. Some babies can't abide being in a playpen. Some parents feel the time to start using one is before the baby can move independently, so she takes a while to understand she is being "penned in". Some babies tolerate short times in the playpen, as long as they have a few favourite toys in there with them. It's not good for a baby to spend long periods in a playpen, as exploring and moving is essential to her development. Be creative – a playpen can be useful for you to sit in instead of your baby if you are involved in something you want to keep her away from, such as sewing.

Safety advice

You should always use a car seat that's right for your baby's weight (usually a forward-facing seat at this age), and use the seat on all journeys. Never place the baby seat in the front passenger seat if the car is fitted with an air bag.

Your health visitor is a good source of information about safety, the equipment you may need, and when and how to change your routines. Some areas have equipment-lending schemes for things like stairgates. When it comes to buying equipment, choose products that meet safety standards. Look for a BS (British Standards) or EN (European Norm) number.

Rough and tumble play is fun, and most babies adore physically active play with you or anyone they know well. Keep it safe by never shaking your baby. Don't swing her round by her arms as you could dislocate her elbows or shoulders; hold her under the arms instead, and swirl gently.

ACCIDENTS WILL HAPPEN

As they become more mobile, babies will inevitably have minor accidents. Some adventurous babies will have many. It can be difficult to tell how hurt your baby is, and to know how best to manage these situations. Here are a few pointers:
- Crying that is instantaneous, loud, and accompanied by frantic searching for adult contact is probably more of an expression of fear and outrage than serious injury. Soothe and comfort your baby and try not to over-react. Remaining calm will help your baby to calm down more quickly. If you appear panicked or fearful she will pick this up and become frightened herself.
- If an accident is followed by silence then an almost immediate scream this may be more serious, but again remaining outwardly calm will help your baby. Most parents will recognize the heart-sinking experience of this pause before crying, as it is one of the more upsetting experiences of early parenthood. However, the loud crying should reassure you as you go to help.
- An accident followed by silence is the most serious. A doctor should see any child who loses consciousness, however temporarily, or who appears drowsy or "shocked" after an accident.
- Most minor bumps and bruises will be soothed by the application of a cold compress (or cloth wrung out in cold water) and lots of cuddles and kisses.
- Blows to the head, especially the temples or back of the head are more serious than bruises on the more fleshy parts of the body. If you are in any doubt about whether to take your child to see a doctor you can ring the NHS Direct helpline for advice, on 0845 4647.

8 NEARLY ONE YEAR OLD

- You've come a long way

- Celebration

- Looking to the future

You've come a long way

Anniversaries are celebrated as significant milestones in the passage of time. They are the points at which we take stock of what has passed and look forward to the future. The anniversary of your baby's birth can be a time of heightened emotions and vivid memories. Looking back you will probably wonder how so much can have happened in just one year. Many parents experience a potent mixture of pride, joy, and possibly some sadness at this time, as they think over the amazing first year of their child's life.

"Looking at our magnolia tree about to bloom, I remembered my thoughts a year ago. I gave birth the same day the first flower opened. A year on and we have all flourished."

As you approach your baby's first birthday you will find yourself back in the season of the year corresponding to the last weeks of pregnancy. Do you remember how you felt back then? Did your pre-birth self predict what would happen and how you would feel in your first year as a parent? Do you miss the old you, or are you happy with the ways in which you have changed? Just as your baby has transformed during the year from a helpless newborn to an active, nearly toddler, you have also transformed from living as an individual to being someone's parent.

As you reflect on this transformation you may feel pleasure and satisfaction, or you may feel sadness and wish that you could turn back the clock and alter events. You may feel concerned about how little you were prepared for the momentous change, and feel a sense of loss for the person that you were before the birth. Perhaps the birth was difficult, or you were unhappy enough in the early weeks to have not enjoyed your new baby. You may still be struggling to find a balance.

Many parents surprise themselves in the first year after birth, by discovering that they are not the parents they thought (and hoped) they would be. It is very easy to have unrealistic expectations. As parents fall in love with their babies many decide that they will be endlessly patient, selfless, loving, and fun. However the realities of tiredness, conflicting demands, and stress make this impossible. While it is good to want to do your best, carrying too much guilt about the ways in which you have been less than perfect is not helpful. Reassure yourself that you are constantly growing and learning as a parent and that most mistakes can be put right.

As well as the larger regrets there may be smaller ones. Perhaps you missed an important milestone; maybe you were at work when your baby took his first steps, or were out socializing when he first said "Dada". It is easy to feel bad about how you "weren't there", while overlooking all the times you were there. It is the day-to-day little moments that go to make up the sum of your relationship with your baby.

Growing at his own pace

Babies at one year are certainly a very mixed group. Some are already walking, have had their first haircut, and look distinctly like toddlers. Others are still immobile, have little hair, and appear relatively baby-like. Looking across the room at first birthday parties, it is easy to compare your baby's progress with the others'. In our society independence is highly valued and a particular significance is placed on learning to walk. If your baby is an early walker it is tempting to assume that he is more "advanced", that he is getting ahead of the crowd. Conversely, if your baby is still sitting or crawling you may have feelings of disappointment, no matter how you tell yourself that you shouldn't be measuring your baby against others (*see* box, right).

Parental pride is normal and natural, but parental embarrassment may be the other side of this particular coin. If you get into the habit of feeling good or bad about your success as a parent based on how your baby "performs" in public you may be in for an uncomfortable time as he grows and establishes his own identity. Every toddler tantrum will also feel like an assault on your self-esteem as a parent. Doing the best you can, asking for support from others, and letting go of the need to do everything perfectly first time will help.

As the end of the first year dawns make every effort to enjoy and take pride in your baby's own individuality and uniqueness. Love him with all your heart and celebrate him; be his number one fan and he will be yours.

ENJOYING YOUR ONE-YEAR-OLD
Make the most of every opportunity you have to spend time with your baby, enjoying all the big and little milestones he reaches, in his own time.

Celebration

Having a new baby may alter how you view birthdays, anniversaries, Christmas, and other religious festivals. In your new role as someone's "parent" in the extended family, expectations about what you should do may change in your own eyes and those of your relatives. You may also be part of a new circle of baby friends with whom you have a new closeness and a wish to share such celebrations.

A CELEBRATION OF LIFE

While your baby will not remember the details in the future, you will want to mark this special first birthday in some way. Whether you throw a large party or simply share a cake with a few friends, do what is right for you as a family.

Now that you are a parent you must make decisions on behalf of your baby as well as yourself. You will need to find a new balance between doing your own thing and living up to other people's expectations. Before your baby was born you may have been used to complying with the wishes of your extended family, but now you may want to take charge of events on behalf of your child.

Your baby's first birthday

Your baby's first birthday is an important milestone and one that you will probably want to mark in some style. However, take some time to think about what you would really like to do. Some parents get swept along with hugely elaborate arrangements to celebrate their baby's first birthday, doing things that they feel they "should" do because everyone else expects it, rather than taking their own initiative and doing what feels right for them. They may decide to have a huge party and find themselves inviting more people than they (or their baby) can cope with. It may feel important to invite all their new "baby friends" as well as family. Perhaps there is even a feeling of having to conform, as other parents are making extravagant arrangements.

If you are a really keen party animal and can organize a lavish party without getting stressed then go right ahead, but remember that a one-year-old child will not remember this event and will have little understanding of what is going on. A typical one-year-old may find such an event overwhelming and unmanageable and the last thing that you will want to do on this special day is deal with the tears and tantrums of an over-extended baby. By having a big celebration you will not be building a future memory for your child. Conversely, by not having a huge party your baby will not feel deprived (after all there will be many, many years in the future when birthday parties will be much more important to your child, and all the party ingredients, such as games, loot bags, and party food, will delight him and his friends).

Some babies find a large, noisy event very stressful so you could choose to have a small quiet event with cake and candles and a few family and friends. The timing of the party can also be important, so plan a short get-together at your baby's "best" time of day.

All you really need to do for a first birthday is to mark the event in some way and have the opportunity to take some pictures for the family album. You could consider the first birthday as a celebration more for the parents and family than the child himself. Celebrate your achievement in giving birth to your child and bringing him through this first demanding year. Raise a toast to yourself and make sure that you get some treats too. (*See* box, right, for further ideas.)

Your baby's first Christmas, Hanukkah, Eid, or Diwali

These celebrations are important family times as well as vital aspects of our culture and traditions. As a new parent you may want to think about how you would like to celebrate these events with your child, both now and in the future. For example, what would you like to take from your own childhood memories and pass on to your children?

With the expectation of family togetherness there may be some difficulty over the issue of who should be included in such celebrations. The get-together may feel incomplete without all the aunties, uncles, and cousins, or you may now feel that you, your partner, and baby are an independent unit. Stress can occur when deciding which relatives have precedence for visiting and sharing events. In some families it is clear that one set of in-laws or the other is the "main" family, but in others this can be a source of real difficulty. New mothers may feel quite strongly that they need to be with their own mothers if the celebration falls soon after the birth.

Some new parents who have difficult or unsatisfying relationships with their extended family feel that with a new baby they can finally assert their need to have a smaller family celebration for themselves and their baby. Others regretfully make this decision based on the fact that their family is geographically too distant to make a visit feasible on a practical level.

Whatever you choose to do in this first year try to make sure that you pay attention to your own emotional needs. Being a new parent is tiring and busy; the last thing you need is to run around making sure that everyone else's celebration goes with a swing. Making your baby a priority may help you to make decisions that have been too difficult before, such as saying "no" to visiting more distant or difficult relatives and friends.

On the other hand, you may feel a new, stronger sense of family following the birth of your baby. Suddenly your place in the family may feel much more important as you see how you and your baby fit into the wider picture. In this case a big family celebration with grandparents, aunts, uncles, and cousins may satisfy you on a deeper level than it has ever done before.

IDEAS FOR CELEBRATING YOUR BABY'S FIRST BIRTHDAY

• A simple party – a few nibbles for the grown-ups, finger food for the children, a few toys – keep it short.

• A very small gathering for grandparents, aunties and uncles, and immediate family.

• A small gathering in the morning for coffee and biscuits with "baby friends", leaving the afternoon and evening free for you to do as you wish.

• Perhaps someone else will host a party for you – grandparents may be keen.

• Take a short family break/holiday, a re-run of the "babymoon" (*see* p.41).

• Give yourself a treat – maybe some time at a spa or an outing to a favourite place that makes you feel good.

• Find a space in the day, maybe at the actual "time anniversary", to pause and reflect on your baby's birth – after all, when he was born your new identity as a parent was also "born".

• Make a special book compiling your memories of the first year; perhaps including "time capsule" information to share with your child in the future.

Looking to the future

As the first year moves into the second your thoughts will turn to the journey ahead. The first year after birth is an especially eventful one. There are many new skills to learn, and experiences that you will not have met before; however, it is only the first step of a much longer journey. Becoming a parent is for life; your relationship with your child will be transformed over the years, but you will never stop being his parent.

Thinking about the future may fill you with pleasure, anxiety, or a mixture of both. If the first year has been difficult you may fear more problems to come; equally, if the first year has been wonderful you may worry that everything will change as your baby transforms into a toddler. You may feel that you still haven't quite come to terms with your new role as a parent, or that you are still not being the parent you would like to be. Some parents find caring for young babies less rewarding and pleasurable than caring for older children. Although you may love your baby deeply, the initial feeling that you are not really a "baby person" may never quite have gone away. It may be useful to remember that some parents who find the baby years a challenge come into their own as their children grow up and need a different style of parenting. Parents who were ill at ease with their infants may thoroughly enjoy the teenage years, which other parents find more difficult.

Although the first year is important for laying the foundations of your relationship, a difficult first year does not mean that your relationship will be difficult forever. All relationships can be improved with understanding and a willingness to change. There are many organizations that offer support to parents, to help them to make the best relationships they can with their children (*see* pp.239–41).

Continuing to take care of yourself

During the first year of parenthood you will have learned many things about yourself, both inspiring and disappointing. Many parents report that they didn't realize before they became parents their capacity for both enormous patience and extreme irritability. Looking after a needy, helpless, and vulnerable infant can drive parents to the extremes of emotional experience, and this is rarely acknowledged.

The common image of parenthood is one of unconditional love and tireless self-sacrifice, and many parents aspire to this difficult ideal. Nobody wants to fail, and failing as a parent holds a particular stigma. However, being a parent is especially emotionally challenging; being so close to a vulnerable baby can put you in touch with deep emotions. If you find you are frequently being hijacked by your emotions and behaving in ways that you are unhappy with, take time to look at your own emotional needs. This will help you to respond more effectively to your child.

"This is our family"

In the years to come you will be creating a family with its own culture, traditions, and expectations. Choices that you make, both big and small, about how you want to live will form the childhood experiences of your child. This can feel like a weighty responsibility, and indeed it is, but it also gives you the opportunity to pass on your values to your children. You may not have the opportunity to give them an "ideal" childhood, with the perfect family, house, school, and friends, but you can choose to give them a family that shares certain principles and beliefs about the world.

It may be that you and your partner have different ideas about what a family should be like; after all you will both have come from separate families of origin and will consider different behaviour to be entirely normal. This can cause consternation and stress if each of you puts too much energy into attempting to prove that your way is best, and such conflict can be confusing to children. Criticizing each other's particular way of doing things can feel like attacking each other's families and defensiveness can set in. When such issues arise it is best to try to sort them out through discussion together away from your child, rather than acting out the problem with baby in the middle.

"I still don't know if I'm doing it right"

All new parents want the best for their babies and are motivated to want to do everything "right", but the trouble is there is no one right way of bringing up a child. While experts and researchers in the field of child development can give guidance about what seems to work for most families, they cannot guarantee that any one thing will work for every individual child. In the end parents have to have faith in their children and themselves, and seek to do the best they can with the knowledge and information that they have.

Babies don't come with an instruction manual, and parenting is not a simple set of skills to perform. The real parenting, the bit that matters, is the development of a secure, loving relationship between parent and child. Our children watch us; they know us and they will go to enormous lengths to love us and to make us love them. They need to have a good relationship with their parents, just as parents need to have one with them. Being a parent is hard work and can sometimes feel overwhelming. At its best it can feel like being in love, such is the joy and pleasure we feel, while at its worst it can feel like being pushed around and disrespected to the most amazing degree. Being a parent is about resilience and flexibility. It is about loving and expressing that love as best we can so that it is passed from generation to generation, to nourish us all.

LOOKING AHEAD

Your baby's first year is just the first step of a longer journey ahead. With your support and guidance he will grow to reach his full potential, as an individual in his own right.

Common illnesses

CHEST PROBLEMS

Asthma

Asthma is not often diagnosed in babies; it is more common for the diagnosis to be made from about the age of two onwards. However, if your baby is wheezy you should contact your doctor's surgery as a baby with a wheeze or a fast breathing rate should be checked promptly. Asthma can be difficult to treat in young babies because treatment is given by inhaler. However, the "spacer" devices, which are used to make inhalers easier for older children, can be fitted with a special mask for babies.

Colds and coughs

It is normal for everyone to have around five colds per year. Babies suffer too, and may develop a fever, runny nose, and cough. Treat a fever with infant paracetamol – there are dosage instructions on the bottle/box. You can try to clear nasal secretions at the very front of your baby's nose using a cotton bud, but for mucus further back you need to wait for it to clear by itself. A baby with a fast, shallow breathing rate, difficulty breathing, and fever may have developed bronchiolitis so contact your doctor's surgery right away. If your baby is otherwise well, and the only problem is a little difficulty latching onto the breast or bottle, it is safe to wait for a few days to see if it clears up on its own.

DIGESTIVE PROBLEMS

Constipation

Breastfed babies rarely become constipated. However, some breastfeeding mothers worry if their baby has only two dirty nappies per week. This is actually very common in babies older than a month, and as long as the baby is otherwise well there is no need to worry. If bottle-fed babies become constipated they should be offered extra drinks of water. After the age of six months they can also have a little pureed fruit or fruit juice. Occasionally they may need the help of a liquid called lactulose to soften the stools. Blood seen in a nappy should always be reported to your doctor right away.

Diarrhoea and vomiting

Most communities will experience two or three "epidemics" of diarrhoeal illness each year. These illnesses are very infectious and pass from person to person, including babies. Handwashing is always important when handling babies, but if you know there is a virus going round then be absolutely scrupulous about hand hygiene.

Gastroenteritis tends to start with 24–48 hours of vomiting, followed by a few days of diarrhoea. If your child has diarrhoea there is a risk of dehydration and it is important to make sure that she is receiving plenty of fluids to make up for those she has lost. Avoid high-sugar drinks; use plain water or rehydration sachets, which are available from your doctor. If there is no vomiting then you may continue to give milk.

In the case of vomiting you can continue to breastfeed, although your baby may not want to if she is very unwell. If so, continue to express milk to avoid engorgement of your breasts, and offer her water or rehydration sachets. It is fine to withhold milk from a formula-fed baby for 24 hours but replace the milk with plenty of fluids. After that you can try full- or half-strength milk depending on the severity of the child's symptoms. For babies over six months who are on solids a little yoghurt is a good first food after an episode of diarrhoea and vomiting.

As has been stated, babies are at risk of dehydration from both vomiting and diarrhoea. Signs to look for are a sunken fontanelle, wrinkly abdominal skin, and dry lips or tongue. A baby who is also very listless should be checked by a doctor. Never give over-the-counter diarrhoea remedies to a baby – all the effective remedies contain morphine or a similar substance and can have serious side effects in a young baby; they are only suitable for adults and older children.

Babies who are breastfed are less likely to suffer diarrhoeal illness than those who are bottle fed. Projectile vomiting means that the vomit is very forceful – so much so that it might reach the other side of the room. Babies who have projectile vomiting may have a problem with the outflow to the stomach and will need to be assessed by a doctor. (Posseting is the term used to describe what happens when a baby has had a little too much milk. There is often a hiccup and a little milk comes back up, hence the cloth or tissue that many mums keep on their shoulder when they cuddle their baby after a feed! Vomiting is, in contrast, nearly always more forceful and there is a greater quantity regurgitated.)

EAR, NOSE, AND THROAT

Blocked noses

Babies often get blocked noses. If your baby has difficulty breathing when feeding, your GP can prescribe some drops to apply in her nose just before you feed.

Croup

Croup is a viral infection that affects the larynx or voice box. It causes laryngitis in adults and older children, but in the very small air passages that babies have it causes a characteristic noise as they breathe in. The noise sounds a bit like a sea lion barking. Croup used to be treated with steam, and it is worth sitting with your baby in a steamy atmosphere for 20 minutes to see if this helps. However, many doctors now feel that the more severe cases benefit from a short course of steroid drugs given by mouth. As the condition is nearly always caused by viruses, antibiotics are unlikely to help. Croup has become quite rare since the advent of the Hib vaccine given to babies at 8, 12, and 16 weeks. Due to the vaccine the most serious complication of croup, epiglottitis, is now hardly ever seen.

Earache

Colds can often lead to ear infections, as the throat and inner ear are linked by a passage called the Eustachian tube. Presumably the same happens to babies, but of course they can't tell us that they have a sore ear. We only know if they become fretful or perhaps pull on their ears. Doctors are now less likely to prescribe antibiotics for ear infections as most of these infections are caused by viruses that are not killed by antibiotics. If you think your baby might have an ear infection try some infant paracetamol. If your baby is otherwise well then wait until you are next visiting the doctor at the surgery. (See Chest Problems on p.232 for information on colds and coughs.)

EYES

Conjunctivitis is very common in babies. If your baby has a sticky or red eye, bathe it with warm water and cotton wool. Use a new piece for each eye so as not to spread infection. If this doesn't clear it, make an appointment at the surgery. Your doctor may prescribe some antibiotic drops. Babies hate having eye drops inserted. Try wrapping your baby in a towel or blanket to put the drops in her eyes. It is easier if there are two of you to do this. Pull the lower eyelid down and squeeze the dropper. Don't worry if most of it seems to come out. Even the tiniest amount will dissolve in the tears and spread over the surface of the eye. Conjunctivitis is very infectious so give your baby her own towel and be scrupulous about washing your hands before and after treating her eyes.

FEVER

You will soon get to know when your baby has a fever. Her skin will feel hot and she will be listless. At the start of many infections it is usual for the body temperature to rise every few hours to a peak, then to go back to normal. Fever should be treated with infant paracetamol and, if necessary, tepid sponging. This means sponging your baby's skin with a sponge or flannel soaked in tepid water. Let

the water evaporate on the baby's skin or fan it dry. Babies usually dislike this process but it is effective in bringing temperature down.

If a baby remains very listless even once you have tried treating the fever you should call your doctor. Babies may occasionally be admitted to hospital for observation if they do not perk up after paracetamol and sponging. Your doctor will check for such things as meningitis (see General Skin Rashes on p.234). Meningitis causes the baby to be very listless. The doctor will also check for skin rashes, especially a rash that looks like tiny bruises that don't go pale, even if you press on them. Remember that even if your baby has been checked by a doctor and given the all-clear things can change, and if new symptoms develop you should report back to your doctor.

Babies who are very listless in spite of infant paracetamol and sponging need to be checked by a doctor. When body temperature rises to a very high level in under fives they may have a febrile convulsion. If this happens a baby may seem to be unconscious and begin to shake. It will last about a minute, although it will seem longer than that. Although this may not be as serious as it looks you should call your doctor right away, as he/she will want to check her over.

Babies may bounce back when their temperature comes back to normal. They may seem quite normal for an hour or two then the whole thing starts again. You may need to nurse your baby through the night when she has a fever. Accept any offers of help because it can be quite exhausting nursing a child with fever through two or three days.

MUMPS

Mumps has become quite rare since the MMR vaccine was introduced in 1988. It is caused by a virus so there is no specific treatment for it. The incubation period is 16-21 days. Children who have mumps will be feverish, lethargic, and have very enlarged glands under the jaw and sometimes in the cheek. A rare complication is that it can affect the testicles (more common in adults). Children should be treated, as with any viral illness, with fluids and infant paracetamol for fever.

SKIN PROBLEMS

Birthmarks

Your baby's skin may look blotchy and wrinkled in the early weeks, and sometimes there are darker areas (so-called strawberry birthmarks) on the forehead, eyelids, or around the back of neck. They can look worrying, especially as they may initially grow, but they will fade as your child gets older. These are sometimes called "stork bites". A "port wine stain" is darker, may be slightly raised, and doesn't usually fade. Whatever birthmark your baby may have, it is best to leave it alone as most will fade on their own over the coming months.

Cradle cap

Cradle cap is a scaly condition that affects a baby's scalp. It may be linked to a condition called seborrhoeic dermatitis, which both children and adults can get, but the exact cause is unknown. The old-fashioned treatment of rubbing olive oil into the baby's scalp at night is still as good as any (the oil should be washed off the next day). Tempting as it is, if you pick off the scales you will pull out the hair at the same time.

Dry skin, itchy skin, and eczema

Dry skin is itchy skin! Eczema and dermatitis mean the same thing: dry, itchy, inflamed skin. We do not know why it occurs but it may run in some families, although breastfed babies are less at risk. Dry skin and eczema benefit from regular moisturizing with creams and prescription bath lotion. If the skin becomes more inflamed doctors sometimes prescribe steroid creams. These can thin the skin if over-used so it is important to use them sparingly and for the shortest possible time. The opposite applies to moisturizers, which are available on prescription. They can also be bought but are expensive. Tell your pharmacist what it is for and he/she will advise you on an appropriate product. You may need to try more than one to find the one that suits your baby. Apply plenty of moisturizer to your baby's skin regularly, especially after baths.

Babies can sometimes get contact eczema from washing powders or fabric conditioners, for example. These are treated in the same way, although you should also change your washing powder and avoid fabric conditioner.

General skin rashes

Possible causes:

1. Dry skin
2. Sweat rash
3. Milia
4. Eczema
5. Allergy
6. Ringworm
7. Fifth disease
8. Hand, foot, and mouth disease
9. Chickenpox
10. Measles
11. Rubella
12. Roseola infantum
13. Meningitis

The last five will be accompanied by a definite fever (see separate entry, below). The fever usually comes on first and then the rash appears. Rubella and measles are less common since the advent of the MMR vaccine. Measles is generally a severe illness with high fever, lots of catarrh, and a profuse rash of red spots. Babies with measles are usually very unwell and would need to see a doctor. Rubella is much less severe and causes a pinhead rash that only lasts a day or two.

Chickenpox causes small blisters that occur in crops over a week and then crust over. Your baby is infectious until the last blister has crusted. If you recognize that your baby has chickenpox and are confident about treatment then there is no need to see the doctor. However, you should always see your doctor if you are unsure about the diagnosis, or if your baby seems more unwell than you would expect.

Roseola infantum is a mild viral illness that can cause a temperature and rash in babies and young children aged between six months and three years. The high temperature and fine, raised, red skin rash can last from a few hours to three to five days. The fever should be treated with infant paracetamol.

Hand, foot, and mouth disease causes small spots on the hands, feet, and mouth (but also up the backs of the child's legs). The spots are usually on the palms, soles of the feet, and on the soft palate at the back of the mouth. It is caused by a virus and is usually a fairly mild illness. Slapped cheek disease, or "Fifth" disease, is also caused by a virus and does not usually result in the infant being very ill. The "slapped cheek" label refers to the very red cheeks that are the effect of this illness.

Meningitis is very rare but very serious. If it is picked up early it can be treated. Contact your doctor if your baby is unusually listless, even after paracetamol. The rash of meningitis is very distinctive: it looks like tiny pink or purple bruises that do not go pale when you press on them. You can see they do not fade if you press a glass against them. If you see these, your baby needs to be checked by a hospital doctor right away.

Milia (also known as milk rash) are small white spots on a baby's face. Although no one knows why they occur, they don't need treatment and will clear up on their own. A sweat rash causes small reddish-coloured bumps that go pale if you press them. They are nearly always in skin folds but can occur in other areas in very hot weather.

Ringworm is a fungal infection, not dissimilar to athlete's foot but affecting dry skin areas. It has nothing whatsoever to do with worms. It looks a bit scaly and can form a ring, hence the name. It is sometimes referred to by its medical name, Tinea. It is easily treated by antifungal creams, which can be bought over the counter, although most pharmacists would advise seeing a doctor first if it the baby is under a year old.

Allergic rashes can take the form of small pinhead spots over the trunk, or sometimes the whole body. They can also take the form of urticaria or "hives". These are red, raised blotches, often with a paler area in the middle if the patch is quite large. Smaller urticarial spots look like a nettle rash. If your child suddenly develops urticaria speak to a doctor or nurse. If the urticaria affects the head or neck go to your doctor's surgery or casualty right away. Urticaria is treated with antihistamines. In the case of urticaria the allergy is often due to something your baby has eaten, but it can also occur with bee, wasp, and jellyfish stings. Allergies to washing powder and so on are more likely to look like eczema – dry, inflamed skin.

Impetigo

Impetigo is a skin infection. It is caused by a bacterium so can be treated with antibiotics. The bacteria are more likely to infect if there is a cut in the skin or if there is inflamed eczema. The patches look inflamed and have yellowish crusts that weep if picked. It is very infectious. Make sure that your baby has her own towel when she has impetigo, and be especially careful to wash your hands frequently.

Jaundice

It is very common for a baby to appear jaundiced in the days following birth. Premature babies are more prone to this. Jaundice is a yellowish discolouration of the skin caused by the build up of a pigment called bilirubin in the blood. If your midwife feels it is necessary, she may check a blood sample to determine the amount of bilirubin. Most cases do not require treatment but some babies will benefit from a form of light therapy known as phototherapy.

Nappy rash and thrush

Nappy rash is caused by one of the constituents of urine being in contact with the skin in the nappy area. It causes red inflamed skin that can become weepy. Treat it with fresh air if you can, make frequent nappy changes, and use barrier creams. If your child is distressed during nappy changes or the skin is weeping you may need a prescription for anti-fungal cream.

Babies may also sometimes develop oral thrush. This causes white patches on the baby's tongue and inside the mouth. It can cause problems with feeding, as the baby appears to have mouth discomfort, and it can be associated with breast thrush in a breast-feeding mother. Oral thrush is treated either with nystatin drops or miconazole oral gel, which are both available on prescription.

Spots

Small white spots are called "milk rash" and they clear up with time (see General Skin Rashes on p.234). If the spots are red with a yellow centre, more like pimples, they are called neo-natal urticaria and are a sign that your baby's skin pores are not yet working efficiently. Again these don't need treatment as they will clear up in time – don't be tempted to squeeze them as you will leave scars.

A–Z glossary

Afterpains are period-like pains, often felt in the first few days after birth as the womb contracts down to its normal size. They tend to be stronger after second and subsequent births.

Amniotic Fluid, commonly known as "the waters", is the clear liquid (mainly made of water) that surrounds and protects the foetus in the womb.

Apgar score is a numerical indicator of the physical condition of your baby after birth. Medical staff observe your baby's heartrate, breathing, muscle tone, reactions, and skin colour, and give a score for each on a scale of one to ten.

Bilirubin is a product of the breakdown of red blood cells and is the yellow skin pigment associated with jaundice.

Caesarean is an abdominal operation to deliver your baby through a horizontal or vertical incision in the abdomen.

Casein is the part of the milk that forms curds. It is produced as the first step in digesting milk in the stomach.

Colic is a term used to describe persistent crying, especially in the evening. The specific definition is crying that lasts for more than three hours a day, more than three days a week, in a baby less than

three months old. Colic is seen in about 20 percent of infants and there are many explanations about why it occurs and what treatment is best (see pp.152–5).

Colostrum is the substance produced by the breasts in the early days after birth. It looks different from usual breastmilk as it is more yellow in colour, and thicker. Colostrum has many beneficial qualities, being high in protein, minerals, and antibodies that protect your baby from infection.

Cystic Fibrosis is the most common serious genetic disease of Caucasian children, caused by a recessive gene being passed to the child from both parents. CF causes the lungs, pancreas, mouth, and gastro-intestinal tract to produce thick sticky mucous, and it also affects the sweat glands of the skin. Early detection means that symptoms can be treated quickly, leading to better long-term outcomes.

Diamorphine is a drug related to morphine that is used to relieve severe pain.

Diurnal rhythms are the natural changes in our bodies that are linked to day and night. Governed by melatonin and other hormones, diurnal changes in our body-temperature and metabolism make it easier for us to sleep at night than during the day.

Doula comes from a Greek word meaning "woman servant" or "caregiver". A doula is a woman who is trained to support women emotionally and in practical ways through the process of birth and in the days and weeks afterwards.

Down's syndrome is a genetic disorder where the affected person carries an extra chromosome in each cell. People with DS have varying degrees of learning difficulty and a characteristic appearance; a proportion also have heart defects.

Engorged literally means "excessively full", but is a term often used in the postnatal period to describe a breast that has become too full of milk. An engorged breast will feel heavy and tight and the nipple may be flattened, leading to difficulty in the baby latching on for a feed.

Entonox is the medical name for what is often known as "gas and air". It is a mixture of 50 percent nitrous oxide (or laughing gas) and 50 percent air. It is often used as a painkiller in the first stage of labour as its effects are short-lived and it can be administered by the woman herself. Entonox is inhaled through a mouthpiece or a mask.

Epidural is a local anaesthetic administered into the spine during labour, which numbs the nerves supplying the womb and cervix, as well as the legs and feet.

Episiotomy is a cut made to the perineum (*see* p.237) to enlarge the vaginal opening in order to aid birth, especially when instruments such as forceps must be used.

Fontanelle is a membrane-covered space between the bones of the skull. To enable babies to pass through the birth canal the bones of their skulls are not fused as they are in adults. Fontanelles close within about two months of birth.

Forceps are long, tong-like instruments used to help the baby be born. They enable the baby's head to be guided through the birth canal.

Gastroenteritis is an acute bacterial or viral infection of the digestive system. If your baby has gastroenteritis she may vomit and will have diarrhoea. Prolonged or severe bouts of gastroenteritis can cause dehydration (*see* p.232 of Common Illnesses).

Immunization is the process in which a baby is given small doses of a modified form of an organism to promote immunity from a particular disease (*see* pp.194–5).

Inoculation is the introduction of an active agent that confers immunity.

Jaundice is seen, in some degree, in 60 percent of newborn babies, and is caused by high levels of bilirubin in the blood. It usually resolves after a few days, although some infants may need phototherapy treatment.

Lactose intolerance is a form of allergic indigestion, with symptoms of nausea, abdominal cramps, diarrhoea, and weight loss, caused by an individual's lack of the enzyme lactase (which breaks down sugars in milk).

Let-down reflex is a point near the start of a breastfeed when the milk starts to flow freely from the milk sacks into the milk ducts and down to the nipple. In most women this occurs after the baby's first few sucks, but it may take up to about a minute. It may be experienced as a tingling, buzzing feeling and is often pleasurable – although a few women find it uncomfortable and even painful.

Lochia is the name for the vaginal discharge after birth. At first lochia is bright red blood; over the course of the first week the blood goes from bright to dark red, and then turns brownish. Lochia becomes increasingly light in colour over time until it stops altogether after about six weeks.

Mastitis is an infection of the breast. Mastitis can make the affected breast very tender, hot, and sore and an infected woman may also experience flu-like symptoms and a high temperature. Sometimes mastitis is diagnosed incorrectly and the problem is simply a blocked milk duct.

Meconium is a very dark, tar-like substance that is found in babies' nappies in the first few days after birth.

Mongolian blue spot is a form of birthmark seen in dark-skinned babies. It is a collection of pigment usually seen in the small of the back or top of the buttocks. It usually disappears by the time the child is three to four years old.

Moro reflex is a primitive reflex seen in young babies. When a baby is moved downwards sharply, as though about to be dropped, she throws out her arms and legs, stiffens her body, and then makes a clinging movement.

Necrotizing entercolitis is a condition in which part of the tissue in the intestines is destroyed. It occurs mainly in under-weight and premature newborn babies.

Oxytocin is known as the "hormone of love", and is thought to be responsible for a mother's need to be near her infant. In the days following the birth oxytocin causes the womb to contract, and it also causes milk to be squeezed out of the breast during feeds.

Paediatrician is a doctor who specializes in the health of infants, babies, and children.

Passive immunity is the protection against disease through antibodies produced by another human being. Passive immunity is effective, but protection is generally limited and diminishes over time (usually a few weeks or months). For example, maternal antibodies are passed to the infant prior to birth; these antibodies temporarily protect the baby for the first four to six months of life.

Perineum is the tissue that lies between the back of the vagina and the anus.

Pethidine is an opiod (related to opium) drug sometimes given to women in labour via injection. Pain relief is stronger than "gas and air", however, some women find that it makes them feel sick and disorientated. Pethedine given to a labouring woman too close to the birth will affect her baby, making him sleepy and disinclined to suck.

Placenta is an organ that feeds a baby in the womb. It is the place where oxygen and nutrients in the mother's blood are passed into the baby's blood and then travel to her body via the umbilical cord.

Postpartum is the official term for the period immediately following childbirth, lasting about six weeks.

Prolactin is a hormone associated with the supply of breastmilk. It begins to be secreted during the final months of pregnancy and then for as long as breastfeeding is established. More prolactin is secreted at night, when milk production increases. High prolactin levels inhibit the menstrual cycle and so stop periods from returning straight after birth in most women.

Resuscitaire is a cot-like piece of special care breathing apparatus for the immediate care of newborn babies, used in neonatal units.

Rooting reflex is the instinctive response of a baby that helps her to feed from the breast. When a hungry baby feels something against her cheek she turns towards the feeling and opens her mouth wide. Using the rooting instinct can help you to get your baby to latch effectively at the breast.

Skin-to-skin means physical contact between the naked skin of the baby and mother. It is thought to be especially comforting and also stimulating to very young infants.

Spina Bifida is a congenital defect in which part of one or more of the vertebra fails to develop properly, leaving a portion of the spinal cord exposed. The severity of the condition varies widely depending on the site and extent of the malformation.

Syntometrine is an artificial hormone that may be given to women in the second stage of labour to speed up the third stage, which is when the placenta is expelled, the womb begins to contract down, and bleeding slows. It is possible to choose not to be given syntometrine and thereby have a "natural third stage".

Thrush is a fungal infection that some infants acquire in their mouths. It can cause discomfort during feeding and can be seen as white patches on the gums and cheeks. Breastfed babies may pass thrush to their mothers, causing sore nipples and possibly pain. Thrush can be treated with anti-fungal drugs, administered to both baby and mother.

Top and tail is a term commonly used to refer to the head and nappy areas of the baby that need frequent cleaning.

Umbilical cord is the gristly cord that connects the baby to the placenta in the womb. After the birth the cord is cut and clipped at a point near to the baby's abdomen. This short piece of cord shrivels and falls off over the first week after birth, leaving the "tummy button".

Urates are compounds sometimes passed in a baby's urine. They may cause red stains on the nappy, although as they occur at the same time as the meconium you are unlikely to notice them.

Vaccines are medical preparations containing dead or de-activated organisms that, when introduced to the body, confer immunity.

Ventouse is an obstetric instrument for helping the baby be born. Using suction to attach a cup-like appendage to the head, the baby can be drawn down the birth canal.

Vernix is a greasy substance that covers the baby's skin and can be seen when she is born. It moisturizes the skin and protects it from becoming waterlogged by the amniotic fluid when she is in the womb.

Useful organizations

CAESAREAN BIRTH
Caesarean Support Network
55 Cooil Drive
Douglas
Isle of Man IM2 2HF, UK
Tel: 01624 661 269
(evenings and weekends)
Email: yvonnewilliams@manx.net
Fax: 01624 266 49
Listens to and offers support and help
to women who have had, or may need
to have, a Caesarean section.

DISABLED CHILD
Contact a Family
209–211 City Road
London EC1V 1JN, UK
Freephone helpline: 0808 808 3555
(Mon-Fri 10am-4pm)
Tel: 020 7608 8702 (minicom)
Tel: 020 7608 8700 (administration)
www.cafamily.org.uk/dirworks.html
Email: info@cafamily.org.uk
Fax: 020 7608 8701
Help specifically for parents and carers
of children with disabilities, rare disorders,
or any kind of special needs.

National Portage Association
PO BOX 3075
BA21 3FB, UK
Tel: 0962 60148
www.portage.org.uk
Email: info@portage.org.uk
Portage is a home-visiting service (England
and Wales only) for pre-school children who
have special needs.

DISABLED PARENT
Disabled Parents Network
Unit F9
89–93 Fonthill Road
London N4 3JH, UK
Tel: 0870 241 0450
Tel: 0800 018 9949 (textphone)
www.disabledparentsnetwork.org.uk/
Email: information@disabledparentsnet-
work.org.uk
Fax: 020 7263 6399
Disabled parent-to-disabled parent support.

DPPI (Disability, Pregnancy, and Parenthood International)
Unit F9
89–93 Fonthill Road
London N4 3JH, UK
Tel: 0800 0184 730
www.dppi.org.uk
Email: info@dppi.org.uk
Fax: 020 7263 6399
Practical information – for example on
bathing or lifting your baby. At the same
address and telephone number is the
National Centre for Disabled Parents.
This organization gives one-to-one support
with ongoing issues such as assessments
or complaints.

REMAP
Hazeldene
Ightham
Sevenoaks
Kent TN15 9AD, UK
Tel: 0845 130 0456
www.remap.org.uk
Email: info@remap.org.uk
Fax: 0845 130 0789
Supplies equipment (including adjustable
baby cribs) for disabled parents.

REMAP (Scotland)
Maulside Lodge
Beith
Ayrshire KA15 1JJ, UK
Tel: 01294 832 566
Fax: 01294 834 162
Supplies equipment (including adjustable
baby cribs) for disabled parents.

FEEDING YOUR BABY
The Breastfeeding Network
PO Box 11126
Paisley PA2 8YB, UK
Tel: 0870 900 8787 (supporters' line:
9.30am–9.30pm every day of the year.
Connects caller automatically to their local
Breastfeeding Supporter. Calls charged at
local rates. Calls from mobiles are accepted.)
www.breastfeedingnetwork.org.uk
Email: email@breastfeedingnetwork.org.uk
Provide breastfeeding information and
support. They have a number of drop-in
centres around the UK (details given on
their website).

La Leche League (Great Britain)
PO Box 29
West Bridgford
Nottingham NG2 7NP, UK
Tel: 020 7242 1278 (24hr helpline: puts
caller in touch with nearest local breast-
feeding supporter)
www.laleche.org.uk
Email: lllgb@wsds.co.uk
Breastfeeding information and support.

HOMEOPATHY/OSTEOPATHY FOR BABIES
Institute for Complementary Medicine (ICM)
PO Box 194
London SE16 7QZ , UK
Tel: 020 7237 5165
www.icmedicine.co.uk
Email: info@icmedicine.co.uk
Fax: 020 7237 5175
Provides the public with information on
complementary medicine. Also holds a
register of professional practitioners.

IMMUNIZATION

HealthchoiceUK
Regus House
Victory Way, Admirals Park
Crossways, Dartford
Kent DA2 6AG, UK
Tel: 0870 442 3993
www.healthchoiceuk.co.uk
Email: info@healthchoiceuk.co.uk
Health care group offering single vaccines
for MMR at clinics all over the UK.

Immunization page of the
Department of Health website
www.immunisation.nhs.uk
Information on immunization research.

Immunization page of the
"What Doctors Don't Tell You" website
www.wddty.co.uk
Information on immunization research.

Informed Parent
PO Box 870
Harrow
Middlesex HA3 7UW, UK
(Please enclose a SAE if writing)
Tel: 020 8861 1022
Questions routine immunization; support
and information on vaccine decisions.

**JABS (Justice Awareness
and Basic Support)**
1 Gawsworth Road
Golborne
Warrington WA3 3RF, UK
Tel: 01942 713 565
Information on immunization research.

MULTIPLE BIRTHS

**Twins and Multiple Birth
Association (TAMBA)**
2 The Willows
Gardner Road
Guildford
Surrey GU1 4PG, UK
Tel: 0870 770 3305 (9.30am–5pm, Mon to Fri)
Twinline: 0800 138 0509 (10am–1pm and
7pm–11pm every day, all year round)
www.tamba.org.uk
Email: enquiries@tamba.org.uk
Fax: 0870 770 3303
Aims to provide information and mutual
support networks for families of twins,
triplets, and more, highlighting their
unique needs to all involved in their care.

PARENT SUPPORT

**AIMS (Association for Improvements
in Maternity Services)**
5 Ann's Court
Grove Road
Surbiton
Surrey KT6 4BE, UK
Tel: 0870 765 1453
Helpline: 0870 765 1433
www.aims.org.uk
Email: chair@aims.org.uk
Fax: 0870 765 1454
Supports parents and professionals
in the UK and Ireland.

Action against Medical Accidents (AvMA)
44 High Street
Croydon
Surrey CR0 1YB , UK
(NB: no unarranged visitors admitted)
Helpline: 0845 123 2352 (10am–12 noon
and 2–4pm Mon to Fri)
Tel: 020 8688 9555 (admin only)
www.avma.org.uk
Email: admin@avma.org.uk
Fax: 020 8667 9065
Team of medically and legally trained
caseworkers who can provide free
and confidential advice on such things
as rights and compensation following
a medical accident.

Birth Crisis Network
Tel: 01865 300 266 (answerphone: calls
will be responded to within 24 hours)
Tel: 01454 299 449
www.sheilakitzinger.com/Birth%20Crisis.htm
Offers reflective listening to women who
want to talk about a traumatic birth.

The Birth Trauma Association
PO Box 1996
SP1 3RQ, UK
www.birthtraumaassociation.org.uk
Email:
enquiries@birthtraumaassociation.org.uk
Provides support for women who have
suffered traumatic birth experiences.

Children 1st
83 Whitehouse Loan
Edinburgh EH9 1AT, UK
Tel: 0131 446 2300
www.children1st.org.uk
Email them directly from their website
Fax: 0131 446 2339
This organization supports families under
stress throughout Scotland, protects children
from harm and neglect, helps children
recover from abuse, and promotes
children's rights and interests.

Doula UK
PO Box 22678
London N14 4WB, UK
www.doula.org.uk
info@doula.org.uk
Doulas provide emotional and practical
support to enable a woman to have the
most satisfying time that she can during
pregnancy, birth, and the early days as
a new mum. Doula UK gives advice on
locating and employing a doula.

**Early Childhood Unit at
the National Children's Bureau**
Sue Owen, Director
Early Childhood Unit
National Children's Bureau
8 Wakley Street
London EC1V 7QE, UK
Tel: 020 7843 6071
www.earlychildhood.org.uk
Email: earlychildhood@ncb.org.uk
The Early Childhood Unit has resources
on baby development, as well as talking
and listening to your baby, that may be
of interest to parents.

Fathers Direct
Herald House
15 Lamb's Passage
Bunhill Row
London EC1Y 8TQ, UK
www.fathersdirect.com
Email: enquiries@fathersdirect.com
Fax: 020 7374 2966
Support specifically for fathers.

Gingerbread
16–17 Clerkenwell Close
London EC2R 0AN, UK
Tel: 0800 018 4318
(advice line: 9am–5pm Mon to Fri)
www.gingerbread.org.uk
Email: office@gingerbread.org.uk
Fax: 020 7336 8185
Local groups for lone parents.

Grandparents' Association
Moot House
The Stow
Harlow
Essex CM20 3AG, UK
Helpline: 01279 444 964
Tel: 01279 428 040 (administration)
www.grandparents-association.org.uk
Email: info@grandparents-
association.org.uk
Support for the grandparent/grandchild
relationship. Services include an advice and
information line, publications, support groups,
and Grandparent and Toddler groups.

Home-Start
2 Salisbury Road
Leicester LE1 7QR, UK
Tel: 0800 068 63 68 (for information about
Home-Start and to find your nearest scheme)
Tel: 0116 233 9955 (administration)
www.home-start.org.uk
International: www.home-start-int.org
Email: info@home-start.org.uk
Fax: 0116 233 0232
"Home-Start schemes offer support,
friendship, and practical help to families
with children under five, in their own homes."

**International Childbirth
Education Association**
PO Box 20048
Minneapolis
Minnesota 55420, USA
Tel: 952 854 8660
www.icea.org
E-mail: info@icea.org
Fax: 952 854 8772
Provides information and support to
expectant and new parents. Believes in
freedom of choice based on knowledge
of alternatives in family-centred maternity
and newborn care.

Irish Childbirth Trust
Denise Garde
Carmichael Centre
North Brunswick Street
Dublin 7, Ireland
Tel: +353 (0)1 872 4501
www.cuidiu-ict.ie
Email: info@cuidiu-ict.ie
Information and support during pregnancy
and parenthood, based on the principle of
informed choice.

National Childbirth Trust (NCT)
Alexandra House
Oldham Terrace
London W3 6NH, UK
Enquiry line: 0870 444 8707 (9am–5pm
Mon to Thu and 9am–4pm Fri)
Breastfeeding line: 0870 444 8708
(8am–10pm 7 days a week)
Administration line: 0870 770 3236
www.nctpregnancyandbabycare.com
Email: enquiries@national-childbirth-trust.co.uk
Caesarean e-group, open to non-members:
http://groups.yahoo.com/group/
nct-caesarean
Fax: 0870 770 3237
Offers support in pregnancy, childbirth,
and early parenthood. Aims to give every
parent the chance to make informed
choices. Tries to make sure that all their
services, activities, and membership are
fully accessible to everyone.

National NEWPIN
Sutherland House
35 Sutherland Square
London SE17 3EE, UK
Tel: 020 7358 5900
www.newpin.org.uk
E-mail: info@newpin.org.uk
Fax: 020 7701 2660
Support for families with young children.

One-parent Families
255 Kentish Town Road
London NW5 2LX, UK
Helpline: 0800 018 5026
www.oneparentfamilies.org.uk
Helpdesk:
www.oneparentfamilies.org.uk/helpdesk
Email: info@oneparentfamilies.org.uk
(Not for personal advice: please phone
the helpline for that)
Fax: 020 7482 4851
Information service for single parents.

Parentline Plus
520 Highgate Studios
53–79 Highgate Road
Kentish Town
London NW5 1TL, UK
Freephone helpline: 0808 800 2222 (24hr)
Tel: 0800 783 6783 (textphone: 9am–5pm
Mon to Fri)
www.parentlineplus.org.uk
Email: centraloffice@parentlineplus.org.uk
Information and support for anyone in a
parenting role. Following the merger with
Parent Network it also runs parenting classes.

Parents Anonymous Inc.
675 West Foothill Blvd.
Suite 220
Claremont
CA 91711-3475, USA
Tel: 909 621 6184
www.parentsanonymous.org
E-mail:
Parentsanonymous@parentsanonymous.org
Fax: 909 625 6304
For parents who are finding things difficult.

PIPPIN (Parents in partnership –
parent infant network)
48 Drapers Road
Leyton
London E15 2AY, UK
Tel: 020 8519 8821
www.pippin.org.uk
Email: tracy@pippin.org.uk
Fax: 020 8519 8831
"PIPPIN is a national charity whose main
aim is to maintain and improve the
emotional health of families through… the
period surrounding the birth of a new baby."
The charity also provides parenting classes.

Planet One Parent
5 Park West
Southdown Park
Haywards Heath
West Sussex RH16 4SG, UK
Tel: 0870 907 2555
www.planetoneparent.com
Email: info@planetoneparent.com
Fax: 0870 907 2666
Support for single parents.

Relate
Herbert Gray College
Little Church Street
Rugby
Warwickshire CV21 3AP, UK
Tel: 01788 573 241 (9am–5pm Mon to Fri)
www.relate.org.uk
Email: enquiries@relate.org.uk
Fax: 01788 535 007
Advice, relationship counselling, sex therapy,
workshops, mediation, consultations,
and support face-to-face, by phone,
and through their website.

Sheila Kitzinger's Homepage
www.sheilakitzinger.com
Information and support on pregnancy,
birth, and parenthood topics.

SPAN (Single Parent Action Network)
Millpond
Baptist Street, Easton

Bristol BS5 0YW, UK
Tel: 0117 951 4231
www.singleparents.org.uk
Email: info@spanuk.org.uk
Fax: 0117 935 5208
Information and support for single parents.

POSTNATAL DEPRESSION
APNI (Association for Postnatal Illness)
145 Dawes Road
London SW6 7EB, UK
Tel: 020 7386 0868
(helpline and administration: 10am–2pm
Mon and Fri; 10am–5pm Tue, Wed, Thurs)
www.apni.org
Email: info@apni.org
Fax: 020 7386 8885
Advises and supports women suffering
from postnatal depression.

Meet a Mum Association (MAMA)
77 Westbury View
Peasedown St John
Bath BA2 8TZ, UK
Tel: 01761 433598 (general information)
Helpline: 020 8768 0123
(7–10pm Mon to Fri)
Email: meet-a-mum.assoc@blueyonder.co.uk
Supports mothers and mothers-to-be in
the UK by putting them in touch with other
mothers living nearby. Provides one-to-one
support for mothers suffering from postnatal
illness, and a helpline service for women
and their families.

MIND
Tel: 0845 7660 163 (information line)
www.mind.org.uk
Working to create a better life for those
experiencing mental distress. Local support
available in England and Wales only.

National Association for
Premenstrual Syndrome (NAPS)
7 Swift's Court
High Street
Seal
Kent TN15 0EG, UK

Helpline: 01732 760 012
Tel: 01732 760 011
(administration phone and fax)
www.pms.org.uk
Email: naps@pms.org.uk
Provides women and men with reliable
information, guidance, and support to
improve diagnosis and treatment, and
to increase awareness of PMS and
hormone-related ill health.

PND Productions
www.postnataldepression.com
Website about postnatal depression, which
includes details of Understanding Postnatal
Depression, an informative and practical
video for GPs, health visitors, and parents.

Surrey Post Natal Depression Support and
Information Website (part of Surrey NHS)
www.surreypnd.org.uk
A very helpful website with lots of
information on postnatal depression.

PREMATURE BABY
BLISS – The Premature Baby Charity
68 South Lambeth Road
London SW8 1RL, UK
Tel: 0870 7700 337 (for general calls from
both parents and health professionals,
9am–5.30pm Mon to Fri)
Parent support and information line:
0500 618 140 (10am–5pm Mon to Fri, but
callers can leave a message at other times)
www.bliss.org.uk
Email: information@bliss.org.uk
Fax: 0870 7700 338
Supports parents of babies in special
and intensive care.

Tommy's, The Baby Charity
Nicholas House
3 Laurence Pountney Hill
London EC4R 0BB, UK
Tel: 0870 777 30 60 (pregnancy information
line: 9am–5pm Mon to Fri)
www.tommys.org
Email: info@tommys.org

Tommy's is determined to end the heartache caused by premature birth, miscarriage, and stillbirth. It funds a national programme of research, education, and information aimed at understanding and preventing these tragedies.

RETURNING TO WORK

ACAS National Helpline
Tel: 08457 474747
See also the Department of Trade and industry employment website: www.dti.gov.uk/er/workingparents.htm
Advice on maternity/paternity rights and benefits.

Childcarelink
Freephone: 08000 960 296
www.childcarelink.gov.uk/index.asp
A government service providing information and advice on childcare.

Daycare Trust
(National Childcare Campaign)
21 St George's Road
London SE1 6ES, UK
Tel: 020 7840 3350 (10am–5pm Mon to Fri)
www.daycaretrust.org.uk
Email: info@daycaretrust.org.uk
Fax: 020 7840 3355
The national childcare charity, which aims to promote high-quality, affordable childcare for all.

Eeziminders
Tel: 01784 435 092
Provides emergency or backup childcare.

International Au Pair Association (IAPA)
Bredgade 25 H
DK – 1260
Copenhagen K, Denmark
Tel: +45 3317 0066
www.iapa.org
E-mail: mailbox@iapa.org
Fax: +45 3393 9676
Official representatives of Au Pair exchange programmes.

Maternity Alliance
Third Floor West
2–6 Northburgh Street
London EC1V 0AY, UK
Tel: 020 7490 7638
(24hr recorded information)
Tel: 020 7490 7639 (administration)
www.maternityalliance.org.uk
Email: info@maternityalliance.org.uk
Fax: 020 7014 1350
Information on maternity/paternity rights and benefits.

Nanny Payroll Service
Tel: 01536 373 111
www.nannypayroll.co.uk
Email: info@nannypayroll.co.uk
For a small fee, this organization can deal with pay, tax, and national insurance, and issue payslips should you employ a nanny.

Nanny Tax
PO Box 988
Brighton BN1 3NT, UK
Tel: 0845 226 2203 (for parents and nannies)
Tel: 0845 226 2205 (for nanny agencies)
www.nannytax.co.uk
Email: mailbox@nannytax.co.uk
(for parents & nannies)
info@nannytax.co.uk (for nanny agencies)
Fax: 01273 322 229
For a small fee, this organization can deal with pay, tax, and national insurance, and issue payslips should you employ a nanny.

National Childminding Association
8 Masons Hill
Bromley
Kent BR2 9EY, UK
Helpline: 0800 169 4486
(10am–12pm and 2–4pm Mon to Fri)
www.ncma.org.uk
Email: gill.haynes@ncma.org.uk
Fax: 020 8290 6834
Information on finding and employing a childminder. Regional offices throughout England and Wales can help with local enquiries about childminding.

Northern Ireland Childminding Association (NICMA)
16–18 Mill Street
Newtonards
Co. Down BT23 4LU, UK
Tel: 028 9181 1015
www.nicma.org/
Email: info@nicma.org
Fax: 028 9182 0921
Gives information and advice on all aspects of quality childminding services.

Working Families
(Formerly "Parents at Work")
1–3 Berry Street
London EC1V 0AA, UK
Helpline: 020 7253 7243
www.workingfamilies.org.uk
Email: office@workingfamilies.org.uk
Fax: 020 7253 6253
Information and support for those families combining paid work with caring for their children.

The Professional Association of Nursery Nurses (PANN)
Tricia Pritchard
Professional Officer (PANN)
2 St James' Court
Friar Gate
Derby DE1 1BT, UK
Tel: 01332 372 337
www.pat.org.uk
Email: pann@pat.org.uk
Fax: 01332 290 310
The nursery nurses' union. The website discusses professional practice. The association issues a Nanny Pack, which includes a sample contract and other useful information for potential employers.

The Recruitment and Employment Confederation
36–38 Mortimer Street
London W1W 7RG, UK
Tel: 020 7462 3260
Fax: 020 7255 2878
and

Albion House, Chertsey Road
Woking
Surrey GU21 6BT, UK
Tel: 020 7462 3260
Fax: 01483 714 979
www.rec.uk.com/rec/home/index.aspx
http://rec.bucksnet.co.uk/search/
(for details of nanny agencies)
Provides details of reputable nanny agencies
in your area. Nanny agencies charge for
their services, but the agency will usually
have checked their nannies and may be
able to provide you with someone quickly.

Scottish Childminding Association
Suite 3
7 Melville Terrace
Stirling FK8 2ND, UK
Tel: 01786 449 063 (advice line)
Tel: 01786 445 377 (administration)
www.childminding.org
Email them directly from their website
Fax: 01786 449 062
Advice on choosing a registered childminder.

Simply Childcare
16 Bushey Hill Road
London SE5 8QJ, UK
Tel: 020 7701 6111
www.simplychildcare.com
A fortnightly magazine available by
subscription (in London and surrounding
area only). It includes listings of parents
seeking childcare and carers offering
childcare, as well as advice, information,
and answers to questions about childcare.

More information on seeking childcare:

Your **local authority** will be listed in
the telephone directory.

Your local **phone book or yellow pages**
will list local day nurseries.

Advertising – put an ad in your local paper
or magazine detailing what you require, or
answer an ad put in by a nanny.

Agencies – your local phone book or
yellow pages may list au pair or mother's
help agencies. If you choose one that is a
member of either the International Au Pair
Association (IAPA) or the Recruitment and
Employment Confederation (REC), they will
have vetted their applicants for you.

SLEEPING
CRY-SIS Helpline
BM CRY-SIS
London WC1N 3XX, UK
Tel: 08451 228 669
(9am–10pm 7 days a week)
www.cry-sis.org.uk
Provides emotional support and practical
advice to parents of babies who cry
incessantly and have sleep problems,
and of older children with problems such
as temper tantrums, clinging, and long-
term crying.

OTHER
Alder Centre
Alder Hey Children's Hospital
Eaton Road
Liverpool L12 2AP, UK
Tel: 0151 252 5391 (information)
A listening service that offers emotional
support to all those affected by the death
of a child. Provides an opportunity to talk
in confidence with someone who has also
experienced the death of a child.

ARC (Antenatal Results and Choices)
73 Charlotte Street
London W1T 4PN, UK
Helpline: 020 7631 0285
(10am–6pm Mon to Fri)
Tel: 020 7631 0280 (admin and fax)
www.arc-uk.org
Email: arcsatfa@aol.com
For antenatal results and choices –
will discuss abnormal test results.

Baby Directory
7 Brockwell Park Row
London SW2 2YH, UK

Tel: 020 8678 9000
www.babydirectory.com
Email: editor@babydirectory.com
Useful advice and information
pre- and post-birth.

Child Accident Prevention Trust
18–20 Farringdon Lane
London EC1R 3HA, UK
Tel: 020 7608 3828
www.capt.org.uk
Email: safe@capt.org.uk
Fax: 020 7608 3674
Provides information and advice to parents
through publications and videos, and via a
telephone information service.

Child Bereavement Trust
Aston House
West Wycombe
Nr High Wycombe
Bucks HP14 3AG, UK
Tel: 0845 357 1000
(information and support service line)
Tel: 01494 446 648 (administration)
www.childbereavement.org.uk
Email: enquiries@childbereavement.org.uk
Fax: 01494 440 057
Support in the event of the death of a
child, including a professional helpline.

Child Death Helpline
Child Death Helpline Department
Great Ormond Street Hospital
Great Ormond Street
London WC1N 3JH, UK
Freephone helpline: 0800 282 986
(7–10 pm daily, 10am–1pm Mon to Fri,
1–4pm Wed)
Tel: 020 7813 8551 (administration)
www.childdeathhelpline.org.uk
Fax: 020 7813 8516

Compassionate Friends
53 North Street
Bristol BS3 1EN, UK
Helpline: 0845 123 2304
(10am–4pm and 6.30–10.30pm)

Tel: 0845 120 3785 or 0117 966 5202
(administration: 9.30am–5pm Mon to Fri)
www.tcf.org.uk
Email: info@tcf.org.uk
Fax: 0845 120 3786 or 0117 914 4368
An organization of bereaved parents and
their families offering understanding, support,
and encouragement to others after the
death of a child or children. Also offers
support, advice, and information to other
relatives, friends, and professionals who are
helping the bereaved family.

Continence Foundation
The Helpline Nurse
307 Hatton Square
16 Baldwins Gardens
London EC1N 7RJ, UK
(Please provide a SAE if writing)
Helpline: 0845 345 0165
(9.30am–1pm Mon to Fri)
www.continence-foundation.org.uk
Email: continence-help@dial.pipex.com
Please give your postal address so that
relevant leaflets etc can be sent (in a
confidential plain envelope)
Fax: 020 7404 6876
Provides information, advice, and expertise
on bladder and bowel problems.

Cruse-Bereavement Care
126 Sheen Road
Richmond-upon-Thames
Surrey TW9 1UR, UK
Helpline: 0870 167 1677
(9.30am–5pm Mon to Fri)
Tel: 020 8940 4818 (administration)
www.crusebereavementcare.org.uk
Email: info@crusebereavementcare.org.uk
Fax: 020 8940 7638
Anyone can contact Cruse if they want
to talk about themselves or someone they
know who has been affected by a death.

Foundation for the Study
of Infant Deaths (FSID)
Artillery House
11–19 Artillery Row

London SW1P 1RT, UK
Helpline: 0870 787 0554
Tel: 0870 787 0885 (general)
www.sids.org.uk
Email: fsid@sids.org.uk
Fax: 0870 787 0725
Funds research, supports bereaved families,
and promotes information on how to
reduce the risk of cot death to health
professionals and the public.

Guild of Pregnancy and
Postnatal Exercise Instructors
www.postnatalexercise.co.uk
A non-profit making organization based in
the UK. Promotes the teaching of specialized
exercise courses for mothers during child-
bearing years and offers support and
training to exercise instructors.

Health & Safety Executive
HSE Infoline
Caerphilly Business Park
Caerphilly CF83 3GG, UK
Tel: 08701 545 500
Tel: 02920 808 5537 (minicom)
www.hse.gov.uk/contact/index.htm
Email: hseinformationservices@natbrit.com
Fax: 02920 859 260
Provides rapid access to the Health &
Safety Executive's wealth of health and
safety information, and access to expert
advice and guidance.

International Association
of Infant Massage
IAIM UK Office
56 Sparsholt Road
Barking
Essex IG11 7YQ, UK
Tel: 07816 289 788 (10.30am–2.30pm Mon
to Fri; answerphone at other times)
www.iaim.org.uk
Email: mail@iaim.org.uk
Fax: 020 7602 7390
Information on benefits of infant massage.
IAIM also trains infant massage instructors,
provides special needs support, and helps

to promote positive touch through massage
nationally. The website gives contact details
for local practitioners, or send an SAE. Also
many international chapters, including:
Susie Fletcher
1891 Goodyear Avenue, Suite 622
Ventura
CA 93003-/8001, USA
Tel: 805 644 8524
www.iaim-us.com
E-mail: iaim4us@aol.com
Fax: 805 644 7699

YMCA England
640 Forest Road
London E17 3DZ, UK
www.ymca.org.uk
Information on exercise and "mind
and body" classes in England.

National Council of YMCAs of Wales
Lord Aberdare House
27 Church Road, Whitchurch
Cardiff CF14 2DX, UK
Tel: 029 2062 8745/8746
www.ymca-wales.org
E-mail: contact@ymca-wales.org
Fax: 029 2052 0552
Information on exercise and
"mind and body" classes in Wales.

YMCA Scotland
11 Rutland Street
Edinburgh EH1 2AE, UK
Tel: 0131 228 1464
www.ymcascotland.org
E-mail: info@ymcascotland.org
Fax: 0131 228 5462
Information on exercise and "mind
and body" classes in Scotland.

YMCA Ireland
Tel: 02890 327 757 (UK)
Tel: 02148 50 015 (ROI)
www.ymca-ireland.org
E-mail: admin@ymca-ireland.org
Information on exercise and
"mind and body" classes in Ireland.

Meningitis Trust

Fern House, Bath Road
Stroud
Gloucestershire GL5 3TJ, UK
24-hour nurse-led helplines:
UK: 0845 6000 800
International: +44 870 124 7000
Republic of Ireland: 1800 523 196
Australia: 1800 129 068
New Zealand: 0800 446 087
www.meningitis-trust.org.uk
Email: info@meningitis-trust.org
Fax: 01453 768 001
Provides support to people affected by
meningitis and septicaemia, whenever it
is needed and for as long as it is needed.

Miscarriage Association

c/o Clayton Hospital
Northgate, Wakefield
West Yorkshire WF1 3JS, UK
Helpline: 01924 200799 (9am–4pm Mon
to Fri, answerphone outside these hours)
Scottish helpline: 0131 334 8883
Tel: 01924 200 795 (administration)
www.miscarriageassociation.org.uk
Email: info@miscarriageassociation.org.uk
Support and information for all those
affected by pregnancy loss. Provides
a network of local telephone contacts
and support groups across the UK.

National Society for the Prevention of Cruelty to Children (NSPCC)

National Centre, 42 Curtain Road
London EC2A 3NH, UK
24-hour child protection helpline:
0808 800 5000
Tel: 0800 056 0566 (textphone)
Tel: 020 7825 2500 (administration)
www.nspcc.org.uk
Email: infounit@nspcc.org.uk
Fax: 020 7825 2525
The UK's leading charity specializing in
child protection and the prevention of
cruelty to children. Helpline has information,
advice, and counselling for anyone
concerned about a child's safety.

NCT Sales Ltd

239 Shawbridge Street
Glasgow G43 1QN, UK
Tel: 0870 112 1120
www.nctms.co.uk
Email: sales@nctms.co.uk
Fax: 0141 636 0606
Beautiful and useful products to help make
pregnancy, birth, and early parenthood
easier and more enjoyable. Order online,
by email, fax, post, or phone.

NCT Special Experiences Register

NCT Enquiries line: 0870 444 8707
(9am–5pm Mon to Thu and 9am–4pm Fri)

NHS Direct

24-hour helpline: 0845 46 47
www.nhsdirect.nhs.uk
24-hour nurse-led, confidential helpline
providing advice and information.

NMC (Nursing and Midwifery Council) – formerly UKCC

23 Portland Place
London W1B 1PZ, UK
Tel: 020 7637 7181
www.nmc-uk.org
Email: advice@nmc-uk.org
Fax: 020 7436 2924
Protecting the public through professional
standards for nursing and midwifery.

Patient Advisory Liaison Service (PALS)

Contact them via your local Primary Care
Trust to complain about local health care.
England and Wales: NHS Direct (0845 46 47)
can give local PALS contact details, and
their website has an online PALS service:
www.nhsdirect.nhs.uk/pals.asp
Scotland: NHS 24-hr helpline: 0845 424 2424
(for the local Health Board/Primary Care
Trust and Local Health Council (PALS),
www.show.scot.nhs.uk/organisations/
orgindex.htm
Northern Ireland: the Health and Social
Services Boards (Primary Care Trusts)
can be accessed from: www.n-i.nhs.uk

Positively Women

347–349 City Road
London EC1V 1LR, UK
Helpline: 020 7713 0222 (10am–4pm Tues,
Wed, and Fri; 10am–8.30pm Mon and Thurs)
Tel: 020 7713 0444 (administration)
www.positivelywomen.org.uk
Email: info@positivelywomen.org.uk
Fax: 020 7713 1020
Works to improve the quality of life of women
and families affected by HIV. specialist
support from women living with HIV.

Real Nappy Association

Tel: 020 8299 4519
www.realnappy.com
All about reusable nappies.

SANDS (Stillbirth and Neonatal Death Society)

28 Portland Place
London W1N 4DE, UK
Helpline: 020 7436 5881
(10am–3pm Mon to Fri)
Tel: 020 7436 7940 (10am–5pm Mon to Fri,
for a broad range of enquiries relating to
stillbirth and neonatal death).
www.uk-sands.org
Email: support@uk-sands.org
Support for bereaved parents and families
when their baby dies at, or soon after, birth.

Scottish Cot Death Trust

Royal Hospital for Sick Children
Yorkhill, Glasgow G3 8SJ, UK
Helpline: 0141 357 3946
www.sidscotland.org.uk
Email: h.brooke@clinmed.gla.ac.uk
Fax: 0141 334 1376
Only Scottish charity working to find cause
of cot death. Offers support to families, and
provides education on the topic, for the
public and for health care professionals.

Tax Credit Hotline

Tel: 0845 609 5000
www.inlandrevenue.gov.uk
Information on working tax credit.

All about the NCT

Having a baby is a major life change. The National Childbirth Trust (NCT) is the charity that campaigns for and supports those who are going through this incredible life event.

The NCT does not tell parents how to manage their pregnancies, how to give birth, or how to feed and care for their babies. We believe that women and their partners are the best people to make these decisions. However, in order to make the best decisions parents need accurate information, based on evidence, free from commercial influence, and written from a parent's point of view. Becoming a parent is a life-enhancing experience, but it can also be challenging and sometimes stressful. The NCT's role is to help make it as joyful a time as possible.

Powerful at a local, national, and UK level, The National Childbirth Trust has over 350 branches across the UK, run by parents for parents. There's bound to be a local branch near you, offering:
- antenatal classes
- breastfeeding counselling
- new baby groups
- open house get-togethers
- support for dads
- working parents' groups
- nearly-new sales of baby clothes and equipment, as well as many events where parents can meet others going through the same changes, for mutual support and friendship. You can also hire a breast pump or a Valley Cushion locally, after birth.

To find the contact details of your local branch, ring the NCT Enquiry Line: 0870 444 8707 or check the branch details at **www.nct.org.uk**

To get support with feeding your baby, ring the NCT Breastfeeding Line: 0870 444 8708

To find answers to pregnancy and parenting queries, ring the Enquiry Line or log on to: **www.nct.org.uk**

To buy excellent baby goods, maternity bras, toys, and gifts from NCT Sales, look at: **www.nctsales.co.uk** or telephone 0870 112 1120.

To join the NCT, call 0870 990 8040 or go to **www.nct.org.uk/join**
Although it's not essential to become a member to enjoy the services and support of The National Childbirth Trust, membership is encouraged because it helps to fund the charity's work supporting all parents.

The National Childbirth Trust
Alexandra House
Oldham Terrace
London W3 6NH, UK
Tel: 0870 770 3236
Fax: 0870 770 3237

References

References are denoted in the main chapters by the symbol ⊙

Chapter 1 – The first few hours

Page 11
On birth partners – doulas
Hodnett ED, Gates S, Hofmeyr GJ, and Sakala C. *Continuous support for women during childbirth (Cochrane Review). In: The Cochrane Library, 3, 2003.* Available from: www.nelh.nhs.uk/cochrane.asp

Scott KD, Klaus PH, Klaus MH. The obstetrical and postpartum benefits of continuous support during childbirth. *Journal of Women's Health & Gender-Based Medicine* 1999;8(10):1257-64.

Page 16
On perineal suturing
Kenyon S, Ford F. How can we improve women's postbirth perineal health? *MIDIRS Midwifery Digest* 2004;14(1):7-12.

Lundquist M, Olsson A, Nissen E, et al. Is it necessary to suture all lacerations after a vaginal delivery? *Birth* 2000; 27(2):79-85.

Kettle C, Hills RK, Jones P, et al. Continuous versus interrupted perineal repair with standard or rapidly absorbed sutures after spontaneous vaginal birth: a randomised controlled trial. *Lancet* 2002;359:2217-23.

Page 21
On baby's first feed
Cattaneo A, Buzzetti R. Effect on rates of breast feeding of training for the baby friendly hospital initiative. *BMJ* 2001;323(7325):1358-62.

Page 23
On vitamin K
Hey E. Vitamin K: can we improve on nature? *MIDIRS Midwifery Digest* 2003;13(1):7-12.

Chapter 2 – Up to six weeks

Page 49
Frequent use of chemical products
Sherriff A, Farrow A, Golding J, et al. Frequent use of chemical products is associated with persistent wheezing in pre-school age children. *Thorax* 2005;60(1):45-9.

Chapter 3 – Feeding

Page 86
Benefits of breastfeeding
Visit www.babyfriendly.org for a summary of the latest research.

Research about snoring
Palmer B. Breastfeeding: reducing the risk for obstructive sleep apnea. *Breastfeeding Abstracts* 1999;18(3):19-20.

Page 86 and 87
On hormones and physiology
Lawrence RA. *Breastfeeding: a guide for the medical profession.* 4th edition St Louis,MO: Mosby; 1994.

Page 88
Colicky symptoms
Woolridge MW, Fisher C. Colic, "overfeeding", and symptoms of lactose malabsorption in the breast-fed baby: a possible artifact of feed management? *Lancet* 1988;332(8607):382-4.

Page 89
Attachment and positioning
Royal College of Midwives. *Successful breastfeeding.* 3rd edition Edinburgh: Churchill Livingstone; 2002.

Page 93
Satiation cues and overriding these
Drewett R, Wright P, Young B. From feeds to meals: the development of hunger and food intake in infants and young children. In: Niven CA, Walker A, editors. *Current issues in infancy and parenthood.* Oxford: Butterworth Heinemann; 1998. pp. 204-17.

Page 94
Scheduled feeds
World Health Organization Division of Child Health and Development. *Evidence for the ten steps to successful breastfeeding: revised.* Geneva: World Health Organization, Division of Child Health and Development; 1998.

Page 98
Hand expressing
Mohrbacher N, Stock J. *The breastfeeding answer book.* 3rd revised edition Shaumberg, Illinois: La Leche League International; 2003.

Page 100
Expressing and storing breastmilk
Hands A. Safe storage of expressed breast milk in the home. *MIDIRS Midwifery Digest* 2003;13(3):378-85.

Page 103
Thrush
Information on this topic is produced by the Breastfeeding Network (BfN) – see www.breastfeedingnetwork.org.uk to order leaflets.

Cabbage leaves
Renfrew MJ, Woolridge MW, McGill HR. *Enabling women to breast-feed: a review of practices which promote or inhibit breastfeeding – with evidence-based guidance for practice.* London: The Stationery Office; 2000.

Page 104
Mastitis
Information on this topic is produced by the Breastfeeding Network (BfN) - see www.breastfeedingnetwork.org.uk to order leaflets.

Page 107
Diurnal rhythms
Walker AM, Menahem S. Normal early infant behaviour patterns. *J Paediatr Child Health* 1994;30:260–2.

Page 108
Scheduled feeds
World Health Organization Division of Child Health and Development. *Evidence for the ten steps to successful breastfeeding: revised.* Geneva: World Health Organization, Division of Child Health and Development; 1998.

Emphasizing the difference between day and night
Pinilla T, Birch LL. Help me make it through the night: behavioral entrainment of breast-fed infants' sleep patterns. *Pediatrics* 1993;91(2):436–44.

Chapter 4 – Sleeping

Page 113
Adults sleep fewer hours than a generation ago
Cropley M, Dijk DJ. Sleep: is the 24/7 lifestyle leaving us seriously short? *Journal of Family Health Care* 2003;13(5):114–5.

Women report extreme fatigue
McQueen A, Mander R. Tiredness and fatigue in the postnatal period. *J Adv. Nurs.* 2003;42(5):463–9.

Page 115
Sleep in babies
Davis KF, Parker KP, Montgomery GL. Sleep in infants and young children. Part one: normal sleep. *J Pediatr. Health Care* 2004;18(2):65–71.

Page 121
Interpreting babies' cries
Daws D. *Through the night: helping parents and sleepless infants.* London: Free Association Books; 1993.

Risks posed by dummies
Renfrew MJ, Dyson L, Wallace L, D'Souza L, McCormick F, Spiby H. The effectiveness of public health interventions to promote the duration of breastfeeding: systematic reviews of the evidence. National Institute for Health and Clinical Excellence (NICE), 2005.

Page 122
Helping your baby to sleep more effectively
St James-Roberts I. Use of a behavioural programme in the first 3 months to prevent infant crying and sleeping problems. *Journal of Paediatrics and Child Health* 2001;37(3):289–97.

Hames P. *NCT: Help your baby to sleep.* Revised edition London: Thorsons; 2002.

Page 124
Babies in the same room as their parents
Blair PS, Fleming PJ, Smith IJ, et al. Babies sleeping with parents: case-control study of factors influencing the risk of the sudden infant death syndrome. CESDI SUDI research group. *BMJ* 1999;319(7223):1457–61.

Page 126
Breastfeeding mothers sharing a bed with their newborn
Quillin SI, Glenn LL. Interaction between feeding method and co-sleeping on maternal-newborn sleep. *J Obstet Gynecol Neonatal Nurs* 2004;33(5):580–8.

Page 131
Babies who have more daylight
Harrison Y. The relationship between daytime exposure to light and night-time sleep in 6–12-week-old infants. *J Sleep Res* 2004;13(4):345–52.

Page 133
Babies and loveys
Pantley E. *The no-cry sleep solution; gentle ways to help your baby sleep through the night.* Chicago, IL: Contemporary Books; 2002.

Further Reading:
pp117–18 Attachment Parenting
Liedloff, Jean, *The Continuum Concept*, Arkana Publishers London, 1989.

Sears, William, *The Attachment Parenting Book*, Little Brown & Co, London 2001.

Chapter 5 – Six weeks to three months – your social baby

Page 138
About the roller coaster of emotions
Kitzinger S. *The year after childbirth: surviving the first year of motherhood.* Oxford: Oxford University Press; 1994.

About primary maternal pre-occupation
Winnicott DW. *Babies and their mothers.* London: Free Association Books; 1988.

Page 139
The need to talk about your baby and be supported in your mothering
Stern DN, Bruschweiler-Stern N. *The birth of a mother: how motherhood changes you forever.* London: Bloomsbury; 1998.

Particular need to talk if you have had a difficult time
Horowitz MJ, Kaltreider NB. Brief therapy of the stress response syndrome. *Psychiatric Clinics of North America* 1979;2(2):365–77.

Birth crisis
Kitzinger S. Birth and violence against women: generating hypotheses from women's accounts of unhappiness after childbirth. In: Roberts H, editor. *Women's health matters.* London: Routledge; 1992. pp. 63–80

Page 141
Looking after yourself
Welford H. *Feelings after birth.* London: NCT Publishing; 2002.

Page 142
The varying temperamental styles of babies
Brazelton TB. *Touchpoints: your child's emotional and behavioral development.* London: Viking; 1992.

Abilities babies are born with
Klaus MH, Klaus PH. *The amazing newborn.* Reading, Mass.: Da Capo Press; 1985.

Murray L, Andrews L. *The social baby.* Richmond: CP Publishing; 2000.

Page 143
Baby states
Brazelton TB. *Touchpoints: your child's emotional and behavioral development.* London: Viking; 1992.

Page 145
Responding to the world
Brazelton TB, Cramer BG. *The earliest relationship: parents, infants and the drama of early attachment.* USA: Da Capo Press; 1990.

Page 146
Understanding the characteristics and needs of your particular baby
Brazelton TB, Cramer BG. *The earliest relationship: parents, infants and the drama of early attachment.* USA: Da Capo Press; 1990.

Extra-sensitive "jumpy" babies
Brazelton TB, Cramer BG. *The earliest relationship: parents, infants and the drama of early attachment.* USA: Da Capo Press; 1990.

Page 147
Restless, irritable babies
Murray L, Andrews L. *The social baby.* Richmond: CP Publishing; 2000.

Page 149
Goodness of fit
Brazelton TB, Cramer BG. *The earliest relationship: parents, infants and the drama of early attachment.* USA: Da Capo Press; 1990.

Page 150
Looking at faces
Klaus MH, Klaus PH. *The amazing newborn.* Reading, Mass.: Da Capo Press; 1985.

Page 151
Focusing on your baby
Klaus MH, Klaus PH. *The amazing newborn.* Reading, Mass.: Da Capo Press; 1985.

Murray L, Andrews L. *The social baby.* Richmond: CP Publishing; 2000.

Noticing when your baby is beginning to tire
Brazelton TB, Cramer BG. *The earliest relationship: parents, infants and the drama of early attachment.* USA: Da Capo Press; 1990.

Page 152
Parents asked to keep records
St James-Roberts I, Halil T. Infant crying patterns in the first year: normal community and clinical findings. *J Child Psychol.Psychiatry* 1991;32(6):951–68.

Variations between babies
St James-Roberts I, Conroy S, Wilsher K. Bases for maternal perceptions of infant crying and colic behaviour. *Archives of Disease in Childhood* 1996;75:375–84.

Page 153
Parents who respond quickly and sensitively
Bell SM, Ainsworth MD. Infant crying and maternal responsiveness. *Child Development* 1972;43(4):1171–90.

Page 154
Crying babies are usually thriving babies
Crowcroft NS, Strachan DP. The social origins of infantile colic: questionnaire study covering 76 747 infants. *BMJ* 1997;314(7090):1325–8.

Observations of "colicky" babies
St James-Roberts I. What is distinct about infants' "colic" cries? *Archives of Disease in Childhood* 1999;80(1):56-62.

Babies' brain development
Barr RG. "Colic" is something infants do, rather than a condition they "have": a developmental approach to crying phenomena, patterns, pacification and (patho)genesis. In: Barr RG, St James-Roberts I, Keefe MR, editors. *New evidence on unexplained early infant crying: its origins, nature and management.* Skillman, N.J.: Johnson and Johnson Pediatric Institute; 2001. pp. 87–104

Page 156
Being out of step with old friends
Maushart S. *The mask of motherhood: how becoming a mother changes everything and why we pretend it doesn't.* London: Rivers Oram Press/Pandora List; 1999.

Page 157
Other parents can help you to negotiate the new territory of parenthood
Stadlen N. *What mothers do, especially when it looks like nothing.* London: Piatkus; 2004.

Page 158
Feeling part of a larger group of women
Stern DN, Bruschweiler-Stern N. *The birth of a mother: how motherhood changes you forever.* London: Bloomsbury; 1998.

Chapter 6 – Three to six months – your settled baby

Page 168
Restlessness and fussing tend to diminish
St James-Roberts I, Halil T. Infant crying patterns in the first year: normal community and clinical findings. *J Child Psychol.Psychiatry* 1991;32(6):951–68.

Page 174
About good quality childcare
Anme T, Segal UA. Implications for the development of children in over 11 hours of centre-based care. *Child Care Health Dev.* 2004;30(4):345–52.
Phillips D, Adams G. Child care and our youngest children. *Future.Child* 2001;11(1):34–51.

Children fare worst in terms of school readiness
Brooks-Gunn J, Han WJ, Waldfogel J. Maternal employment and child cognitive outcomes in the first three years of life: the NICHD Study of Early Child Care. National Institute of Child Health and Human Development. *Child Dev* 2002;73(4):1052–72.

In forming early social relationships
Phillips D, Adams G. Child care and our youngest children. *Future.Child* 2001;11(1):34–51.

Page 175
Language and activities linked to the development of language skills and school readiness
Brooks-Gunn J, Han WJ, Waldfogel J. Maternal employment and child cognitive outcomes in the first three years of life: the NICHD Study of Early Child Care. National Institute of Child Health and Human Development. *Child Dev* 2002;73(4):1052–72.

Children in full-time childcare before their first birthday
Lowe Vandell D. Early child care: the known and the unknown. *Merrill-Palmer Quarterly* 2004;50(3):387–415.

Page 182
Children who have their needs met consistently
Waters E, Weinfeld NS, Hamilton CE. The stability of attachment security from infancy to adolescence and early adulthood: general discussion. *Child Development* 2000;71(3):703–6.

Chapter 7 – Six to nine months – your active baby

Page 204
A reasonable level of dirt does a baby no harm and may even strengthen her immune system
Strachan DP. Hay fever, hygiene and household size. *BMJ* 1989;299:1259–60.

Strachan DP. Family size, infection and atopy: the first decade of the "hygiene hypothesis". *Thorax* 2000;55 Suppl 1:S2–10.

Page 206
Babies benefit from six months of exclusive breastfeeding
Kramer MS, Kukuma R. *Optimal duration of exclusive breastfeeding (Cochrane Review) In: The Cochrane Library, Issue 1, 2003.* Available from: www.nelh.nhs.uk/cochrane.asp

Developmental readiness
Naylor AJ, Morrow A. *Developmental readiness of normal full term infants to progress from exclusive breastfeeding to the introduction of complementary foods: review of the relevant literature concerning infant gastrointestinal, immunologic, oral motor and maternal reproductive and lactational development.* San Diego,CA.: Wellstart International; 2001.

Page 207
Babies grow well and healthily if solids are introduced at around six months
Naylor AJ, Morrow A. *Developmental readiness of normal full term infants to progress from exclusive breastfeeding to the introduction of complementary foods: review of the relevant literature concerning infant gastrointestinal, immunologic, oral motor and maternal reproductive and lactational development.* San Diego,CA.: Wellstart International; 2001.

Kramer MS, Kukuma R. *Optimal duration of exclusive breastfeeding (Cochrane Review) In: The Cochrane Library, Issue 1, 2003.* Available from: www.nelh.nhs.uk/cochrane.asp

Cohen RJ, Brown KH, Canahuati J, et al. Effects of age of introduction of complementary foods on infant breast milk intake, total energy intake, and growth: a randomised intervention study in Honduras. *Lancet* 1994;344(8918):288–93.

Solids at an early stage could reduce the overall calorie intake
Kramer MS, Kukuma R. *Optimal duration of exclusive breastfeeding (Cochrane Review) In: The Cochrane Library, Issue 1, 2003.* Available from: www.nelh.nhs.uk/cochrane.asp

Babies who are given solids are no more likely to sleep through the night than babies on milk only
Heinig MJ, Nommsen LA, Peerson JM, et al. Intake and growth of breast-fed and formula-fed infants in relation to the timing of introduction of complementary foods: the DARLING study. Davis Area Research on Lactation, Infant Nutrition and Growth. *Acta Paediatr* 1993;82(12):999-1006.

Baby-led weaning
See www.babyfriendly.org.uk/weaning.asp

Page 210
Breastmilk protects the vulnerable baby's gut
Labbok MH, Clark D, Goldman AS. Breastfeeding: maintaining an irreplaceable immunological resource. *Nat Rev Immunol* 2004;4(7):565–72.

Introduction of allergenic foods
See www.eatwell.gov.uk/agesandstages/baby/weaning

Page 212
Some protective factors in breastmilk increase as a baby grows older
Goldman AS, et al. Immunologic components in human milk during the second year of lactation. *Acta Paediatrica Scandinavia* 1983; 72: 461.

Page 213
Concern about the level of phytoestrogens
Chief Medical Officer's Update, Jan 2004, Dept of Health; www.dh.gov.uk/assetRoot/04/07/01/76/04070176.pdf

Index

Acknowledgments

Your Baby's First Year

First published in Great Britain in 2005 by Mitchell Beazley,
an imprint of Octopus Publishing Group Ltd,
2-4 Heron Quays, London E14 4JP

All reasonable care has been taken in the preparation of this book, but the information it contains is not intended to take the place of treatment by a qualified medical practitioner.

ISBN 1 84533 063 3

A CIP record for this book is available from the British Library

Set in Avant Garde and Wingdings

Colour reproduction by Eray Scan in Singapore
Printed and bound in China by Toppan

Commissioning Editors Vivien Antwi / Jonathan Asbury
Executive Art Editor Yasia Williams
Senior Editor Emily Anderson
Designer Gaelle Lochner
Illustrator Debbie Rowlands
Production Gary Hayes
Picture Research Jenny Faithfull
Proofreader Colette Campbell
Indexer Helen Snaith

At the NCT: Lynn Balmforth, Roz Collins, Rosie Dodds, Mary Newburn, Kate Pearce, Belinda Phipps

The NCT would like to acknowledge the following writers for their contributions to the book:

Adela Stockton: "The first few hours"

Caroline Deacon: "Up to six weeks" and "Feeding"

Juliet Goddard: "Sleeping", "Six weeks to three months – your social baby", and "Nearly one year old"

Vicki Bevan: "Three to six months – your settled baby"

Heather Welford: "Six to nine months – your active baby"

Thanks also to the following people and organizations:

Fiona Barlow	Gillian Fletcher	Diz Meredith	Tanya Tunley
Debbie Chippington Derrick	Nancy Gedge	Cathy Neale	Liz Wise
Cynthia Clarkson	Anne Humphreys	Judith Ockenden	Maternity Alliance
Sheila Company	Nicola Jones	Joy Oxenham	Bliss
Rosie Dodds	Sue Maguire	Kieron Smith	Tamba
Jane Evans	Morag Martindale	Kim Thomas	

Mitchell Beazley and the NCT would like to thank the following for their permission to reproduce their photographs:

Front cover: © Comstock Images
Back cover: Photodisc/Andersen Ross

3 © Comstock Images; 6 Ania Huxtable; 8 Angela Hampton Family Life Picture Library; 11 Catherine Eden; 12 Dhillon Rai-Green; 15 Roz Collins; 17 Andrew Florides; 18 Alamy/SHOUT; 20 Jayne McCoy; 22 Roz Collins; 25 Dhillon Rai-Green; 26 Angela Hampton Family Life Picture Library; 31 Alamy/SHOUT; 32 Angela Hampton Family Life Picture Library; 35 Bubbles/Gena Naccache; 36 Donna Nestor; 39 Sarah Cutler; 40 Belinda Phipps; 43 Dhillon Rai-Green; 47 Shirlayne Dunwoodie; 48 Belinda Phipps; 53 Vivienne Foster; 55 NCT/Emma Penrose/A Green Armytage/HarperCollins; 57 Ania Huxtable; 60 Angela Hampton Family Life Picture Library; 63 Alamy/Picture Partners; 64–72 Angela Hampton Family Life Picture Library; 74 Bubbles/Chris Rout; 76 Alamy/ Photofusion Picture Library; 79 Angela Hampton Family Life Picture Library; 80 Octopus Publishing Group Ltd/Peter Pugh-Cook; 83 Tina Bolton; 84 Sandra Lousada; 87 Angela Hampton Family Life Picture Library; 88 Tina Bolton; 90 NCT; 92 Dhillon Rai-Green; 95 NCT/Jacky Chapman; 97 Photodisc/Ryan McVay; 98 NCT; 99 Octopus Publishing Group Ltd./Peter Pugh-Cook; 100 Mother & Baby Picture Library/Ruth Jenkinson; 101 Roz Collins; 103–104 Science Photo Library/Dr P Marazzi; 105 Tina Bolton; 106 © Comstock Images; 108 Roz Collins; 110 Angela Hampton Family Life Picture Library; 115 Melanie Munday; 117 Kate Ness Pomroy; 118–126 Angela Hampton Family Life Picture Library; 131 Kate Ness Pomroy; 133–136 Dhillon Rai-Green; 138 Roz Collins; 141 Dhillon Rai-Green; 143 Angela Hampton Family Life Picture Library; 144 NCT; 147–155 Angela Hampton Family Life Picture Library; 156 Sally and Richard Greenhill; 159 Tina Bolton; 160 Caroline Gowing; 164 Roz Collins; 166 Alamy/ Profimedia.CZ.sro; 169 Bubbles/ Frans Rombout; 171 Paige Sinkler; 177 Alamy/David Hoffman Photo Library; 179 Alamy/Stock Connection Distribution; 180 Bubbles/ Loisjoy Thurston; 183 Angela Hampton Family Life Picture Library; 187 Alamy/Medical-on-Line; 188 Octopus Publishing Group Ltd./ Peter Pugh-Cook; 193 Angela Hampton Family Life Picture Library; 194 Bubbles/Jennie Woodcock; 196 © Comstock Images; 199 Jo Homan; 201 Belinda Phipps; 203 Philippa de la Isla; 205 Belinda Phipps; 206 Tina Bolton; 209 Jo Homan; 211 Alamy/Craig Holmes; 214 Belinda Phipps; 217 Photodisc/E Dygas; 218 Augusta Harris; 220 Angela Hampton Family Life Picture Library; 222 Dhillon Rai-Green; 224 Belinda Phipps; 227 Photodisc/Bronwyn Kidd; 228 Catherine Eden; 231 Angela Hampton Family Life Picture Library